4

EVERY

OTHER

BED

EVERY

OTHER

BED

BY MIKE GORMAN

CLEVELAND AND NEW YORK

THE WORLD PUBLISHING COMPANY

COPYRIGHT ACKNOWLEDGMENTS

Blakiston Division, McGraw-Hill Book Company, Inc., for material from *Psychosomatic Case Book*, by Drs. Roy R. Grinker and Fred P. Robbins, copyright 1954 by Blakiston Division, McGraw-Hill Book Company, Inc.

The Curtis Publishing Company, for material from "Is Mental Disease Mental?" by Albert Q. Maisel, from the July, 1953 issue of the *Ladies' Home Journal*, copyright 1953 by The Curtis Publishing Company.

The Ronald Press Company, for material from *Studies in Psychosomatic Medicine—An Approach to the Cause and Treatment of Vegetative Disturbances*, by Drs. Franz Alexander and Thomas Morton French, copyright 1948 by The Ronald Press Company; for material from *Psychoanalytic Therapy*, by Drs. Franz Alexander and Thomas Morton French, copyright 1946 by The Ronald Press Company.

Library of Congress Catalog Card Number: 56-5310

FIRST EDITION

HC256

Designed by Abe Lerner

CONTENTS

Research Progress Against the Major Mental Illnesses

Psychiatric Research: The Future

INTRODUCTION

THIS book has been written for the express purpose of bringing to the American people the facts about the parlous state of psychiatric research and training in a country fat with prosperity, two-toned automobiles, and refrigerators which open from either side.

Few will dispute the contention that our treatment of the millions of mentally ill in this country still smacks of superstition, negativism, niggardliness, and unimaginativeness. The much-heralded genius of the American productive economy, so daring in the fashioning of hosts of mechanical gadgets up to and including electronically controlled weapons of destruction, falters badly when confronted with the basic problems involved in understanding the complexities of mind and emotion.

Successive waves of reform have succeeded to some degree in bettering the physical housing of those afflicted with ills of the mind, but the big job of accumulating a body of scientific knowledge, and a large corps of practitioners capable of dispensing it, still lies ahead of us.

If there is an angry note of impatience in this book, it is long accumulated and difficult to restrain. Eleven years ago, when as a newspaperman on *The Daily Oklahoman* I started waving the reek and stench of our state mental hospitals under the public's nostrils, I thought American know-how would make short work of the deficiencies in the system. I reckoned little with either the stifling hold of comfortable tradition or the granite power of professional intransigence.

By 1948, when the condensation of my book, *Oklahoma Attacks*

9

Its Snake Pits, appeared in *The Reader's Digest,* I had become acutely aware of the fact that an organized offensive would have to be mounted to break down the powerful resistance of the self-appointed guardians of the past.

During the next few years, as I wrote, lectured, and took an active part in mental health reform movements in a number of states, I began to see the utter futility of disconnected, sporadic bursts of citizen indignation. In looking back over those years, I see much patching and filling, small bands of righteous souls acting with compassion and mercy, but no real attempt to tear down the whole rotting structure and build afresh.

A wearisome accumulation of such experiences convinced me that I should devote my full time to welding the disparate voices together in support of a clear-cut set of objectives. In 1953, I therefore assumed the position I still hold—Executive Director of the National Mental Health Committee, with forty-six state Governors as my Honorary Chairmen.

We have made a small beginning, but the typical state mental hospital of today is an anachronism, a vestigial appendix of earlier superstitions which pictured the mentally ill as incurably possessed of evil thoughts and demons and therefore to be consigned to asylums far removed from the eye and conscience of "civilized" society. It is still incredibly isolated from the main stream of American medicine, a stagnant and weary tributary cut off from the bubbling river. The story of this unconscionable isolation forms a sorry chapter in the history of American medicine and I, for one, am not possessed of enough blessed charity to exculpate the many practitioners of the medical arts who knew better but turned their backs on their sick brethren.

In spelling out the many deficiencies in our present handling of the mentally ill, I have foregone much of personal opinion and, wherever possible, used documentation from general medical, psychiatric, and official sources. This was a difficult chore, since my whole impulse was to write from the heart and let the hot adjectives fall where they might. However, I became convinced that this is not the time for that kind of book. I have therefore quoted at length from official papers and documents. The particularly long quotations from psychiatric research papers I believe to be necessary in giving the feel of an area difficult of comprehension.

There also may seem to be an undue emphasis upon money. Some of my sophisticated psychiatric friends recoil at tables and charts pointing up the financial malnutrition of psychiatric research or the shortages of psychiatric personnel. Attempts to reduce complicated problems to simple, pragmatic levels within the comprehension of the many offend their highly developed sensibilities. They accuse us of a lack of appreciation of the subtleties of the research mind, of the intricacies of medical education, of the tenuous nature of the therapeutic process.

I accuse them of living in a cream-puff world of fantasy. I commend to them a story told about the late Dr. Joseph Mountin, one of the great architects of our modern U. S. Public Health Service. After listening to one all-day conference devoted to a follicle-splitting dissection of every wearisome aspect of a public health problem, Dr. Mountin barked, "Look, it all boils down to this—give us the money and we'll do the job."

The Public Health Service itself is an instance in point. The National Institutes of Health at Bethesda, Maryland, now administers a budget of close to a hundred million dollars a year in a Clinical Center which cost sixty million to build. Yet a short twenty years ago the entire present site of the Institutes was a sleepy Maryland farm. During World War II, when Senator Claude Pepper's Committee on Education and Labor conducted an investigation of Federal support of medical research, it was told by the then director of the Institutes that the two million dollar annual appropriation he was allotted was "about all he could spend." Every time we agitated for an expansion of the Federal effort, we were told we didn't understand the complexities of the research process and, besides, you could never get the researchers anyway. Today there are several thousand employees at the Institutes, operating what is probably the largest medical research program in the world. Came the money, came the men.

Granted there is much more to a successful psychiatric research program than basic financing, but I have yet to see a major research program operating without funds. And too many times in the past decade I have seen promising research projects plowed under because the money ran out. My fainthearted friends should take a leaf from the book of Dr. Will Menninger. One of the giants of American psychiatry, he is on the road at least one hundred days in every year pleading with industrial tycoons, Rotarians, Kiwanians, Lions, Elks, Eagles, and sundry others to support psychiatric research.

I am aware of the fact that this book will be criticized for its "excessive" emphasis upon the physiological factors underlying mental illness. I am cheerfully prepared to be read out of the Inner Temple by the High Priests of the Oedipus Complex and the rampant Id. For a number of years, I was an active communicant in that Temple, cocking an attentive ear while its psychiatric theologues concocted a witches' brew of sterile terminology to describe psychiatric phenomena they had no capability of treating. The annual incantations of the psychoanalysts, with their ritualistic excommunication of the deviationists and their Sacred Bulls quoting obscure sentences from the pen of Sigmund the Master, appear to me now as remote and fantastic as the practice of the Black Mass in the Middle Ages.

I also actively solicit the remonstrances of the vast horde of self-constituted "experts" on human behavior, the blithe popularizers who fear not to tread where scientists are wary to walk. Fortified by a massive ignorance of the physiology of the human mind and nervous system, they lecture, write, preach, and advise about juvenile delinquency, thumb-sucking, marriage, and so on. Send your problem in, make sure you enclose a stamped return envelope, and all the world will be fine again. There is a saying that any nitwit thinks he can run the country better than the politicians, produce better movies than Hollywood, and run baseball clubs much more competently than the present crop of managers. The numbers of people who think they can accomplish these things are as a handful compared with the legions who, without ever having examined or even seen you, can advise you on your most serious emotional problems. This is a tragic business, and it has spawned some terrifying personal misfortunes.

Then there are the moralizers—I've got them on my list. Cheerful practitioners of the Do-It-to-Yourself School, they exhort their listeners to buck up, hop out of the chair, and whip the world with a pillow full of platitudes. There's nothing really wrong with you that a good dose of grit, gumption, and go won't cure! And then they tell you an inspirational story about old Jim Wilson who at the age of seventy-three, after curing himself of the seven-year itch, learned the Charleston and bagged himself a wealthy widow of eighty-five who drives brewery trucks for a hobby.

I am not trying to deprecate the importance of a scientific understanding of the psychological factors involved in mental illness. Personality and social stresses play an enormous part in aggravating emotional disturbances. An insight into your personality difficulties is of prime importance in handling them, but, as Dr. Paul Hoch has emphasized time and time again, insight is not enough. Many schizophrenics who have been in analysis for a number of years have remarkable insight into the twistings and turnings of their personalities, but they lack the *metabolic* strength to rise out of the pit of despond. Many alcoholics have a very clear notion of why they drink, but in times of crisis this is of little help when the inside sweats and the jangled nerves render them defenseless. You step in your car, you have a clear idea of your geographical goal, but you cannot get there if the basic mechanism of your car is faulty. We are turning up increasing evidence of the physiological distortions underlying mental illness, and we are developing drugs and other physical therapies to alleviate these distortions.

Anxiety is a telling case in point. At a recent psychiatric convention, one analyst described anxiety as the *raison d'être* of mental illness. Every mother's son of us, born into a world we did not make, has moments of profound anxiety and insecurity. When anxiety overwhelms us, we either strike out at the world or withdraw from it. Psychiatric conversation does little to allay serious anxiety. What does the analyst do when confronted with a hysterical, anxiety-ridden patient who is smashing the furniture in a blind attack of rage? He calls the police.

Physiological research is beginning to change this picture. It is developing scientific data on the transmission of anxiety from the hypothalamus, the seat of emotions in the brain, through nerve pathways to the cerebral cortex. Drugs are now in use which somehow inhibit the transmission of anxiety. Dr. Frank Ayd, Jr., a Baltimore psychiatrist, gave a dramatic illustration of this in testifying before a Senate committee last May. At 1:30 A.M. on the very day he testified, he was called to the home of a thirty-year-old woman who was so disturbed she was tearing up the furniture. Dr. Ayd frankly confessed that, if he hadn't had the

new drugs at his disposal, he would have called the police and
had the woman carted off to a state institution. However, with
one injection of Chlorpromazine the patient's hysterical attack was
abated, and she was transferred to a general hospital for further
drug treatment and probable release at the end of a few weeks.

All of us have to bear stress, all of us have to live with anxiety.
This is the human condition. By the same token, a tall building has
to withstand the ravages of wind, rain, heat, and hurricane. Its
builders therefore make sure its foundation is as solid as the
proverbial oak. We are beginning to learn that we must do the
same with the human frame if it is to withstand the lacerating
buffetings of a fast-paced atomic age.

Dr. Ayd raised an even more important point at that hearing
when he told the Senators that modern psychiatric research was
producing medications within the economic reach of all. He
cited the case of a pair of twin sisters who suffered from an
almost identical schizophrenic psychosis. A few years back, one
of the twins developed a psychotic episode. She was hospitalized
for six months, during which she received innumerable shock
treatments. She was then treated for another year, and the total
bill for her illness came to more than $3,000. Early in 1955, the
other twin suffered an identical psychotic break. She was brought
to Dr. Ayd's office by five men who had to hold her in restraint
because of her disturbed behavior. She was placed in a nursing home
for a week, and Chlorpromazine was administered to her. She
was then given the drug for another eleven weeks in her home
and was relieved of her psychosis. The total cost was $325.

It is the bounden duty of modern psychiatry to develop therapies
within the economic reach of all. When mental illness tears across
the country like an unspent hurricane, what value the Park
Avenue analyst with his precious annual case load of four to eight
highly distilled neurotics? We must go out and fight mental
illness on the highways and the byways, and to do this we must
put potent medicines into the black bag of the general practitioner
as well as the psychiatrist. You can't fight a raging epidemic with
an overstuffed couch. We must treat mental illness where we find
it—in the home, in the clinic, in the general hospital.

I harbor no illusions about the magical properties of the new
drugs. In fact, I find it quite annoying that a few of the more

hyperbolic articles refer to them as "wonder" drugs. The only wonder I can see in the situation is perplexity as to why American medicine and the American drug industry, with all of their vaunted skills, have continually drawn a blank in the production of chemical weapons against mental illness. There is no point in kidding ourselves: we are constantly cribbing drugs developed and tested by foreign scientists. Reserpine is a derivative of the snakeroot used for centuries in India to calm the mentally ill, and Chlorpromazine is the accidental by-product of a French scientist's efforts to find an antihistamine with reduced side-effects. Both drugs achieve some remarkable therapeutic effects, but they are a far cry from what American science might have achieved if it had devoted even a small amount of its resources and ingenuity over the past few decades to a research attack upon mental illness.

However, I readily admit to marching behind the banner of those who have demanded that the new drugs be given a full and fair trial. To those of you who question the extent and ferocity of the medical resistances to the drugs, I commend the October, 1955, proceedings of the Mental Hospital Institute of the American Psychiatric Association. At the panel on drug therapy, some of the top state hospital superintendents in the country spelled out incredible resistances from within their own staffs and from the psychiatric community outside the walls. Dr. Douglas Goldman, brilliant researcher and Clinical Director at Longview State Hospital in Cincinnati, pointed out that the very medical men who fought his pioneer use of electric shock in the late thirties are the ones who today refuse to give up electric shock for the drug therapies. To them, and their like-minded colleagues, any new therapy is ipso facto a "flash-in-the-pan" and any psychiatrist who advocates it is either "endangering his professional reputation" or "reacting against past failures."

What is it that these defenders of the past are trying so zealously to preserve? Is it really the present state mental hospital system, with its freightage of despair, defeatism, despondency, filth, futility, and failure? Maybe so. I remember a remark of Dr. Karl Menninger's after we had both completed a day's tour of a medieval almshouse known as Topeka State Hospital back in 1947.

"This place is too damned quiet," he remarked angrily. "The staff people tiptoe around like they were all working in a funeral parlor. We've got to get some noise in here to shake them out of their complacency. We'll start with three pianos, and we'll build from there."

By the same token, the new drugs have shaken up the stagnant air of many institutions. As Dr. Fritz Freyhan, a conservative clinician who has had fifteen years of state hospital experience, emphasized recently, they served a supreme purpose in breaking down the "anti-therapeutic climate" of the mental hospital, cutting the violence, terror, and physical restraint to the point where the medical staff could turn for the first time to clinical objectives leading to "the emancipation of the mental hospital" from its ancient doldrums.

I am also prepared to be accused of "sensationalism," just as was Dorothea Lynde Dix a century ago when she exposed the filth and rottenness of nineteenth-century mental hospitals. I plead guilty, not to the charge of sensationalism, but to one of willful understatement. There are many psychiatrists, some of them in high official positions, who go about the land decrying the "excesses" and "hysteria" of modern journalistic exposés of conditions in state hospitals. Others say that there was a time for this sort of exposé but that the necessity for it has long since passed.

Whereof do they speak? In 1954 and 1955, scores of average citizens of the Commonwealth of Pennsylvania were asked by their state mental health association to tour their local hospitals and report on conditions. The following eyewitness comments, sparse and free of professional jargon, are little different from those recorded in the notebook of Miss Dix when she toured the Pennsylvania mental hospitals in the eighteen-forties.

"I walked through ward after ward. Patients were sitting in rows in baggy, hospital-style garments with nothing to do. There was nothing to read."

"I saw patients strapped to lawn chairs to control their hyperactivity."

"In the isolation ward, a patient with a contagious disease was placed between two other patients who were seriously disturbed. In a corner of the room, on piled-up bedding, a patient lay without clothes. These patients were together five hours without a doctor or nurse visiting them."

"I saw a patient brought in handcuffed by the police and listened to the staff joke with the police while the patient and his relatives were present."

"I saw buildings, old and inflammable, which had been condemned years ago, being used because of overcrowded conditions. The hospital had to resort to double-decker beds and cots in corridors."

"This school for the mentally retarded was about 30 per cent overcrowded, I was told. There are 750 crib cases. The wards are so filled that there is no space whatever between beds and the needs of the patients must be administered over the foot of their beds."

In February of the prosperous, give-it-the-big-smile year of 1955, Pennsylvania's newly appointed Secretary of Welfare, former State Senator Harry Shapiro, toured a mental institution devoted to the "care" of helpless, mentally deficient women thrown upon the mercy of their compassionate brethren for succor and survival. Commenting on what Shapiro found, the conservative Philadelphia *Inquirer* editorialized:

"What Shapiro says he has found at Laurelton which houses more than 900 mentally deficient women is something right out of the dark age era of torturing the deranged.

"As described by him, eight-foot steel isolation cells in one of the buildings have been used for the punishment of patients who have disobeyed regulations. . . . The mentally retarded women are not prisoners, they have been convicted of no crime. They have been sent to this state institution to be cared for and trained, not to be penalized for their misfortune.

"Yet Shapiro charges that these patients were punished by keeping them in solitary confinement for periods up to six months, during which no one was permitted to talk to them, cold water· was furnished once a day only for washing purposes and food, shoved through a slot in a sealed door, was restricted to as much oatmeal, mashed potatoes or stew as could be placed on a single slice of bread."

This in joyous 1955, when everything was booming but the guns! And the situation in Pennsylvania is far, far from an isolated instance of the sorry condition of our state mental hospital system. During that same year, progressive state mental health commissioners in a number of states were forced, under the relentless hammerings of the press and the public, to take action to clean up institutions sinking in a quickstand of filth and in-humanity. In some cases, superintendents and other key officials were relieved of their jobs. In others, the Psychiatric Union rushed to the aid of notorious incompetents, preserving their jobs and issuing statements critical of state officials.

Slumber peacefully those of you—state mental health officials, private psychiatrists, and "respectable" laymen—who prefer peace at any price, even if it be at the expense of thousands upon thousands of mentally ill who have no recourse. And to those scores of your colleagues in all parts of the country who chose craven silence when a word of protest was needed, a peaceful good night. But a gentle note of caution to all of you: Keep some barbiturates handy at your bedside. For there are some of us, however limited our capabilities, who seek goals other than craven conformity and the sop of professional respectability. We follow other stars, and we venerate these words of slavery's greatest foe, William Lloyd Garrison:

"I will be as harsh as truth, and as uncompromising as justice. On this subject, I do not wish to think, or speak, or write, with moderation. . . . Urge me not to use moderation in a cause like the present. I am in earnest. I will not equivocate; I will not excuse; I will not retreat a single inch; and I will be heard."

MENTAL ILLNESS: AMERICA'S NUMBER ONE HEALTH PROBLEM

1. AN EPIDEMIC
SWEEPS
THE LAND

DR. ROBERT H. FELIX, Director of the National Institute of Mental Health, was testifying in October, 1953, before a Congressional committee investigating the extent of the major illnesses in this country. He had a seventy-page statement filled with carefully documented statistics on the overwhelming cost of mental illness in terms of human suffering, tax dollars, loss in income and industrial productivity, juvenile delinquency, crime, alcoholism, dope addiction, and so on. The documentation was so far-ranging in its impact that it was almost impossible to digest: It was somewhat like conceiving a clear picture of the holocaust resulting from the dropping of a series of hydrogen bombs upon our major cities.

Sensing the difficulty, Dr. Felix tried to project the impact of mental illness in the simplest way.

"Mr. Chairman," he said, addressing Representative Charles A. Wolverton, "I should like to mention one other figure, and I hesitate because I do not want to discourage you. . . . If the present birth rate remains constant, if the number of mentally ill who are hospitalized remains constant, and if the cost for hospitalizing the mentally ill remains constant, each year's crop of new babies will, because of the percentage of them who will go to mental hospitals, cost the taxpayers—this is just the taxpayer and not any private foundation—$800,000,000 before they die."

THE CHAIRMAN: It is time somebody began to think about this in a very serious way.

DR. FELIX: (*Deeply moved and pounding the table*) I wish to God they would, Mr. Chairman. . . . For some reason or another, gentlemen, there seems to be a feeling among many of the people in our country—the people on the highways and byways and my home in Kansas and your home wherever it may be—that if you forget about mental illness and ignore it, it will go away. . . . We hide this thing and cover it up; we alibi for it and bury our heads in the sand, gentlemen, and this is the greatest problem, the most expensive health problem, we have in this country (*Pounding the table hard*). Excuse me. I have to live with it every day.

THE CHAIRMAN: Your emphasis is excusable.

There are nine million people in the United States today suffering from some form of mental illness severe enough to warrant treatment. Few get this treatment. If there were nine million people suffering from typhoid fever—or merely nine hundred thousand—we would mass all our public-health preventive efforts into a gigantic effort to smash so crippling an epidemic. But is it not appallingly apparent that mental illness has reached epidemic proportions—that it smashes thousands of minds each year; that, hurricane-like, it spares neither big city, small town, nor rural community; that, like the polluted waters that breed the bacteria causing typhoid fever, it breeds and proliferates millions of social bacteria which are eating into the very warp and woof of our democracy?

No one denies that mental illness and other personality disturbances are usually significant factors in criminal behavior, juvenile delinquency, suicide, alcoholism, drug addiction, and the breaking-up of marriages. How can we overestimate the seriousness of the problem when:

a. About 1,750,000 serious crimes are committed each year.

b. There are about 100,000 thefts from department stores in the United States *every week*. According to Dr. Fabian Rourke, head of the Department of Psychology of New York's Manhattan College, a recent study in that city showed that twenty-nine department stores there caught 7,000 shoplifters and dishonest employees in *one year*. According to Dr. Rourke, fewer than 10 per cent of those arrested by store detectives were professional thieves, and fewer than 3 per cent of the amateur thieves stole for material gain. The great majority, he pointed out, stole because of problems of personality adjustment.

c. There are estimated to be 3,800,000 problem drinkers in the United States, 950,000 of whom are people with severe chronic alcoholism.

d. About 17,000 people commit suicide each year, and many times that number make suicide attempts.

e. For every four marriages in a year, there is one divorce.

f. Approximately 265,000 children between the ages of seven and seventeen are brought to juvenile courts each year for serious offenses against society. At the present rate of increasing delinquency, one of every five boys coming of military age in the next few years will have a juvenile court record, according to a report submitted to the 1954 Congress of Correction.

In an appearance before a Congressional committee in May, 1954, Dr. Leo Bartemeier, Chairman of the Council on Mental Health of the American Medical Association, delivered some strong observations on our callous treatment of emotionally disturbed children.

"Just a few months ago, the Child Welfare League of America published the first nation-wide study of treatment centers for disturbed children," Dr. Bartemeier told the committee. "The report, citing studies placing the number of children from homes broken by death, divorce or desertion at 6,000,000 and the number born out of wedlock annually at 150,000, pointed out that 80 per cent of American communities fail to provide adequate facilities for emotionally disturbed children. According to the report, twenty-five states have no child-guidance centers, and there are only thirty resident treatment centers in the country, which altogether are capable of treating only 1,500 children per year. These centers have ten times as many applicants as they are able to handle each year....

"Even more arresting," Dr. Bartemeier continued, "are the figures from a just completed three-year research project conducted under the auspices of the Columbia University Department of Psychiatry. It reported that 10 per cent of public-school children in the United States are emotionally disturbed and need mental guidance, but that the majority of the schools lack the trained personnel or facilities to aid these disturbed children. . . . The psychiatric personnel shortages in the schools are appalling—one psychiatrist for every 50,000 children, one psychologist for every 10,964 children, and one psychiatric social worker for every 38,461 children."

Manpower wastage is a burning topic these days in Washington. Experts produce reams of reports on ways in which our precious military manpower can be preserved. We are using civilians as kitchen police in Air Force mess halls so that more men may be spared for fighting units.

No number of civilian KP's can begin to make up for the tremendous military manpower losses caused by mental illness. In World War II, rejections for mental illness before induction, or discharges during service, deprived the armed forces of 2,564,184 young men in the prime of life. Forty per cent of our medical disability losses were due to neuropsychiatric disorders—a group large enough in size to man 177 Army infantry divisions, and larger than the total number of men the Army sent to the Pacific Theater of Operations during all of the last World War.

Our civilian losses are equally staggering. In terms of industrial productivity, at least one million man-years are lost each year because of mental illness. This is an economic loss of several billion dollars a year in wages, and several hundred million dollars a year in lost federal income taxes. Recent studies have pointed up the fantastic industrial losses due to the three Evil A's of industry—Alcoholism, Absenteeism, and Accidents. According to Dr. Ralph Collins of Eastman Kodak, one of only four psychiatrists employed by industry to reduce these losses, the vast majority of them are due to severe personality disturbances.

There are close to six hundred hospitals for the mentally ill, and their total bed capacity is in excess of 700,000. This is approximately one-half of all the hospital beds, both public and private, in this country.

Because 97 per cent of these patients are in tax-supported hospitals, it costs the American people more than one billion dollars a year to care for them and to pay pensions to veterans with psychiatric disorders. And the cost is rising at the astronomic rate of $100,000,000 a year, with no end in sight.

Every three minutes, the gates of a mental hospital open somewhere in the country to admit a victim of this disease. Each year, there are from twelve to sixteen thousand more patients in our public mental hospitals than there were the year before.

Testifying before a Senate committee in 1954, Dr. Kenneth Appel, then the President of the American Psychiatric Association, had this to say:

"We are on a treadmill, and we are losing 16,000 a year—that is, there is a 16,000 increase over the previous year. . . . And that means in ten years over $1,200,000,000 for bed construction alone."

Dr. Appel then pointed out that thousands of the mentally ill could not be admitted to mental hospitals because there were no beds available. Senator Edward Thye, incredulous, queried Dr. Appel:

"Where are those mental cases then if there are not facilities and beds available? Where are they? They cannot be at home if they get too violent."

"Some of them are in jails," said Dr. Appel, "some of them are lying on floors, and some of them are lying in triple-decker beds in state hospitals."

In the period between 1903 and 1950, the percentage of our population in long-term mental hospitals has doubled. Since 1939, the remarkable increase in our population has been outstripped, percentage-wise, by the increase of our mental hospital population.

The state governments, which have assumed the major responsibility for care of the mentally ill since Colonial days, have made heroic efforts these past few years to keep abreast of the increased flood of mental illness. In the past decade, state expenditures for mental health programs have increased more than 300 per cent, amounting to more than $560,000,000 in 1953. In a number of states, these programs cost more than one-third of the total operating budget. New York State, for example, spent $160,000,000 last year for care of its mentally ill. This was not only by far the largest departmental allocation in the budget, but was actually about 38 per cent of the entire State Purposes budget of New York.

Particularly since the close of World War II, state after state has floated bond issues to construct hospital beds to meet the mounting tide of admissions. Since 1945, an average of $200,000,000 a year has been appropriated by state legislatures for this purpose. A few years ago, New York appropriated $200,000,000 to provide sixteen thousand new beds in forty buildings. But the epidemic of mental illness mounts, and in November, 1954, New York voters approved a bond issue for an additional $350,000,000 of badly needed mental hospital construction. Will this bond issue be the last one? Not one mental health official I talked to in New York believed so.

Late in 1953, the Council of State Governments summarized the building situation this way:

"Overcrowding runs as high as 50 per cent in many states and estimates indicate an immediate national shortage of approximately 300,000 beds, which computed at the rate of $10,000 per bed, would call for immediate expenditure of three billion dollars for buildings alone.

"However, the problem does not cease even with expenditures of this magnitude. The number of people entering mental hospitals increases each year and one estimate for 1960 indicates a total mental hospital population of around 750,000. This figure would call for additional expenditures of $250,000,000,000 for buildings, or a total of $5,500,000,000. To this sum must be added the replacement of obsolescent structures."

If the future is dark at the state level, it is equally, if not more, dark at the Federal level. Back in 1945, when the Veterans' Administration launched its modern psychiatric program, the cost of caring for mentally ill veterans was about $44,000,000. In the fiscal year 1954 it had gone up 500 per cent—to more than $200,000,000 a year. In fiscal 1955, with pension and compensation costs included, the psychiatrically disabled veteran cost the Federal taxpayer approximately $632,000,000. And this is exclusive of construction costs; the Veterans' Administration has spent several hundred million dollars for construction of new beds since the end of World War II.

Depressing? As the average age of the veteran increases, more and more hospital beds will be needed. Authorities estimate that the hospital and compensation bill for psychiatrically disabled veterans will exceed one billion dollars within a few years.

Why are these figures so astronomical? Is it because we are pampering the mental patient, lavishing excess medical and social attention upon him?

In the Year of Our Lord 1955, in this democracy which is the apogee of civilized man, we were still spending less than $3.00 a day to feed, clothe, and give "medical care" to our mentally ill. In 1953, in one of the great states of the Midwest, patients were being fed on a budget of 17 cents a day. By contrast, we spend more than $20 a day for those suffering from physical ailments and bedded down in our general hospitals.

In the year 1953, the sovereign Empire State of New York spent less per capita to care for its mentally ill than it did to feed and maintain criminals confined to its prisons.

If we are spending only a few dollars a day to care for these unfortunates, how come total costs in the billions? Because, penny wise and pound foolish, we spend a pittance and sow the ugly harvest—thousands upon thousands of suffering human beings wasting their lives away in custodial institutions. According to figures compiled by the National Institute of Mental Health, the average length of stay of a mental patient in a state institution is eight years. Figured at an approximate annual per capita cost of $1,000, the more than 700,000 patients comprising the average daily mental hospital census in 1955 will cost the nation more than $5,500,000,000 (five and a half *billion* dollars) before they either die or are returned to society. If the maladies of these people could have been prevented or cured before the need for hospitalization, these people could have earned more than sixteen billions over the eight-year hospital span, and they would have paid Federal income taxes totaling several hundred million dollars on these earnings.

What is wrong with our mental hospitals? Why can't they achieve the improvement and recovery rates of our general medical and surgical hospitals?

Over the past several years, the Central Inspection Board of the American Psychiatric Association has officially inspected more than one hundred state mental hospitals. As its yardstick, it has used the minimum, rather lenient personnel standards of the American Psychiatric Association. At the 1954 National Governors' Conference, Dr. Mesrop A. Tarumianz, Chairman of the Inspection Board, told the assembled chief executives that not one state hospital inspected had met these minimum standards of the American Psychiatric Association! Several were placed upon the "approved" list because they came close to meeting the standards, and another handful were "conditionally approved" because they met 70 per cent of the standards.

Of late, a number of professional workers in the mental health field have begun to deplore frank discussion of the inadequacies of our mental hospitals. At meetings usually devoted to the problems of thumb-sucking in infants or the psychogenic rash in adolescence, they inform their lay audiences that these exposés of mental hospital conditions are destroying the "faith" of the general public in their work. They conveniently forget that from the pioneer crusading of Dorothea Lynde Dix and Clifford Beers on through the modern journalistic work of Albert Deutsch, Albert Maisel, and many other reporters has stemmed the limited improvement in our state mental hospital system.

Dr. Tarumianz, who has run one of the better state mental hospitals for thirty years and who is one of American psychiatry's most distinguished leaders, has carefully examined the reports on every hospital inspected by the American Psychiatric Association. Reporting on these findings at the 1954 National Governors' Conference, he turned to the governors assembled on the dais and hurled this bombshell at them:

"Conditions in our state mental hospitals are rotten. For want of a more adequate word, and I don't know that I could find a more adequate word, I can only tell you the state mental hospital system stinks."

His distinguished colleague, Dr. Kenneth Appel, was equally frank. As President of the American Psychiatric Association, Dr. Appel had this to say to several hundred hospital superintendents at the Fifth Mental Hospital Institute of the American Psychiatric Association:

"There are snake pits, more than have been written about. . . . Treatment can hardly be spoken of for the majority of the 700,000 patients in mental hospitals. It is mostly care and custody. For the most part, the care appears to be adequate from the point of view of clothing, food, sanitation, and kindness. However, it smacks of packing boxes, as a distinguished professional man who is familiar with our mental hospitals said to me. Mass methods, herding, and regimentation are the rule. Electroshock is available in most hospitals, but not insulin treatment in 40 per cent of our hospitals because of lack of adequate staff. Individual treatment, personal contact and conference, which are the keystones of modern psychiatric treatment or psychotherapy, are absent except in the rarest instances. It is practically absent in the majority of hospitals. Acute, intensive treatment which is imperative for good results is absent in many hospitals, or is done in a hasty, haphazard, super-ficial way. . . .

"The greatest frustration of the psychiatrist as a physician and a great tragedy from the humane point of view is that the majority of the state mental hospitals are omitting or greatly restraining the use of more successful methods of treatment chiefly because of lack of staff and facilities. Imagine what it would be like if you, as a physician, could not give insulin for diabetes, liver extract for anemia, or penicillin for peritonitis. This is the practical situation of the psychiatrist today in the state hospitals. This is un-businesslike, it is un-economic, it is inefficient, and it is un-American."

The problem of mental illness is not confined within the walls of our state mental hospitals. It is authoritatively estimated that for every in-patient hospitalized, there is another out in the community who is in immediate need of hospitalization. But there are no beds. The average hospital is already 20 to 30 per cent over-crowded. So the mentally sick person staggers wildly down the street, smashing himself and bruising those about him.

True, recent years have seen the establishment of more and more out-patient clinics where emotionally sick people can receive psy-chological first aid. But there are only about a thousand mental hygiene clinics in the entire country, and less than half of these are full-time operations.

Testifying before the Congress, Dr. Leo Bartemeier laid the facts on the line.

"Testimony presented at a health inquiry conducted by the House Interstate and Foreign Commerce Committee last fall indicated a national need for 840 additional full-time clinics," Dr. Bartemeier told the congressmen. "I daresay there is hardly a clinic in any part of this country which does not have a long waiting list. Even in New York City, where there are more clinics per person than anywhere else, a sick person has to wait six months to a year before receiving his first appointment. This is a very dangerous situation—thousands of upset, emotionally troubled people are capable of all sorts of antisocial activities during such a trying period."

There is not space enough to treat of the impact of the tensions of living in this modern society in which the pedestrian still moves at a leisurely pace, but the automobile hurtles along at seventy and eighty miles an hour and the jet-propelled airplane smashes the sound barrier. In his closing address as President of the American Psychiatric Association, Dr. Appel summed up the present challenge to psychiatry in these memorable words:

"Certainly psychiatry needs to rally every resource in meeting the problems it faces. In this period of instability, conflict, and rapid change, man's life is shot through with apprehension and fear, dissatisfaction and hostility—the primal, psychological reactions to danger and frustration. Anxiety and hostility, which arise when man's love, devotion, longings, and ambition are frustrated, are reflected in the rising burden of mental illness (a bigger problem than cancer, tuberculosis, and infantile paralysis combined); increasing juvenile delinquency; a divorce rate that in 1946 reached the figure of one in four (a 2,000 per cent increase in seventy-five years); an alcoholic bill of eight billion dollars (our bill for education is five billion dollars); nine million citizens handicapped by psychological illnesses; the repeated breakdowns from time to time of our economic machinery, and the international hostilities which, with the hydrogen bomb, the jet airplane, and biological warfare, menace our civilization. These are all destructive forces in men and society. Will Titan of Technology swallow and destroy us as the Titan Cronus devoured his own offspring?"

2. A PITTANCE

FOR THE

HUMAN MIND

WE ARE supposedly living in the Golden Age of Medical Research. Theoretically, all of us in this splendiferous country are persuaded of the great contributions of medical research in combating deadly diseases and prolonging our lives.

The President's Commission on the Health Needs of the Nation, which completed a five-volume survey of medical care in 1952, capsuled the attitude of the American people toward research in these words:

"Perhaps no field of human endeavor offers more in the way of possibilities for human betterment than that of medical research. During the past half century, medical discoveries have been key stepping stones to fuller and longer lives for the American people. Many of the diseases that claimed their victims with dramatic speed in 1900—typhoid fever, scarlet fever, whooping cough, measles, diphtheria, smallpox and malaria—have now become much less frequent causes of death. . . . In the short time from 1937 to 1949, the death rate has declined 14 per cent. . . . After sifting the evidence, both at panels in Washington and public hearings in the field, we conclude that the American people are aware of the enormous dividends to be reaped from intensified medical research. They desire to see it extended. The earned income of the American people has been accelerated several billion dollars a year through the rapid decline in the death rate since 1937; this same dramatic decline has brought several hundred million dollars of additional tax revenues to government each succeeding year."

However, when the Presidential report moves from attitudes to facts, it tells a different story about medical research expenditures:

"Last year's [1951] total expenditure of $180,000,000 amounted to only three-tenths of one per cent of the Nation's defense budget. It was less than the amount spent on monuments and tombstones."

And when the report gets over into the field of psychiatric research, all euphoria has departed:

"We received evidence at all of our field hearings and at several panels in Washington of the appalling lack of research in the field of mental disease," the report concludes. ". . . In the year 1950, Federal and State governments together spent about a billion dollars for hospital care and pensions for the mentally ill. . . . In the face of this enormous expenditure, the Nation spends only $6,000,000 a year for research in this neglected field. Over the five-year period 1946–51, grants for mental health research were less than 5 per cent of grants and contracts for all types of medical research. Our knowledge of mental illness today is in many ways as limited as that of undefined infections in the days when we lumped them all together as 'fevers.' "

The corrected figure for fiscal 1955 is $10,786,253 spent by Federal, state, and national voluntary agencies for research on mental illness. This munificent sum is the approximate cost of a single B-52 designed to drop a hydrogen bomb. The new program of the Department of Defense contemplates the construction of a fleet of these B-52's at a total cost in excess of $4,000,000,000. There is always money for more B-52's, but when those of us who testify for more psychiatric research ask the Congress for an additional million or two, the screams of "economy" and "where will we get the money?" can be heard over in Virginia.

For a number of years, the psychiatric profession was anything but outspoken in attacking the inadequate sums spent on psychiatric research. In hearings which I have observed and reported on both at the national and state level, psychiatrists invariably assumed the role of mendicants; they held their hands out in supplication and were appropriately rewarded with some splinters from the bottom of the barrel. However, they have recently taken courage from the example of a few outspoken laymen who come before the Congress each session and give their representatives a real working-over. Typical of these is a wealthy Alabama lumberman, Ben May, who comes up to Washington several times a year and gives luncheons for key congressmen. After the congressmen have consumed the thick steaks, Ben gets off his haunches and, in a high-pitched voice lubricated with deep conviction, takes them to task for the way they are spending his and the other taxpayers' money.

"If the Du Ponts were running this country," Ben told a group of Senators at one luncheon, "we would be spending ten times as much on research as we are spending now. Why? Because they learned that research pays off, that new discoveries create new wealth. Each year, the Du Ponts spend many times more on industrial research than we are spending on our most precious commodity—the human mind."

At a luncheon in June of last year, Ben got really worked up. After pointing out that the American people spend as much on goldfish as Federal, state, and private sources spend on psychiatric research, his voice hit a high, indignant contralto and his index finger waved accusingly as he chastised them.

"It is not a case of whether or not our country can afford to spend money for research into the mental diseases," he pointed out. "The proposition is better stated as follows: We are not rich enough, and we are not strong enough, to heedlessly accept this ever-continuing hemorrhage of lost manpower, lost military power, and lost money occasioned by mental illness when research can show us how to stop a considerable part of the hemorrhage."

Despite the eloquent pleas of Ben May and other dedicated laymen, psychiatric research is still getting the splinters at the bottom of the barrel. Last year, this country spent more than $4,000,000,000 in both governmental and nongovernmental research. Industry alone spent more than $1,000,000,000 searching for new products, and a number of industrial companies spent individually much more for research activities than the country spent collectively for psychiatric research.

Of late, much has been made of the fact that the Federal government is spending for scientific research and development twenty times what it spent before the outbreak of World War II. On the surface, a jump in research from $100,000,000 in 1940 to $2,000,000,000 in 1954 looks tremendously heartening. However, a breakdown of the over-all figure is a quick disillusioner. More than 85 per cent of the $2,000,000,000, about $1,700,000,000, is allocated to military research—how to build better and more potent weapons of destruction. Way down near the bottom of the list is psychiatric research, which is allocated its "proper" share of our national government's expenditures—less than one four-hundredth of the total!

Dr. Lawrence S. Kubie, distinguished psychoanalyst and Clinical Professor of Psychiatry at Yale University School of Medicine, has done some extensive studying of the financing of psychiatric research. In one project, he carried out a meticulous examination of support for psychiatric research in both an independent psychiatric facility and a medical school subdivision devoted to psychiatric research. He then matched these findings with the financing of organic medical research units in both these kinds of facilities. In matters of over-all budgets, ratio of research space to patient space, ratio of researchers to number of beds, ratio of laboratory technicians to number of beds—in all of these, and many more, the organic medical research facilities far outstripped the psychiatric ones.

"What impresses one first is that in neither of these outstanding psychiatric organizations are any beds endowed for purely research purposes," Kubie wrote in *Science*. "As a result, research must be carried on almost as a side issue, paralleling the main stream of clinical and teaching services. . . . Another study of two more such psychiatric units, one independent and one a subdivision, confirms these figures in every essential feature. Furthermore, from a fairly close knowledge of leading psychiatric institutions all over the country, it can be said that, although there are some in which the picture may be a shade more favorable, there is none that departs materially from the general level of equipment for reseach, none that in research facilities, research space, research personnel or research budget compares even remotely with those great research units that have been our pioneers of research in organic medicine."

On the basis of these laboriously accumulated findings, Kubie concludes:

"Psychiatric research in this country is indeed being starved to death, starved for lack of funds, starved for lack of space, and starved for lack of a personnel adequate either in numbers or in maturity. . . . Evidently, in spite of the enormous amount of talk about psychiatry in this country, there is an even greater failure on the part of the country to meet the challenge of its psychiatric needs. America is still only talking about mental hygiene. It is not acting. . . . When we look at our figures, we need no longer feel surprise that, in spite of all the popular talk about psychiatry, not one of the psychiatric discoveries of the past fifty years was made in this country."

The 1954 session of the United States Congress provided an illuminating contrast in the kinds of support given various programs.

During the week of April 12, the House of Representatives opened debate on appropriations for the Department of Agriculture for 1955. The House Appropriations Subcommittee had allocated $82,059,453 solely for agricultural research, $3,324,730 more than the year before, but $4,206,255 under what the Administration had asked for.

From the opening bell of the debate on the bill, the screams about the cut in agricultural research reverberated with a mighty fury from the well of the House. Dire predictions were made of the holocaust which would follow if the cut were allowed to stand. Mr. Matthews of Florida cried out in a voice charged with emotion: "I believe historians will agree that one of the chief reasons for the decline of any civilization has been the ruin of the soil. Certainly Rome is a great example of what will happen when people turn away from the land and permit it to fall into ruin."

For three days, the debate raged. Each speaker in turn pointed up the perils if research were to be reduced on the Citron black fly, the Mexican fruit fly, Hall's scale eradication (affecting two counties in California), grasshopper and mormon cricket control, cattle ticks, scabies, the Hessian fly, rust-resistant grains, the golden nematode, commercial fertilizer, the corn borer, swine feeding, etc., etc.

Mr. Horan of Washington delivered himself of a massive oration on the value of agricultural research:

"To produce enough for the 1975 population, our present flocks would have to average 241 eggs per hen. It is virtually impossible on the basis of present knowledge. The 241 average exceeds the best average records obtained in such an example of advanced application of available knowledge about breeding, feeding and care of poultry as the Connecticut egg-laying contest. . . . Since a ceiling on the frontiers of knowledge about egg production has persisted, obviously the backlog of unused information that farmers can adopt has been considerably reduced."

The House members, stunned by this depressing knowledge, stared at the ceiling. Mr. Horan began warming up:

"Research has made a great contribution to agriculture. I recognize that important contributions have been made by the extension service, by financing institutions, machinery manufacturers, farm-management specialists and many others. The alertness and initiative of the American farmer and the American system of free enterprise have been especially important. Nevertheless, in every case, research was the foundation on which these accomplishments were based."

To any House member who doubted the potency and supreme value of research, Mr. Horan cited a few benefits:

"Research was the vital key that opened the way to an average increase of 45 per cent in crop yields in the last twenty-five years, of 20 per cent in milk per cow, and of more than 50 per cent in eggs per hen.

"Hybrid corn has increased average yields about 30 per cent, resulting in an increase of at least $750,000,000 in farm income for the Nation as a whole.

"Development of rust-resistant grains has added an estimated $500,000,000 a year to farm income.

"Use of vitamin B-12 as a feed supplement for chickens produces three-pound broilers on two pounds less feed and in two weeks less time than is required using an animal protein diet, which is more expensive.

"Research into the habits of the Hessian fly has made it possible to eliminate losses as high as $100,000,000 annually by postponing wheat planting until after the fly lays her eggs in the fall."

And then, a note of urgency in his voice, Mr. Horan implored his colleagues to move quickly to meet the emergency:

"The time to begin the intensive effort that will be necessary is now. Time is especially important in research if scientific experiments are to be of maximum usefulness. And if science cannot produce the answers in time, where will we get them? . . . The materials and methods farmers will be using in 1959 or 1960 already for the most part have passed the laboratory and test-pilot stages, but additional research, in some cases of considerable proportions, is needed at once if the clues of today are to be developed into practices, materials or methods for use when needed after 1960."

Mr. Horan's colleagues moved quickly. Mr. Hoeven of Iowa, up to then a solid member of the economy bloc, rose and bellowed forth:

"Proper research always takes money, and lots of it. . . . The future of Iowa agriculture depends largely upon agricultural research. . . . Specifically, we need more research in combating the corn borer, a pest which does immeasurable damage to our corn crop. . . . We want to know whether it is best to spread the fertilizer on the land or to place it in the furrows between the corn rows. Much remains to be done in this field, and only research can give us the needed answers. . . . We must find the best method of drying our grain and corn at the least possible expense."

Mr. Laird of Wisconsin rose to talk of the Extension Service, which takes the results of research out to the farmers in the field. Although the House Subcommittee had raised the allocation for this service more than $3,000,000 over the previous year—to a new high of $38,876,514—Mr. Laird worried aloud about the future of American youth.

"Only one out of five farm families now enjoy the advantages of 4-H club work," Mr. Horan told a shocked House. "An average county Extension agent carries a load of 600 4-H members per year of time given to 4-H club work. . . . The present generation of twenty million children and youth growing up on farms and in rural areas need knowledge, skills, and attitudes based on the very latest and best technology that science has to offer if they are to achieve success in the atomic age ahead of us. . . . Education lags behind all other phases of agriculture. We need research, but we are far behind our knowledge now."

When the bursts of oratory had subsided, amendment after amendment hit the floor to raise the allocations, not only over the Subcommittee recommendations, but even over the much higher Administration requests. Some of the economy bloc's most famed knife-wielders joined in the fun. Representative Clarence P. Cannon, who has been accused of having actuarial ink in his veins, offered an amendment to raise the School Lunch Program to $83,000,000, fifteen million more than the Committee wanted and six million more than the high Administration request. The amendment swept through.

Representative H. Carl Andersen, who was trying to defend the bill as Chairman of the Subcommittee, cried out bitterly as the hurricane of amendments struck. Pointing out that his committee had been most generous, that, for example, it had given $150,000 more for control of the pink bollworm than the Eisenhower Administration had requested, Mr. Andersen warned House members:

"Lists distributed in this Chamber today appeal to you on the basis of what your State stands to gain by the proposals for increases being sought. Are you going to succumb to such pressures? I personally am not. My committee has brought a good bill to the floor, not a dime over the budget, and I intend to stand by it."

As member after member succumbed to the powerful pressures of the bloc, Mr. Andersen rose again and, in words rarely heard on the House floor, castigated his own leadership:

"There came to me news that a meeting was held in the White House, that pressure had been brought to bear from certain groups throughout the Nation. Farm groups, dissatisfied with our allocation of funds in this bill, appealed to the White House for aid—yes, and evidently these groups were sustained in their pleadings, because seemingly suggestions were relayed to my leadership here to agree today to considerable increases in this bill. . . . My leadership has deserted me."

The understatement of the year. The House rammed through a whopping $191,700,000 for the Agricultural Conservation Program despite this outright attack upon the program by Representative Leslie Arends of Illinois, one of the Republican Party's big guns:

"Those of us who are tremendously interested in agriculture—all of us, of course, believe in true soil conservation practices; however, during the past years, and we are still at it . . . we are still making available payments for fertilizers for our farmers, paying them to put lime on their land and to do terracing and engage in other practices. Can the gentleman give any good reason why we should pay the farmers of this country to continue these practices that have proven so beneficial to them through all these years? Do they not want to improve this farmland themselves?"

The Soil Conservation Service, which provides technical aid to farmers, was voted a booming $71,427,000 despite the outcry of a number of members that the Federal government was already putting up $14 for every state dollar spent in conserving the soil.

Finally, Mr. Andersen could take no more. The Washington *Post* of April 15, in a story headlined "HOUSE RESTORES SLASHES, VOTES AGRICULTURE A BILLION," described Mr. Andersen's final moments in these words:

"Eventually, Andersen declared that since there appeared to be wide agreement to blow the ceiling off the Agriculture bill, he was 'not going to be put in the position of voting against the farmers' interests. . . . I'll do what I've wanted to do all along, and give the farmers what I've thought they should have, regardless of the cost.

" 'If the lid has been blown off,' said Andersen, 'and I have no fiscal responsibility, why God bless you.' "

About a month later, hearings were held before a Senate Appropriations Subcommittee on the fiscal 1955 budget proposed for the National Institute of Mental Health. The Eisenhower Administration requested $12,460,000 for all the activities of the Institute—research, training, clinical and community services, and the operation of intramural psychiatric research at the Institute's Clinical Center. The National Mental Health Committee appeared at the hearings to protest the grave inadequacy of the Administration sum. In its prepared testimony, it pointed out that the Administration did not allow one cent for construction of badly needed psychiatric research laboratories, although there were carefully screened and validated requests totaling more than $22,000,000 from hard-pressed medical schools, private hospitals, and research centers in all parts of the country. Furthermore, the Administration proposed the retention of a severe cut it had instituted the year before in governmental aid for the establishment of mental health clinics. The Administration cut the year before had resulted in the closing of ten desperately needed clinics, and reductions in services in eighty-four other clinics; this in the face of official testimony by the Director of the National Institute of Mental Health that there was an immediate need for 840 more full-time mental clinics.

On the morning of May 20, the hearings opened in a small room in the Senate wing of the Capitol. There were no television cameras present; they were busy in another part of the Capitol covering that outbreak of mental illness formally described as the "Army-McCarthy Hearings." The hearing was scheduled for 10 A.M., but it was 10:20 before it got under way. Of the eleven Senators who were members of the Subcommittee, only two were present at the outset. Three others came in later in the morning.

One of the witnesses appearing to testify for the National Mental Health Committee's budget proposal of $29,550,000 was Dr. Kenneth Appel, President of the American Psychiatric Association. There wasn't time to hear the carefully prepared formal statement that Dr. Appel had labored over for several weeks and had come to Washington at his own expense to deliver. However, Dr. Appel, an outspoken, courageous individual who pulls no punches, used the little time at his disposal to decry the low salary scales and general financial malnutrition prevalent in the field of psychiatric research. In answer to a query as to what his profession was doing about research, he forthrightly replied:

"If you were in a medical school, as I am or as Dr. English is, and had a bright young fellow who wants to go into research and finds no funds with which to devote his life to research, and finds his colleagues have gone out into the community making $15,000 and $18,000 a year after five or seven years of training, and you have two or three bright young fellows, as I have at the present time, and you have $4,000 or $5,000 to offer him for research, and he is trying to raise his family, you would feel very distressed, not only for this fellow and for your science but for the community and for your country."

SENATOR THYE: He would have to be so imbued with the desire to be that specialist that he would deprive his family and everything else; otherwise he would not take that course.

DR. APPEL: And I know young fellows who are not having children, who are interested in research, because there are not funds to support them to do research in this field.

Senator Harley Kilgore of West Virginia, intrigued by Dr. Appel's statement, had a question:

"Has it not been a fact that for a long time we have starved our basic research and relied upon European research in this country?"

DR. APPEL: There is no question about it.

SENATOR KILGORE: In other words, shall we say we have starved the research people by low salary jobs and things of that kind and made it unattractive?

DR. APPEL: There is no question about that. That is so. Not one of the modern methods being used in psychiatry has been discovered in this country.

Senator Thye then moved into the questioning:

"There was a question I was going to ask, Doctor. You said that we have not made the actual basic findings in psychiatry in this land. Where were they made and by whom, Doctor? Who has made the greatest progress in psychiatry?"

DR. APPEL: Sakel in insulin, Cerletti and Bini in electroshock, Moniz in brain surgery, and Freud in psychoanalysis.

SENATOR THYE: In other words, in electroshock, and so forth—who first conducted electroshock?

DR. APPEL: Cerletti and Bini.

SENATOR THYE: In what country?

DR. APPEL: Italy, Sakel in Vienna, Freud in Vienna, Moniz in Portugal.

SENATOR THYE: That is what I wanted the record to show. Here, with all our vast brains, which have shown that they can produce and invent in industry, we have not channeled these brains into this great problem of mental disease. . . .

Despite the excellence of Dr. Appel's testimony, time was running out on the National Health Committee. The last witness, Dr. O. Spurgeon English, Chairman of the Department of Psychiatry at Temple University and one of the biggest names in American psychiatry, had also come down at his own expense to testify. He filed his formal statement to save time and was giving a five-minute highlighting of his major points when the Chairman interjected:

"Will you now highlight your statement? We are running way over the schedule. Will you please now highlight what is in your report so that we can try to get back on schedule? We have some people here who are supposed to be testifying at eleven o'clock, you see."

Dr. English cut off his remarks. There were six witnesses, including some very distinguished medical authorities, waiting to be squeezed into the hour devoted to the hearing on the 1955 budget for the National Institute for Neurological Diseases and Blindness.

Two months after the hearings, the National Mental Health Committee got the bad news. The House of Representatives had tacked an extra million on to the Administration request, and the Senate had added to this only $687,500. The final figure—$14,147,-

500—was more than $15,000,000 short of the minimum budget asked by the National Mental Health Committee. And not one cent for construction of research laboratories.

This $14,147,500 was not all for research; only about $6,000,000 went for that. Contrast this, if you will, with the action of the House of Representatives in adding more than $14,000,000 for agricultural research, raising the total sum for that activity to more than $92,-000,000!

Agriculture fared even better during the 1955 session of Congress. Under the headline "PRESIDENT GETS FARM BILL THAT TOPS HIS FUND PLEA," the morning newspapers of May 18, 1955, noted that, for the third straight year, Congress had voted farm funds far in excess of those requested by President Eisenhower. One item is worthy of particular note. Despite continued protests that soil conservation subsidies to farmers were bounties ladled out to them on the simple proviso that they pledge not to ruin their own soil, Congress voted a fantastic $250,000,000 for this program. This one item in the Agricultural Appropriations Bill was more than fourteen times the sum the 1955 Congress voted for all the activities of the National Institute of Mental Health.

One important qualification is required at this point. While it is true that the United States Congress is far from lavish in its support of psychiatric research, its interest and support are exemplary when contrasted with the actions of most of the state legislatures. Up until a couple of years ago, it was practically impossible to get a state legislative committee to hold a hearing on psychiatric research, much less appropriate any significant sums for it. As one state Senator remarked to me just a few years ago when I asked him to take an interest in psychiatric research:

"What kind of research can you do on a bunch of nuts? If they're crazy, what can you learn from them? The only thing they need is food and a place to sleep."

But research on hens? Yes, a thousand times yes! Our whole way of life depends on the highly productive hen!

3. OBSTACLES TO PSYCHIATRIC RESEARCH

OF ALL the millions spent for the care and treatment of the mentally ill and the mentally retarded, only about one per cent of the total is spent on research—on trying to find out the causes of mental illness and the best methods of treatment. No modern industry could stay in business if it so neglected research. I say we are not fooling anyone but ourselves when we brag of accomplishments in the field of mental health and I challenge any Governor or Legislature, including our own, to deny that mental hospitals are abominable, undesirable and unfavorable to the recovery of patients. It is only through the Grace of God that so many patients get well. In the forty years that I have been in this work there have been vast improvements in the United States—in scientific advances, in the raising of living standards, in every field but that of mental health, and there we have scarcely advanced at all. The reasons for mental illness cannot be found unless we have research such as industry has."

The above is part of a speech delivered on May 18, 1954, by Dr. Mesrop A. Tarumianz to sixty outstanding citizens appointed by Governor Caleb Boggs to a Delaware Committee on Research and Training. Dr. Tarumianz runs a state mental hospital at Farnhurst which, up until very recently, was the only state mental hospital in the sixteen-state Southern region approved for a three-year residency in psychiatry. Moreover, as Chairman of the Central Inspection

Board of the American Psychiatric Association, he has at his disposal more facts about our mental hospitals than any other American.
His psychiatric colleagues know this, and they are actually afraid to
tangle with him at public meetings. However, their guilt feelings
about the situation are strong, and they release them in technical
journals or within the safe confines of professional meetings.

For the past twenty years or more, there have been articles galore
attempting to explain the paucity of psychiatric research. Back in
1933, Drs. John Whitehorn and Gregory Zilboorg tiptoed into the
safe waters of *The American Journal of Psychiatry* with an article
entitled "Present Trends in American Psychiatric Research."

"A definite increase in facilities for psychiatric research, both
within older institutions and in newly organized agencies, is to be
noted," Drs. Whitehorn and Zilboorg wrote, although they failed to
specify where these supposed increases were taking place. "Complete data regarding these increased facilities are still lacking. It
would be one of the valuable functions of a research committee to
compile such data and keep them up to date; such data should also
include a detailed record of research projects which various investigators happen to work on. Some information along these lines
is being gathered by the National Committee for Mental Hygiene."

Many an autumn leaf has fallen since 1933, and the National
Committee for Mental Hygiene, reconstituted but not revivified as
the National Association for Mental Health, is supposedly still
gathering information. In desperation, the governors of the forty-
eight states ordered their own survey of the extent of research in
state mental hospitals, and that superb study was published in 1953.
In 1954, the National Mental Health Committee brought out *What
Progress Against Mental Illness?*, a brochure detailing research
projects in various parts of the country.

In their 1933 article, Drs. Whitehorn and Zilboorg also touched
upon the formation of psychiatric cults whose feuding impeded the
progress of sound scientific observation.

"It is unfortunate when the cool and intelligent study of such
important matters becomes obscured by heated misunderstandings
over terms like 'Oepidus complex' and 'the castration threat,'" the
learned doctors wrote. "It is earnestly to be desired that, in this
difficult field, questions of absolute truth and universal validity be

set aside and attention concentrated upon the experimental study of working hypotheses and provisional concepts."

Some more autumn leaves have fallen, but the feuds are still blooming. Psychoanalytic institutes in all parts of the country are still expelling disciples for doctrinal deviations, casting them out of the pure-oxygen castles into a cruel world tarnished with carbon dioxide. At the 1954 meetings of the American Psychiatric Association, a woman psychiatrist who served brilliantly in the Armed Forces and with the Veterans' Administration told me of how the then President of the American Psychoanalytic Association had informed her she couldn't become part of his Institute because of her lack of appreciation of the importance of the Oedipus complex. This same former President of the American Psychoanalytic Association also writes letters to university presidents attacking chairmen of departments of psychiatry who want to incorporate psychoanalytic training into the curriculum of the medical schools. The fact that the psychiatric residents demand this training, and that the state mental hospital systems and medical schools must offer it or lose many desperately needed trainees, is very much beside the point to this individual. The main object is to hold the doctrinal line against heresies, and the patient be damned.

So serious has this cultist feuding become, and so detrimental to research progress in the field, that Dr. Kenneth Appel devoted a major part of his 1954 farewell address as President of the American Psychiatric Association to a discussion of it.

"Dichotomies in psychiatry should be mentioned," he told several thousand of his squirming colleagues assembled in the Kiel Auditorium in St. Louis. "There are the psychiatrists who use electroshock very frequently and others who employ psychotherapy almost exclusively. It is easy for psychiatrists using shock to neglect psychotherapy. The psychotherapists at times overlook opportunities when shock would be helpful. In personal attitudes, these psychiatrists often look down on one another. You cannot see eye to eye with a person you look down upon. We need more 'looking eye to eye' in psychiatry. As in so many things, 'either-or' thinking is an artificial attempt to simplify. . . .

"Much of psychotherapy, it seems to me, is too conscious, too intellectual and conceptual, too verbal and reflective, too formalized and too artificial, obsessive, and ritualistic. It neglects feelings, impulses, sub-verbal, and physiological communications. The spontaneity of human responses and human potentialities are often not capitalized on in trying to put feeling into words. Serendipity and the circumstances of life at times produce changes that elaborate therapies do not seem to touch. There is a tendency to be deductive rather than inductive and experimental. Much therapy tries to make a sophisticated mature adult out of an infant or child."

Dr. Appel then dealt very frankly with the war of words which has done immeasurable harm to psychiatry, jeopardizing public confidence in it.

"There is too much name-calling, which used to be applied to Kraepelinian descriptive psychiatry," he warned his colleagues. "One school of thought may be called superficial, another conservative; this one is rigid, controlling, classical, and historical; that one flexible, experimental, radical, and revolutionary. This one is described as vaguely eclectic. One school emphasizes libido and its development, another hostility. One builds its theory on basic anxiety. Another uses conscious analysis, reasoning, and even exhortation. This one relies too much on anthropology and religion. Many, perhaps all, rely on serendipity. All this is understandably disturbing to many young psychiatrists and to the public. As a matter of fact, results of different intellectual formulas do not seem to show significant differences in therapeutic efficiency. . . .

"Psychoanalysis has brought the greatest contribution in the history of psychiatry; it brought light where there was darkness, order where there was chaos, and understanding where there was only description. It was built up, however, on the model of nineteenth-century thinking with regard to cause and effect and determinism, a system now changed by present-day mathematicians and physicists. I believe that some of these early prepossessions, assumptions, and emphases account for some of the failures in psychoanalytic and psychodynamic therapy—in addition to the fact that younger physicians often tend to carry the principles of psychoanalysis into the practice of general psychiatry when it is not appropriate and not indicated by psychoanalytic theory. . . . Psychotherapy is not definitive, proven, with rules established for all time."

Finally, Dr. Appel dealt with the weaknesses apparent in so much of current psychiatric research.

"Most groups do not recognize the selectivity of observation, emphasis and interpretation," he charged. "Observations are selected, eliminated, or suppressed following deductive methods. Curiosity, observation, and independent thinking are guided and often controlled—processes our patients are urged to avoid. Therapy may become a deductive search for confirmation of theory, instead of being flexible and varied, inductive and individualized according to the needs of the patient. Partial remedies for this situation are: more objectivity in our studies and training; more historicity; more scientific methods and evaluation; more extension of the ideas of a university education in training a psychiatrist. Much of our training is assertion, conviction, and indoctrination rather than education. Restriction of interest, curiosity, and spontaneity is constricting, devitalizing, and castrating.

"It would be well to ask: What is the proof of the value of this type of treatment? What is the evidence of that theory? What are the results? Have they been subjected to statistical scrutiny? Are ideological tools being used with unwarranted assumptions, personal preferences, or just convictions? What do evaluation studies as to psychotherapy show? What is psychotherapy? Forty experts give forty different answers. Institutes and clinics exist where practice is purely psychological, where medical examinations, medical supervision, laboratory examinations, the use of drugs are not practiced. Psychotherapy and psychodynamics have been so emphasized that they are taken for the whole of psychiatry."

Another giant of American psychiatry, Dr. Karl Menninger, has given much thought of late to the inhibitory effects of the current psychiatric residency upon the development of the research attitude. Over the past generation, Dr. Karl has supervised the training of more psychiatrists than any of his contemporaries. Although a leading teacher and writer in the field of psychoanalysis, he has been outspoken in pointing out its limitations.

In "The Contribution of Psychoanalysis to American Psychiatry," a brilliant lecture delivered before the Royal Medico-Psychologic Society of Medicine in London in July, 1953, Dr. Karl had this to say about the current psychoanalytic craze:

"Freud, it will be recalled, always had grave misgivings about the overpopularity of psychoanalysis in America. He was afraid that its essential principles would become diluted and compromised.

Many of those of us who do both psychiatric and psychoanalytic teaching have shared his concern in recent years, although for somewhat different reasons than those of Freud. For there is no doubting its popularity. Thus, although there is a great shortage of psychiatrists in America, there are approximately one thousand candidates now registered as undergoing pyschoanalytic training. This is almost as many as the total number of doctors currently receiving basic psychiatric training. ... What happens is that after completing a residency in psychiatry, those residents who can get staff positions in the hospital or in the medical school then begin their psychoanalytic training, and as soon as they have finished this, the trend is for them to leave the medical school or the public hospital and go into private practice, limiting themselves to psychoanalytic treatment.

"The reasons for this are numerous: it is indeed a fascinatingly interesting subject; it is more remunerative than public hospital service; it requires less exertion; it has fewer frustrations; it is often more fashionable; it enlists one in a closely linked group of scientific workers concentrating upon a speciality within a speciality, and it makes for a kind of security and steadiness of income which is very appealing to young men entering private practice. But, nonetheless, it has serious drawbacks both for the physician and for the public. It restricts the experience of the physician to a very small number of patients; as one young doctor put it, 'I hate to face the prospect of spending the rest of my life treating an average of four patients a year' (that is, eight patients a day seen daily for an average period of two years). It is a disadvantage for the public in that it makes for a situation in which a private patient is either considered a proper subject for psychoanalytic treatment or else a case for someone else; and that 'someone else' is apt to be a colleague who similarly overspecializes and treats most of his patients with electroshock therapy. The psychiatrist who functions with catholicity as a counsellor for troubled people is to be found less frequently in general practice than in the public psychiatric hospital and psychiatric clinics which, as I have intimated above, are woefully understaffed."

Dr. Karl then told his distinguished audience of the harmful effects of psychoanalytic training upon research:

"But quite aside from these effects on distribution of psychiatric skills in the national community, the great success of psychoanalysis in America has had other negative effects. For one thing, it has definitely impaired descriptive clinical observation. The young physician, intent on understanding and explaining symptoms on the basis of a hypothesis, is less inclined to be interested in learning to describe accurately what the patient seems to be experiencing and manifesting. An attitude of patronizing indifference toward the acquisition of systematic historical material, either biographic or pathographic, is justified by the glib excuse that since the patient has probably forgotten or repressed the most significant incidents in his life, it is a waste of time to collect conscious memories. . . ."

Another leader in American medicine, Dr. Alan Gregg, has tried over several decades to improve both the quantity and quality of psychiatric research and training. As Director of the Medical Sciences Division of the Rockefeller Foundation, he was invited to deliver a critique of psychiatry at the Centenary Meeting of the American Psychiatric Association in Philadelphia in 1944.

"No other speciality of medicine has had a history so strange, nor a relation to human thought so intimate as psychiatry," Dr. Gregg told his audience. "The three most powerful traditions or historical heritages of psychiatry are still, as they have been from time immemorial, the horror which mental disease inspires, the power and subtlety with which psychiatric symptoms influence human relations, and the tendency of man to think of spirit as not only separable but already separate from body. These are the inherent, the inevitable handicaps of psychiatry.

"So great is the horror of mental disease that the fear of madness has stimulated madness itself in the unreasoning conduct it precipitates. For centuries the insane were imprisoned or put away and no one thought of insanity as a condition directly comparable with other diseases. And when the confinement became kinder—a blessed relief that is crystallized in the word 'asylum'—the insane were still segregated from the rest of society, still feared and loathed. Generations of physicians who assumed that mind and body were separate merely speculated about insanity when they should have observed, compared, and classified."

Dr. Gregg then dealt with psychiatry's isolation from the main stream of medicine, one of the major obstacles in the path of multidisciplinary research.

"We would all agree that psychiatry is the most isolated of the specialities in medicine," he said. ". . . As a natural consequence of their isolation, psychiatrists speak a dialect, a special lingo more productive of resentment than comprehension or interest on the part of their medical brethren, and so defeat the very object of language, which is communication of ideas. Another consequence of isolation, provincialism, with all its clannish distrust of outsiders and its equally petty loyalties, appears too often as the signature of your speciality in the estimation of other medical men. . . . I cannot escape the impression that psychoanalysts usually resent or spurn requests for proof or experimental verification of their postulates, that they ride causation to the virtual exclusion of chance or correlation as explanations for human conduct, and that as a theory of human conduct psychoanalysis seems curiously sterile of success in orderly social co-operation—at least as far as one can judge from the chronic disharmonies prevailing among analysts."

Finally, a plea for well-trained research workers:

"In suggesting a new orientation for psychiatry, I could mention a number of points of reference. For example, a valuable addition to the ranks of psychiatry would be some recruits whose training and formation of mind in the more exact sciences would operate in the direction of insisting on more precision, a search for measurable phenomena, more emphasis upon phenomenon and less upon noumenon, and more discrimination in the examination of evidence."

When one turns from the academic debate about the reasons for the paucity of psychiatric research to recent studies based upon the accumulation of considerable evidence, one is all the more impressed with Dr. Kubie's thesis that psychiatric research is starving to death.

In 1951, the National Governors' Conference unanimously passed a resolution introduced by Governor G. Mennen Williams of Michigan calling for a study of research and training programs conducted by the states. In the course of its two-year study, the Council of State Governments came up with some remarkable figures. Its first surveys indicated that all forty-eight states together were spending only about $4,000,000 on psychiatric research—this against a forty-eight-state expenditure of $500,000,000 a year for care of the mentally ill. The Council study listed 621 research projects at the state level, a somewhat imposing figure until it is analyzed in detail. Actually, only 61 of the 621 projects cost $25,000 or more—a really minimum figure for a research project of any scope. More than two hundred of the projects were budgeted at less than $750 apiece, not even enough to pay janitorial services on a going project.

Perturbed by this evidence, the Council sent lengthy questionnaires to all state mental health officials and directors of research projects in an effort to discover the major obstacles to more adequate research. Both the state officials and the research directors agreed in pinpointing three big bottlenecks to more research: insufficient appropriations, shortages of research workers at current low salaries, and lack of time of hospital personnel for research due to the pressure of daily care of patients.

Noting that only ten states included specific research items in their 1952 budgets, and that state expenditures for research averaged less than one per cent of state mental health budgets, the Council then asked state mental health officials to grade their opinions of the adequacy of present research levels on a scale ranging from "much too much" to "much too little." Of the forty-four officials who replied, twenty said "much too little" research was going on, nineteen voted for "too little," only five thought it was "about right," and nary a one checked off the "too much" or "much too much" categories.

When they were asked what percentage of the mental health budget should be devoted to research, the overwhelming majority of state officials answered that it should be 4 per cent or more. If the minimum percentage figure were adopted as an appropriations base, it would entail an annual forty-eight-state expenditure of about $20,000,000, as against the $4,000,000 being spent now.

A follow-up query asked several hundred psychiatric research project directors this: "If you had adequate money and personnel, would the situation in your institution permit you to develop few or many mental health research projects?" The vast majority of answers fell into the "many" or "very many" categories.

A few months after the publication of the Council of State Governments study, the Group for the Advancement of Psychiatry, which represents the most progressive and dynamic thinking in psychiatry today, published an even more detailed and meticulous diagnosis of the maladies besetting psychiatric research.

"The relative absence of research activity in psychiatry has a complex basis," the 1954 report noted. "Some of the most obvious reasons are: (1) lack of personnel; (2) lack of professional time; (3) lack of funds; (4) lack of training in research methodology; (5) lack of rewards for research; (6) the complexity of the psychiatric field; and (7) lack of administrative support."

On the key question of shortage of personnel, the Group presented some telling figures:

"There are 7,608 fellows and members of the American Psychiatric Association as listed in the 1953 directory. Many of these psychiatrists have in one way or another indicated interest in research and list scientific publications, but the number of them actually engaged in full-time or major research activities is very small. The extent of published research, if we eliminate that which bears directly upon therapy, is almost negligible. There is, in fact, relatively little systematic research being carried out by psychiatrists if we exempt the therapeutic and diagnostic areas."

In the discussion of funds, the GAP report pretty much substantiated the findings of the Council of State Governments:

". . . Few psychiatric institutions have funds per patient that can compare with the funds per patient of non-psychiatric institutions. Free time for research demands not only administrative officers who understand the need, but also funds which these officers may use to support research, so that they can shift the patient-load to enable a competent investigator to spend his time on psychiatric research. Moreover, research in psychopathology requires space and equipment; it cannot be conducted effectively in ward corridors, in offices which are subject to invasion by telephone calls or visitors, or in unused porches or linen closets—all of which have been the locus of some research projects."

However, the report makes its most significant contribution in its analysis of the professional inhibitions and complexities which impede psychiatric research. Its discussion of the lack of training in research methodology is most penetrating:

"Medical students and interns rarely receive even the most elementary training in research methodology for work in psychopathology. No amount of courage and enthusiasm can counterbalance this lack. Since few hospitals have available an expert on the design of behavioral experiment and clinical psychopathological investigation, the would-be research worker without such training has difficulty in conducting competent research. Also, only a few teachers of psychiatry at the level of either undergraduate medical training or residency training are research oriented and, more important, even fewer are themselves engaged in any research project. All this contributes to the relatively large proportion of reports of single cases and simple statistical studies found in current psychiatric literature. . . . An important factor in the lack of training in research methodology is the absence within many medical school departments of psychiatry of sections or divisions of psychopathology or psychodynamics where basic research can be carried on without concern for clinical demands."

And the twin questions of lack of rewards balanced against the heartbreaking complexity of the field:

"Though research in some fields, notably in physics and chemistry as well as in general medicine, has a kind of mystical glamour, the same prestige and status do not appear to be accorded to psychiatric research. No important research tradition exists in psychiatry with which the young psychiatrist can identify. . . . Another handicap to the recruitment of researchers in the area of psychopathology is the apparently overwhelming complexity of the field. . . . He [the investigator] may even reach the position of throwing up his hands in despair, believing that it is impossible to apply ordinary scientific methodology to the subtle manifestations of psychopathology. His despair may increase with the recognition of the intangibility of many psychopathologic concepts, the lack of well-defined and precise units of measurement, the multiplicity of causes for psychopathologic phenomena, and the many plausible though untestable hypotheses to account for these phenomena."

After this detailed and thorough analysis of the obstacles to more widespread psychiatric research, the GAP study makes a basic plea for collaborative research in which the various medical specialists— biochemists, physiologists, pharmacologists, internists, neurologists, psychiatrists, etc.—join together in a specifically planned investigation of a single mental malady.

"Even though more fruitful research, perhaps most of it, is now done by individuals working alone," the report states, "the basic sciences underlying the practice of psychiatry are rapidly advancing to a point where better integrated formulations may be hoped for. . . . Usually this involves the work of an investigator or a group of investigators concerned with a central problem or area, to which the research workers may devote a good portion of their scientific life. There are not many examples of this kind of activity in the mental health field. Such integrated programs of research, however, are likely to be quite fruitful and should be encouraged."

The GAP study cites the team approach of the Worcester State Hospital studies on schizophrenia, which started back in the nineteen-twenties, as an example of a collaborative psychiatric research effort using a number of biological and psychiatric disciplines. As a more recent example, it cites the Columbia-Greystone project in psychosurgery.

There are a number of other team approaches, for some reason overlooked by the GAP study, which are inherently more promising than, for example, the rather restricted Columbia-Greystone study. At the New York State Psychiatric Institute, Research Director Dr. Lawrence Kolb and Dr. Paul Hoch, now New York State Mental Health Commissioner, are furthering a number of team approaches to specific syndromes. One of the outstanding is the Brain Research Project under the direction of Dr. J. Lawrence Pool. At New York's Rockland State Hospital, Dr. Nathan Kline has organized a team attack upon some of the mysteries of schizophrenia. The Psychobiological Unit at Creedmoor State Hospital in New York has also done some multidisciplinary studies.

In other parts of the country, there are some significant collaborative efforts in psychiatric research. Certainly the work of Dr. Hudson Hoagland and his colleagues at the Worcester Foundation for Experimental Biology should be mentioned. Down New Orleans way, Dr. Robert Heath has developed a magnificent multidisciplinary team at Tulane for work on schizophrenia. At Galesburg State Research Hospital in Illinois, Dr. Harold Himwich directs a collaborative research division.

From the point of view of excellence of experimental design and attention to the mechanisms of collaboration, the team project on chronic schizophrenics at the University of Chicago is the most challenging. Headed by Dr. Nathaniel S. Apter, Chairman of the Division of Psychiatry, the team includes distinguished organicists like Dr. Charles Huggins, pharmacologists from the University of Illinois, Drs. Hoagland and Gregory Pincus from the Worcester Foundation, state hospital staff members, and a large group of psychiatrists.

In a recent issue of *The Bulletin of the Menninger Clinic,* Dr. Apter reported on the first four years of the project. The fundamental design of the project is an attempt to produce profound physiological changes in chronic schizophrenic patients, and then to evaluate the behavioral changes emerging as a result of metabolic changes. As Dr. Apter points out, this kind of long-range study will indicate a way in which the biological sciences can open up new avenues of approach in schizophrenia, and also a way in which clinical psychiatric methods may give further insight to biological scientists in their study of schizophrenia.

Despite these scattered attempts, it is still undeniable that financial malnutrition is the major hindrance to expanded psychiatric research. It takes a sizable chunk of money to finance the facilities and personnel needed for a long-range research effort. However, looking through the psychiatric journals, you find very few references to so mundane a matter. This conspiracy of silence was attacked in the January, 1954, issue of *The American Scientist* by Dr. Lawrence Kubie in an article which concentrated on the plight of the individual researcher.

"A failure to warn the prospective student-scientist about the practical problems which lie ahead is like training soldiers for war with no emphasis on the fact that many will be wounded and killed," Dr. Kubie wrote. "Yet our system of education for scientists engages in a silent conspiracy to deceive the student by never confronting him frankly with the basic facts about the economics of his future career. . . .

"What are some of the economic realities which the young scientist fails to anticipate? First of all, he rarely seems to realize that a day in the laboratory is the same for a rich scientist or a poor one, while the price of poverty will be paid by his family at home. He does not accept the full import of the fact that his wife and youngsters are the ones who will have to spend twenty-four hours a day in quarters so crowded that they will lack space for peaceful family living and the dignity of privacy. Furthermore, because he is young and takes health and longevity for granted, he rarely includes in his calculations the fact that if he has no personal capital he will have to allocate throughout his life a significant share of his small salary for an over-all insurance program; since insurance will be the only way in which his meager earnings can give his family any protection against illness, ensure the future education of his children, or provide a modest independence for his own old age."

If a medical school graduate contemplating a possible career in psychiatry picked up the August, 1954, issue of *The American Journal of Psychiatry,* he would find the results of a questionnaire survey conducted by the University of Michigan's Neuropsychiatric Institute on conditions in psychiatric residencies in university centers. After sifting through the data, the survey came up with this profile of the average psychiatric resident: he is twenty-eight years of age, married and the father of at least one child, and his total monthly income is $275!

Anyone for psychiatric research?

4. WHERE WILL WE
GET THE MONEY?

FANTASY, the psychiatrists tell us, is a great revealer and exposer of our basic wishes and desires. Well, Doctor, I have one recurrent fantasy that has stayed with me pretty persistently during the past six years. The setting for my fantasy is neither a Turkish harem nor an island in the bejeweled Pacific. It is a rather bare, unattractively furnished Congressional committee room in the airless catacombs of our national Capitol. Hearings are taking place on the Federal mental health budget. In my fantasy, the hearings drone on at a routine pace, and the untrained observer might ask: "Why do you call such humdrum proceedings a fantasy. There is actually nothing unusual going on in your daydream?" The hell there isn't, my untrained friend. Haven't you noticed that, during the entire pleadings of our psychiatric witnesses, not one congressman has interrupted to bellow forth, "But where will we get the money?"—said question accompanied by a triumphant obbligato of "harrumphs" from his colleagues.

One hundred billions of dollars for roads. Of course, harrumph, the only sensible thing to do. Twenty-five billion dollars of new Federal money for an interstate network of highways. Only logical, despite unanimous resolutions at both the 1952 and 1953 National Governors' Conferences requesting the Federal government to relinquish its two-cent gasoline tax and turn the whole business over to the states. States Rights is a convenient rallying cry—to be taken off the book shelves when needed, and buried when expedient. Apply the States Rights principle to health programs; forget it when it comes to big, fat roads.

Late in May, 1954, Dr. Jacques Gottlieb, one of America's most distinguished research psychiatrists and Chairman of the Committee on Research of the American Psychiatric Association, appeared before a Congressional committee to plead for $8,000,000—the price of one B-52 Stratofortress—for the construction of desperately needed laboratory facilities for psychiatric research in all parts of the country.

"Since the National Institute of Mental Health was set up by law in 1946, it has not received one cent of research construction money," Dr. Gottlieb told the committee. "At the present time there are on file with the Institute applications for research construction totaling approximately $22,000,000 from hard-pressed nonprofit foundations, medical schools and hospitals all over the country."

Dr. Gottlieb then detailed for the committee's benefit some outstanding examples of the rickety, paper-shack physical structure of modern psychiatric research.

"Let us start with the famed Menninger Foundation in Topeka, Kansas," Dr. Gottlieb testified. "A few years ago, having no endowment of its own, it launched a nation-wide campaign for funds to further its research and training programs. Despite the herculean efforts of the two Menninger brothers, Doctors Karl and Will, it has only been able to raise enough money in the research area to support a small number of research projects. This foundation has a world-wide reputation, yet here is a description of its present research facilities in a letter dated January 7, 1954:

" 'Present physical facilities for research are generally makeshift and seriously overcrowded,' Dr. Will Menninger writes. 'One building devoted exclusively to research is a one-story frame structure which was formerly the workshop of a tombstone manufacturer. Most of the research work is scattered throughout the foundation in various buildings, and there is a laboratory and workshop in the basement of one of the clinical office buildings. Altogether, there are approximately fifteen scattered offices which are used primarily for research purposes.' "

Ironically, Dr. Menninger is deeply interested in industrial psychiatry. In 1954, the Menninger Foundation completed a massive survey of emotional ills in industry, which cost this nation billions of dollars in productivity each year. Absenteeism costs more than nine billions a year; accidents, 80 to 90 per cent due to psychological causes, an untold sum; and alcoholism in excess of a billion dollars (one out of every fifty workers is a problem drinker, and 89 per cent of them are in the 35-55-year range). The survey concludes: "In the whole United States there is only one training program which tries to prepare psychiatrists for industry and its maximum capacity is two psychiatrists at a time. There are no specialized programs preparing clinical psychologists and social workers for service in industry. Industry supports none. . . . Despite its research-mindedness and despite its growing concern about human problems, *industry's contribution to mental health is practically nothing.*"

So, in the discarded workshop of a tombstone manufacturer, the Doctors Menninger and their colleagues analyze the basic causes holding down our national productivity and wealth. In more plush research surroundings, their fellow scientists are given millions in personnel and equipment to work on Dacron, Nylon, plastics, refrigerators with a two-way stretch, superficial television with deep, deep dimension, etc.

Is the situation of the Menningers an unusual one? Up in Stockbridge, Massachusetts, there is the Austen Riggs Center. Its famed director, Dr. Robert P. Knight, describes his research facilities thus:

"A converted and remodeled residence, many decades old, contains the research offices, library, conference room, and filing rooms. Every inch of space is in use through repeated remodeling. The building is sagging, barely passes the test for safety against fire, and is thoroughly inadequate for our research needs which have developed in new projects undertaken in the past three years. At the present time there are no actual funds on hand for building construction, although $330,000 was raised in the last three years for the support of research work. If we were to be successful in being allotted Federal funds for research construction, the trustees would put on a special fund-raising drive to raise a large portion of the balance of the total cost and our borrowing capacity would take care of the remainder."

Commenting on these and other statements from renowned psychiatric institutions in all parts of the country, Dr. Gottlieb set the record straight in these understandably angry words:

"These expressions of need do not come from people who think the Federal trough is an open spillway for easy money. On the contrary. During the past few years, Dr. Knight and both the Menninger brothers have practically given up psychiatric practice in order to go about the land, hat-in-hand, seeking funds to keep their foundations from going into bankruptcy. They have succeeded in raising some money for operating costs, but the big moneys for major construction are almost impossible of attainment through private solicitation. Dr. Will Menninger points out that he wants to double his research staff within the next five years; however, he notes this will be impossible without a research building where these investigators can work."

Dr. Gottlieb then turned to the plight of the nation's eighty medical schools. For a number of years, the medical school deans have been pleading for some kind of Federal aid for capital construction. The National Fund for Medical Education, headed by former President Herbert Hoover, recently estimated that the nation's medical schools need from two to three hundred millions in construction moneys, in addition to from ten to thirty millions a year to overcome existing operating deficits. Despite the urgency of these needs, the National Fund has raised only a little more than a million a year since its inception in 1949. Yet these medical schools are the bulwark of our medical research effort in this country. In the 1954–55 academic year, they received more than $43,000,000 for basic and applied medical research. However, it cost them considerably more than that to finance this research, since the grants provided an inadequate sum for overhead and no money for the construction of needed laboratory facilities.

In a letter to the National Institutes of Health, Dr. Lowell T. Coggeshall, Dean of the University of Chicago Medical School, expressed the position of the medical schools very clearly.

"It would be my point of view that a great amount of necessary assistance, primarily in the form of funds to assist schools in maintaining adequate laboratories and research facilities, as well as to erect new structures, could be given with major benefit to the country," Dr. Coggeshall wrote early in 1954. "Furthermore, rather than consider the assistance in construction as an outright gift to the schools, it is my opinion that there is a definite obligation involved. The obligation stems from the fact that practically all scientists in this country now engaged in medical research in various United States public hospitals, Armed Forces hospitals, and other Federal groups, must rely entirely on the medical schools for their talent. In other words, private institutions today are providing professional and near-professional assistance without adequate compensation. Further, because of the superior facilities and salaries and other emoluments, many of the government institutions are cannibalizing the medical schools, the very source of their talent, by attracting some of the teachers and investigators who are responsible for the development of the younger men."

Dr. Gottlieb told the committee that, if time permitted, he could place upon the record "scores of examples of the inability of the medical schools to finance major research construction. . . . Right here in Washington you have Georgetown University Medical School, one of the finest research centers in the country. Its reputation is nation-wide, but Dr. Francis M. Forster, Dean of the school, wrote in January, 1954:

"'A single laboratory is often shared by three departments. Research is often carried out in the corner of a routine laboratory or in an area of space abandoned by another department. The clinical work in psychiatry is being done on an out-patient basis and without actual assignment of specific offices. Corridor space is used for access of records; the electroencephalograph records are banked in a side room in the department of surgery. However, I must convey to you the unusual qualities of the Georgetown faculty. This is a most highly dedicated group, and men will carry on research in a corner when there is no laboratory space available. It is this fine spirit of co-operation and selflessness which has brought so much true scientific accomplishment from our group, and with adequate facilities how much greater our contribution would be.'

"From little Albany Medical College comes this plea:

"'We have some superb clinical men, who are academically minded, on our staffs. If we don't provide them with reasonable facilities for research soon, they will give up in despair and return to the more lucrative practice of medicine and surgery for a living. We are a growing institution, we are fighting our major financial battles for operation and survival, but we desperately need outside governmental support for the construction of the research facilities indicated.'

"And from the gigantic New York University-Bellevue Medical Center in New York City, this statement:

" 'The present research program has had to be severely curtailed because of the lack of proper facilities. We are in the unfortunate position of having to refuse research grants from outside agencies because of lack of space to house them.' "

Queried by committee members, Dr. Gottlieb told something of his own situation. A distinguished researcher who has published more than fifty papers on the physiological aspects of schizophrenia, Dr. Gottlieb came to Miami in 1952 to head the Department of Psychiatry at the newly established Medical School of the University of Miami. He was also appointed director of a one-hundred-bed psychiatric institute tied in with the Medical School. Since this is the only large psychiatric facility in southern Florida, Dr. Gottlieb has plenty of clinical (patient) material at his disposal. However, Dr. Gottlieb wants to do basic laboratory research, with a considerable amount of work on animals. Pointing out that he had requested the modest sum of $250,000 for construction of this laboratory equipment, Dr. Gottlieb told committee members:

"Unless these additional facilities are made available, research must be limited to clinical studies. At present there are four senior staff members, all of whom have published significant papers in research, who form the nucleus of our program. There are additional staff vacancies. If additional facilities become available, the staff can be expanded to include physicians, technicians, biochemists, physiologists, psychologists, statisticians, and cultural anthropologists. . . . I tell you this very frankly—unless I am able to provide proper laboratory facilities for my staff in the very near future, I have very little hope of retaining them for any length of time, or of developing the type of unit where research and education are handmaidens."

Dr. Gottlieb wasn't bluffing. Repeated failures to obtain the necessary laboratory facilities forced Dr. Gottlieb to abandon his research work at the University of Miami. In the summer of 1955, he accepted the post of Director of the Lafayette Clinic, a new institute set up in Detroit by the State of Michigan to foster psychiatric research and training.

At noon on May 25, 1954, the hearings came to a close. Several months later the Congress of the United States voted a national budget in excess of sixty billions of dollars. Not one cent of this handsome sum was for construction of medical research facilities.

Why not? The psychiatrists are ready with a number of explanations, ranging from fear of mental illness to all sorts of minor phobias and anxieties. The real explanation is much simpler, and it became crystal clear to me during the year I served as chief staff writer and director of public hearings for the President's Commission on the Health Needs of the Nation.

In the course of a year of investigations, during which we accumulated millions of words of testimony and documentation, the Presidential Commission came to the unavoidable conclusion that this nation's health services were poorly financed and badly distributed. However, when the time came to draw up the recommendations for financing additional health services, there was considerable backing and filling among some members of the Commission. It was generally agreed that there was an immediate necessity for about a billion more dollars in Federal expenditures for health services; the announcement of this sum abruptly precipitated the faint-heart syndrome in a number of the commissioners sitting around the table.

To resolve this question, it was decided to call upon a number of economists to give us the pros and cons. The key witness was Leon Keyserling, Chairman of the Council of Economic Advisers to the President of the United States.

Mr. Keyserling approached the problem very directly. Testifying in October, 1952, he estimated that our gross national productivity for that year would be about $350,000,000,000. Projecting a decade ahead, he told the Commissioners this:

". . . We will have within ten years a technology, a labor force, a degree of business skills so vast that, in order to avoid wide-scale unemployment of manpower and materials both on the business side and on the labor side and on the farm side, we will have to find about one hundred billion dollars worth of additional markets in the United States for consumer goods and services. . . . Now, where are we going to find in the United States this market for one hundred billion dollars of additional consumer goods and services? It seems to me that a great expansion of the health services of the American people over the next ten years, with the allied expansion of housing facilities, is one of the great outlets that we have for the progressive expansion of our standard of living. . . . The people of the United States have financial problems in a sense, but so long as we have productive resources begging to be used in the servicing of our people, dangerous financial problems will arise only if we let those resources run laggardly, that is, if we do not use them. . . . There is room within the United States within the next ten years for an enormous expansion of health services to the people. We have the manpower for it, we have the brains for it, we have the physical resources for it, we have the plant for it, and we have the means of financing it."

Several of the commissioners were puzzled by Mr. Keyserling's insistence that we had the plant and manpower for considerable expansion of our health services. They pointed out to him that we were short by some twenty thousand doctors and scores of thousands of nurses, social workers, and allied personnel of achieving even minimum medical care standards; they also emphasized the weak financial condition of the physical plant used in providing these health services.

Mr. Keyserling, in reply, explained some of the A B C's of the utilization of manpower. Pointing out that by 1962 we would have a civilian labor force of approximately ten million more than in the previous decade, he posed the problem of what could be done with these new workers. The increasing introduction of machines in the basic industries was releasing thousands upon thousands of men who would seek other employment. He cited the example of an auto-engine factory in Cleveland, where the introduction of fantastically precise heavy machinery had reduced the labor force in that factory from five hundred workers to three.

"I think a relatively larger portion of that ten million will have to go into these service activities, including medical care, both from the viewpoint of employment as such, which is of secondary consideration, and from the primary viewpoint of employment for the things that we, the people, need most," he told the commissioners. ". . . Now, you don't automatically create that man-

power by having people leave the farm or having people dis-
employed by industry. You have to have a training program going
along with it. You have to train doctors, you have to train nurses,
you have to have the hospitals and other plants in which they are to
work, but that is all a part of the problem of building on a balanced
basis an expansion of all the types of facilities, both human and
physical, which are needed to enlarge and distribute on a wider
basis adequate medical care. . . . I would say that, in our kind of
economy, I would not be concerned about several billion dollars a
year more going into the health services of the American people
than is now going into that particular priority, because I think it is
a very high priority, and I think that it is one of the areas where
we have lagged behind. . . . I think there are many parts of the
country where we are now operating at a relatively low standard of
productivity for the very reason that health services and educational
services and other basic services are not at a high level. I think the
history of our industrial development will show very clearly that it
is where these services have been most adequately performed that
we have most fully released the energies and initiative and the vari-
ability which have been at the source of our industrial growth."

During three hours of cross-questioning, Mr. Keyserling could
not disguise his bewilderment, nor could any of the other economists
who testified, at the essential paradox—there was an enormous need
for more physical plant and more personnel in the health field, and
yet the people who best understood this need were so timorous they
asked only for pennies and fringe benefits.

Puzzled by the defeatist manner in which the production of more
doctors was discussed, Harold M. Groves, Professor of Economics at
the University of Wisconsin, pointed out the simple economic
truism that we have enough doctors only when a freely recruited
supply is equated with a freely manifest demand.

"We do not have enough doctors, competitively speaking, until
all those qualified people who want to enter the profession are
allowed to do so," Professor Groves told the commissioners.
". . . There is ample evidence that many qualified people cannot
obtain access to the facilities which constitute the exclusive channel
by which the medical profession is recruited. The major reason is
that states or cities have been unable or unwilling or insufficiently
pressed to provide these facilities."

They still have not been sufficiently pressed. Although the Presidential Commission recommended an additional Federal expenditure for health services of over a billion dollars a year in the five-volume report it released in December, 1952, the three years since then have seen only small increases in these items.

And the Federal, state and local health officials—with a few notable exceptions—still assume a defensive, mendicant air when pleading with legislative bodies for a few more pennies. All they want to do is to develop the facilities and the personnel to save thousands of people from dying prematurely each and every year, but their message is invariably drowned out by the loud bleatings of those who want more roads, more guns, fatter pigs, and better-laying hens.

5. IS RESEARCH

A GOOD

INVESTMENT?

WHEN mental health commissioners, private psychiatrists, and assorted citizens appear before governmental bodies and appeal for more money for psychiatric research, solemn and close actuarial attention is theoretically given to the impact of these requests upon the health of our economy. In actuality, this close attention is largely confined to platitudinous yelps about pending fiscal bankruptcy. For the sake of sanity, however, let us suppose a Congressional committee or a state legislative committee really decided to examine the cold dollars-and-cents arguments behind the requests for more research money. In other words, is investment in research a very good risk, just a fifty-fifty gamble, or a poor risk with a slim possibility of dividends? The facts, sir, just the facts.

In the incredibly short period of eight years, medical research has added five full years to the life expectancy of the average American. This increase, which encompasses a reduction of about 10 per cent in deaths from all causes, occurred between 1944 and 1952. The many research discoveries put into use since 1944 include penicillin, streptomycin, aureomycin, chloromycetin, terramycin, isoniazid, ACTH, and cortisone. These, along with new surgical techniques and blood plasma, have brought about these percentage reductions in the death rates of some of the major killers and cripplers:

Influenza	77%
Appendicitis	69%
Acute rheumatic fever	66%
Syphilis	56%
Tuberculosis	50%
Pneumonia	50%
Kidney diseases	43%

Translated into terms which any legislator should be able to understand, medical research saved the lives of 845,014 Americans during those short eight years. Now, let us transmute this into the folklore of the legislator—the pay-off in fiscal terms. These 845,014 people, who would otherwise have died, earned and added $1,488,-000,000 to the national income in 1952 alone.

And now something a congressman can grasp pretty quickly: From these earnings in 1952 alone, the Federal Treasury received approximately $234,000,000 in income and excise tax receipts. Furthermore, this increase in tax receipts was approximately seven times the $33,000,000 spent on research in 1952 by the U. S. Public Health Service in all its major Institutes—cancer, heart, mental health, arthritis, neurological diseases and blindness, microbiology, etc. In other words, medical research has returned seven dollars in Federal taxes for every dollar spent by the U. S. Public Health Service.

It has had some fine side-effects, too. In an age when the Communists and their satellites outnumber the forces of the free world by better than two to one, it has bolstered our manpower resources and increased our productive strength. It has reduced immeasurably the tragic toll of human suffering.

It has even made for fatter and healthier cows, pigs, and chickens. The antibiotics provided by medical research have been used in feed to increase the quality and quantity of livestock and poultry production. Of course, cows, pigs, and chickens don't vote, but the farmers do a lot of voting for them.

The foregoing would seem a fairly convincing body of evidence substantiating the need for far greater research expenditures. However, some government officials are not easily convinced.

Take the case of heart disease. Heart disease is our number one menace, killing more than 800,000 Americans each year. In recognition of this fact, the last budget of the Truman Administration provided for an increase of about $5,500,000 in funds for the National Heart Institute. A few months later, the Eisenhower Administration cut back practically the entire increase authorized by the previous Administration.

In the early summer of 1953, Mrs. Anna M. Rosenberg, a former Assistant Secretary of Defense who has devoted a tremendous amount of time over the past decade to furthering public understanding of the need for more heart research, appeared before a Senate appropriations subcommittee to protest this vicious cut.

"For most of my life, I have been deeply concerned with the problem of manpower and conservation and utilization of manpower," Mrs. Rosenberg told the two Senators of the subcommittee who appeared; the others were presumably busy on more important matters. "During recent years, I have come before you a number of times as Assistant Secretary of Defense to testify on military manpower problems—on the drafting of our young men. That draft was to protect ourselves against a military enemy and other potential enemies; but gentlemen, we have an active, immediate enemy of the American people right here on the home front—heart disease. . . . On the mobilization front, heart disease causes tremendous productive and economic losses. No less than 654,000 man-years are lost each year in industry to heart disease disabilities. According to the U. S. Department of Commerce, this meant a loss to our economy of more than two billion dollars in the year 1951 alone."

Mrs. Rosenberg then spelled out these losses in terms of age groups:

"In looking at this staggering manpower loss, we often overlook the fact that heart disease cuts down many people early in life, thereby removing them from the productive economy and making them tax recipients rather than taxpayers. Among children under fifteen, more than twice as many died of diseases of the heart in 1950 as died of infantile paralysis. Heart disease cuts down one out of every three in the prime of life—in the years from forty to sixty-five. Only very recently has American industry begun to face one of the most serious challenges of our productive economy—that many of its young executives, after years of training for peak posts, fall victim to coronary heart disease and hypertension just as they begin to realize their full potential."

In the few minutes at her disposal, Mrs. Rosenberg could only highlight the many drug and surgical treatments which have added years to the lives of many Americans.

"Anyone who doubts the value of research need only glance at arteriosclerosis—the most deadly and widespread of all heart diseases," Mrs. Rosenberg told the subcommittee. "All over the country, our research has begun the long battle against hardening of the arteries. This work is pointing to a routine blood test to detect early hardening of the arteries, and to a possible preventive treatment through administering a substance to inhibit premature hardening. Think of what this would mean in preserving the physical and mental health of the middle-aged and elderly citizens whose accumulated wisdom our nation now loses too soon. . . . I think it equally clear that the American people want Congress to increase our effort. Just a few years back, the Gallup poll showed that 79 per cent of the people wanted the government to spend $200,000,000 on research to find the causes and cure of heart disease and, what is even more to the point, four out of five of them were willing to pay more taxes to provide the money."

Mrs. Rosenberg then got down to the heart of the heart matter. She pointed out that in the fall of 1952, after learning that there were fully documented requests on hand from 122 of our leading medical schools and institutes for the construction of $36,000,000 of heart research laboratory facilities, the Bureau of the Budget allowed $4,000,-000 for fiscal 1954 as a start toward catching up with the construction backlog. However, the revised Eisenhower budget submitted in April, 1953, ripped out the entire laboratory facility sum. Commenting on this, Mrs. Rosenberg said:

"The lack of adequate laboratory and clinical facilities is holding up a number of very promising projects, and it is unthinkable that this situation should be allowed to continue. The research men must be given the means to do their job. The complex machines and equipment of modern heart research cannot be housed in an inadequate basement room or a screened-off alcove in the outpatient clinic of a medical school. Many medical school deans wired the House Appropriations Committee that they could not do justice to their research projects until adequate physical facilities were built. The medical schools don't have the funds to build the facilities themselves—they are deeply in debt."

Mrs. Rosenberg's pleas were in vain. Although the Congress did rebuke the Eisenhower Administration by upping considerably the heart research and training items, it appropriated not one cent for laboratory facilities.

The short history of successful research upon tuberculosis presents an entirely different set of resistances to expansion of financial support for investigative work. Although the disease was known and described in full diagnostic detail in the medical literature many decades ago, the study of tuberculosis was cloaked for many years in a pall of fatalism, purposeful mystification, and punditic philosophizing. Its causes and course were described in hundreds of medical papers distinguished chiefly by fuzziness, elaborately woven clichés, and faint echoes of romanticism rubbing off from *Camille* or *The Magic Mountain*. The self-proclaimed pulmonary specialists recommended a high, dry climate, plenty of bed rest, and the reading of languorous literature.

With the discovery and distribution of the antibiotic streptomycin in 1946, the dreary picture brightened. The death rate started a dramatic downward trend. When streptomycin was combined with para-aminosalicylic acid (PAS), further spectacular declines in the death rate occurred. In the period from late 1945 to 1951, the combination of streptomycin and PAS, plus energetic case-finding, reduced the tuberculosis rate by 50 per cent.

But the guardians of the past dragged their feet. So direct an attack on this mystifying, philosophic disease was anathema to them. I was a medical reporter on *The Daily Oklahoman* in those days, and I did quite a euphoric series on the new tuberculosis treatments. One day I received a call from the chief sachem of pulmonary disease in Oklahoma. Arriving at his office, I was ushered in and subjected to a tedious tirade against all things new. The drugs wouldn't last—after all, new and spectacular treatments for tuberculosis had been hailed many times in the past fifty years. This kind of approach I was prepared for, but I was really astounded when he attacked the modern chest X-ray campaign which was turning up so much undetected, dangerously infectious tuberculosis. He said that the average technician couldn't be depended upon to take a good picture, and even if he got one, you couldn't trust the average doctor to make a sound interpretation. The best methods, he assured me, were still bed rest, a dry climate, and sometimes the collapsing of a lung.

The same kind of resistance greeted the introduction in 1952 of the new isonicotinic-acid drugs and their miraculous action in restoring many hopeless tuberculosis patients to new activity and life. The National Tuberculosis Association dragged a powerful professional foot, and the tuberculosis experts of the U. S. Public Health Service expressed their skepticism a year later in testimony before the Congress.

But the voodoo couldn't suppress the facts. At the 1954 convention of the National Tuberculosis Association, Dr. Arthur B. Robins, Director of the TB Bureau of the New York City Health Department, reported, on the basis of treatment of 348 clinic patients over a six-month period, his conviction that public health agencies everywhere, including those in Oklahoma, should make the new isoniazid and PAS drugs available to all unhospitalized TB patients. Dr. Robins told the distinguished pulmonary experts of the Association that 69 per cent of the clinic patients with active pulmonary tuberculosis had been rendered noninfectious by the drugs. Describing the treatment as simple and safe, he pointed out that the patients visited the clinics once a month to collect their ration of isoniazid and PAS pills and to have their progress checked by X rays and sputum tests.

In the face of overwhelming subsequent evidence, the resistance of the romantics gradually collapsed. In the fall of 1954, the famed Trudeau Sanatorium at Saranac Lake, citadel of bed rest, closed its doors for lack of patients.

On January 15, 1955, Dr. Basil McLean, New York City Commissioner of Hospitals, announced that the city had closed three tuberculosis hospitals with a total capacity of more than one thousand beds. Pointing out that only two years before the city's TB hospitals had been plagued by overcrowding and delays in admission, he cited the 1955 figure of 4,439 beds as against only 3,922 patients.

Giving chief credit for this remarkable development to the new drugs, Dr. MacLean said the saving to the city as a result of the closing of the three institutions would be $2,700,000 a year. Furthermore, the medical staffs of the institutions would be transferred to other city hospitals where there were desperate personnel shortages.

Finally, the Public Health Service capitulated. On January 29, 1955, it issued an epoch-making statement: for the first time in the history of vital statistics, tuberculosis was no longer among the first ten causes of death! The death rate from tuberculosis in 1954 had dropped to 10.6 per 100,000 people, compared with 194 per 100,000 in 1900. Furthermore, the most spectacular declines had occurred since 1951, with a 21 per cent annual drop each year since then.

It is difficult to overstate the savings accruing from this relatively small investment in medical research. The National Tuberculosis Association has estimated that each case of hospitalized tuberculosis costs in excess of $14,000. If the new drugs had not come into the picture, this would have meant a national expenditure of approximately $5,600,000,000 for the four hundred thousand Americans now ill with active tuberculosis. And this figure does not include any costs for the eight hundred thousand who have inactive tuberculosis. Certainly extensive use of drugs now available, and the development of effective new compounds, will mean total savings to the American taxpayer of hundreds of millions of dollars.

Anyone for bed rest?

When we turn to psychiatric research, we find more of the same fatalism and defeatism plaguing those who want to mount a major research offensive against mental illness. This general air of skepticism as to the efficacy of psychiatric research is puzzling when viewed in the light of the spectacular gains it has achieved with the expenditure of incredibly small sums of money.

The ever-increasing conquest of paresis is a case in point. Paresis, a generalized paralysis with accompanying psychosis, is the end result of uncontrolled syphilis. In the 180-year history of our public mental hospital system, thousands upon thousands of paretics spent their last miserable years in confinement in our mental institutions. Physically repelling, and generally avoided by both staffs and fellow patients, these unfortunates added incalculably to the pall of gloom and despair engulfing the back wards of our mental hospitals.

The first great research break against paresis occurred back in 1913 when two bacteriologists, Hideyo Noguchi and J. W. Moore, proved beyond a shadow of a doubt that the spirochetes of syphilis infected the brain and caused paretic insanity. During World War I, Austria's Wagner-Jauregg developed the high-fever malarial treatment for cases of paresis.

However, the major research attack upon paresis came about with the introduction of penicillin. Used against syphilis, the powerful antibiotic killed the spirochetes before they had a chance to multiply and infect the brain and nervous system. The subsequent drop in admission of paretics to mental hospitals is one of the great chapters in modern medical research. In the New York State mental hospital system alone there has been better than a 50 per cent reduction in first admissions for paresis in the five years since the initial widespread use of penicillin in 1946. Dr. Walter Bruetsch, the distinguished neurologist at Indiana's Central State Hospital, has remarked that in his first years at the hospital, paretics accounted for as many as one out of every three male admissions. Last year, admissions for paresis were less than 3 per cent of total admissions.

The victory over pellagra psychosis is an even more dramatic story. Physically weak, deeply disoriented mentally, pellagrins crowded thousands of mental hospital beds, particularly in the South. In the nineteen-twenties and nineteen-thirties, pellagra caused more than ten thousand deaths a year.

Dr. Tom Spies, a brilliant researcher at the Hillman Hospital in Birmingham, devoted fifteen years to tracking down the causes of pellagra. He finally pinned it down to one physiological cause, a nutritional deficiency due to lack of the vitamin niacin. Treated with niacin, most cases of pellagra were soon cleared up. So rapid and remarkable was the conquest of this once "incurable" disease that in 1952 there were only 51 pellagra deaths in the entire United States. At the Southern Regional Mental Health Conference in Atlanta in July, 1954, state hospital superintendents pointed out that pellagra, which used to fill entire wards of overcrowded hospitals with its victims, is now a medical rarity.

In recent years, the dread disease of epilepsy has yielded more and more ground as research has produced new diagnostic and treatment tools. Neurological research produced the electroencephalograph, whose measurement of brain waves demonstrated conclusively that epilepsy is a disorder of the energy and economy of brain cells. Further research disclosed that the aberrant activity of these cells could be controlled by chemical means, and such drugs as tridione and dilantin have proved successful in reducing the number and severity of seizures. Today 80 per cent of epileptics can lead normal lives, and thousands of victims who would formerly have spent a lifetime in a mental institution are now working and paying taxes. In the past several years, a number of state institutions for the care of epileptics have been closed, marking a singular victory against this ancient curse of mankind.

There are many more exceedingly promising research attacks upon mental illness. Indiana's Dr. Bruetsch has recently published several scientific papers detailing his discovery that between 4 and 5 per cent of all the mental hospital patients he studied suffered from previously undetected rheumatic brain disease, the end result of untreated rheumatic heart infections. Further testing is needed, but if Dr. Bruetsch's hypothesis holds up new avenues of treatment and cure will be opened up for thousands of patients now confined in mental institutions.

Chronic alcoholism is no longer regarded as a hopeless affliction. A whole armamentarium of drugs and vitamins is being thrown into the fight against this disease, and many victories are already being reported.

Out at the University of Chicago, a brilliant multi-disciplinary research team has already demonstrated that many cases of mental illness previously thought to be psychological in origin are actually due to physiological causes: undulant fever, hypertension, and other physical ailments.

In the attack upon senile dementia, the feeling that this syndrome is the inevitable end result of the aging process is giving way to the new view that premature arteriosclerosis can be prevented and thousands of elderly people kept out of mental institutions.

There is little doubt, then, that research is a blue-chip investment paying enormous dividends. Even the prevention of mental illness in a few hundred citizens pays off at a huge rate. For example, male admissions for paresis in New York State mental hospitals in 1931 totaled 774. Dr. Benjamin Malzberg, Director of the Statistical Division of the New York State Department of Mental Hygiene, has estimated the net loss of earnings of these paretics at $9,500,535. In 1948, with a reduction to 390 first admissions for paresis, the net loss of earnings dropped more than $5,000,000.

How much we could save, in both productivity and human life, if only we would push our petty resistances aside and really get on with the job!

6. WHY NOT
MORE ORGANIC
RESEARCH?

In no field of medicine are the resistances to basic physiological research more pronounced or more violent than in the relatively new speciality of psychiatry.

"The observation and classifications of mental disorders have been so exclusively psychological that we have not sincerely realized the fact that they illustrate the same pathological principles as other diseases, are produced in the same way, and must be investigated in the same spirit of positive research. Until this be done, I see no hope of improvement in our knowledge of them, and no use in multiplying books about them."

Dr. Henry Maudsley penned the above statement in 1870. Some of us who follow the literature can attest wearily to the fact that Dr. Maudsley's stricture has had little effect during the past eighty-five years in stemming the flow of psychiatric books running the gamut from outright metaphysics to downright mumbo jumbo. The past decade has seen a cascade of volumes whose average length is inversely proportional to the amount of solid, scientific knowledge contained therein. On schizophrenia alone there have been hundreds of books and magazine articles, each of them invariably touting a "new" definition of schizophrenia—followed by a single case history which, of course, gives scientific validity to the definition.

In a recent article in *The Bulletin of the Menninger Clinic,* Dr. Jules H. Masserman, noted for his twenty years of work on behavior patterns in animals, referred to the harmful effects of "the seductive use of typically mythological thinking in lieu of more precise formulations and operational deductions."

"This is exemplified in attempts to explain fundamentals of human behavior on the basis of highly selected parables such as those of Narcissus or Oedipus," Dr. Masserman wrote. ". . . And so too, in seminars supposedly devoted to the discussion of unconscious dynamics, we are sometimes treated to serious accounts of how in one case 'the ego bribed the superego' while 'really being in secret alliance with the id,' whereas in another instance the 'id masqueraded as the superego' and thus 'gained an advantage in a bitter battle with the ego' in which it also succeeded in 'splitting' the latter nearly in two—all this until a casual visitor might think he were really listening to a quasi-Homeric tale of how three Fates plotted and fought among themselves inside some poor mortal's skull for the control of his body. I am not opposed to poetic license in exposition, but perhaps even in our modern thinking the bright seductive spirit of mystery and fable still shines through the thin, drab Mother Hubbard of pseudoscience in which we pretend to clothe her."

Dr. Masserman to the contrary notwithstanding, the psychiatric boys are still hard at the business of parables, myths, and fables. At the 1954 meeting of the American Psychoanalytic Association in the incongruous milieu of staid, beer-drinking St. Louis, there were learned papers on "Decorating the Home: A Traumatic Neurosis of Women"; "The Holiday Syndrome"—all about how nervous you get on the Fourth of July or at Easter time; "The Phobic Impact of Aspects of Domesticity"—or don't let your phobias disturb the washing machine, and so on. At the December clinical meeting of the same group, such important psychiatric phenomena as "The Christmas Neurosis" and "The Naming of Tom Sawyer" were dealt with at great length.

In his presidential address to the ninth annual convention of the Society of Biological Psychiatry, a group formed in 1946 to bring psychiatry back from mythology to medicine, the famed researcher Dr. L. J. Meduna took some powerful swings at our latter-day coiners of cumbrous parables and fables.

"If the heroine of the modern novel runs away with her lover, leaving her husband and her children, she just wants to liberate her Id from the Electra-complex," Dr. Meduna protested. "If you kiss your wife's lips, it is an expression not of love but of oral fixation; and if the rich woman's husband suffers from diarrhea, his excrements are her money. But why pile up examples of what has become commonplace since a large and voluble minority of the 'psychiatrists' have reverted to the magic thinking of the pre-Judaic time, a thinking in which nothing is what it is but in which everything is something else, something that only the high priests of the sympathetic magic can decipher and interpret to the uninitiated.

"After half a century of mummery came the reaction; and the Society of Biological Psychiatry was founded by a few men, good and true. Our main tenet is that the Thing is what it is—that mental disturbances are disturbances of the brain. All mental disturbances, therefore, have to be expressed and defined, not in terms sociological or religious, or in symbols philosophical and magic-phallic, but in terms physiological and biological. . . . In the human brain there are no symbols, there are only the cells and their magnificent but silent biochemical and physiological processes. A nerve cell can be stimulated by no symbol, but only by another nerve cell. . . . Our flag is a flag of revolution upon which I should like to write the rebellious, the defiant motto: 'A telegraph pole is a telegraph pole.' "

Fortunately, a number of the leaders of American psychiatry have, in recent years, initiated a manful effort to clamp down on the proliferating palaver and swing psychiatry back to its rightful niche in the discipline of medicine. At the 105th annual meeting of the American Psychiatry Association in 1949, Dr. William S. Terhune, one of the nation's leading psychiatrists, delivered a magnificent lecture entitled "Physiological Psychiatry."

"Although psychiatry now emphasizes the psychological interpretations of mental disease, we doctors know that these psychological phenomena occur only as a result of physical processes and basic biochemical reactions in the nervous system," Dr. Terhune told his colleagues. "Fifty years ago medicine had no explanation to offer as to the nature of these reactions, and medical research contributed little to solve the mystery. Factually, there was no understanding and practically no approach to the treatment of mental illness. In this situation, psychiatry accepted Freud's original and dynamic concepts of mental disease, together with his related methods of psychotherapy, as the foundation of modern psychiatry. But it would seem that the situation is changing and we have reached a point where we must attempt to correlate the findings of organic medicine with those of psychodynamics, psychopathology, and psychotherapy, and that if we wish to continue to dwell in the house of medical science we must study the organics of psychodynamics and study them in accordance with the principles of scientific medicine. . . . Not until psychiatry can correlate the physiological and biochemical reactions of the nervous system with the apparent psychological results will psychiatry and psychodynamics stand on a firm scientific foundation, and only in this way can the true pathogenesis of mental disorders be understood."

Dr. Terhune then reviewed the recent swing toward an organic approach to mental illness:

"With the gradual increase of scientific knowledge, the number of mental disorders previously interpreted on a functional [psychological] basis have steadily decreased," Dr. Terhune pointed out. "A review of the standard classification of psychiatric disorders shows that three-fifths of them are now accepted as being organic. As you know, we now unhesitatingly classify as organic the psychoses due to infection, intoxication, trauma, disturbance of circulation, convulsive disorders, disturbance of metabolism, growth, nutrition, or endocrine functions; those due to new growth; and the psychoses due to unknown or hereditary causes—an impressive list when it is remembered that most of these were formerly considered functional. . . . Although many pieces of the organic jigsaw puzzle of mental disease are still missing, and in some instances the design only surmised, I believe the conclusion is inescapable that all mental disorder, like other disease, is the result of a disturbance in the normal physiology of the body with resultant pathological processes, the whole doubtless influenced, as is the case in other fields of medicine, by disturbing environmental factors."

In another section of the lecture, Dr. Terhune dealt with the important question of the inadequate training of psychiatrists in organic methods:

"Today there are some physicians certified as psychiatrists, trained principally in psychodynamics, with no interest in the all-important physical basis of psychiatric medicine," Dr. Terhune said. "In the psychiatric clinics of some medical schools, the psychological implication of case histories is minutely studied with no reference to important physical implications, and little or no attempt to correlate these closely connected factors."

In the current literature, there is an increasing wave of protest against this narrow kind of training. In the July, 1954, issue of *The Atlantic Monthly,* an anonymous English psychiatrist described as "the author of standard works in his field" pictured the kind of training he would seek if he could do it all over again.

". . . I should first of all, before entering psychiatry, try to learn more basic biochemistry, neurophysiology and electronics instead of concentrating on psychology or philosophy," he wrote. "Or I might seriously consider becoming a neurosurgeon with a specialized psychiatric training. Either way, one's future would then be more certain as far as finding out how to help the greatest number of nervously ill patients was concerned. Skilled treatment of the mentally ill must still remain the overwhelming priority and concern of psychiatry today. For, first of all, we must demonstrate our abilities to cure our patients before even thinking of daring to advise the world and his wife on their numerous everyday problems."

Hear, Hear! All psychoanalysts who continue to lecture at Town Halls on subjects metaphysical and mythological, and at Mothers' Clubs on the phallic significance of Junior's thumb-sucking, and all of whom have yet to cure their first schizophrenic, please note.

Our British friend then gives a very interesting description of the kind of psychiatric education he received:

"To show the reason for my present attitude of mind, it is only necessary to look back to the time twenty years ago when I first entered psychiatry from general medicine. The dogmas and techniques of Freud, Adler and Jung were in existence then and very little different from those of today. They had been practised in England for some years previously, but had made no appreciable dent in the number of the nervously ill. It is sometimes forgotten how old Freudian practice really is. After the First World War, medical students at one of the London teaching hospitals were being told by one of the founders of the English school of psychoanalysis that some people were possibly afraid of zeppelins because they were phallic symbols. No increasing number of patients, however, are provenly leaving mental hospitals because of an increasing use of psychoanalytic methods in the last thirty years, and by now it is becoming extremely doubtful that they ever will."

And, as to the status of treatment in the early nineteen-thirties: "Only one mental disease was really being cured in 1934, and that was early syphilis of the brain. This discovery had at last been made when it was shown that the giving of a series of malarial rigors could kill effectively the spirochetes of syphilis in the human brain. The illness had at one time been called the 'moral neurosis.' . . . Today, since injections of penicillin given in a general hospital may be all that is needed, psychiatrists may see as few as one of these patients a year. . . . I was also taught as a student that the flushings of women at the change of life could result from a subconscious protest at the impending change in their sexual status, and even saw patients being psychoanalyzed for this complaint. Since the discovery of cheaply produced female sex hormones, however, the symptoms can now be cured with the greatest ease and simplicity despite all the postulated efforts of the subconscious mind. . . . Epilepsy, also previously treated by attempted exorcism of the Devil, is now being controlled by ever more efficient anticonvulsant drugs, and sometimes by operations on the brain to cut out small damaged areas where electrical discharges are occurring."

Reflecting on these matters, the author concludes:

"It is a pity that medical philosophers have had to seek an asylum in psychiatry in more senses than one, for psychiatry's main proven hope of *practical* progress is to return to a general medical outlook instead of seeking to create an ever-widening gulf between medicine and itself. It is too often forgotten that medicine has been able to make its spectacular advances in the last hundred years only by deliberately giving up all-embracing metaphysical theories, seeking for empirical physical remedies, and then perhaps only many years later finding out how and why they work. Even now we do not know how penicillin or insulin really acts, though the lives of tens of thousands have already been saved by them."

The short history of psychiatry is replete with examples of

stubborn refusals to recognize the physiological bases underlying many mental diseases. As Albert Q. Maisel has pointed out on a number of occasions, paresis for generations was dealt with in the medical and psychiatric literature as an insanity of purely psychological origin. Dr. Richard von Krafft-Ebing, one of psychiatry's greatest pioneers, wrote a study of paresis in 1877 in which he listed, as some of the possible causes of the disease, dissipation in alcohol, the smoking of too many Virginia cigars, excessive love-making, the rigors of making a living, and fright. As Maisel pointed out in a magazine article, "Is Mental Disease Mental?" Krafft-Ebing "never so much as mentioned the spirochete of syphilis as a possible cause."

For many years, despite increasing evidence that paresis was a physically induced infection, the resistance to a physiological explanation for it was fierce.

"Even as late as 1898," Maisel writes, "the famed German physician, Virchow, heatedly denied even the possibility of paresis' having a syphilitic origin."

Pretty much the same story can be written of resistances in other mental diseases now amenable to physical treatment. The invention of the electroencephalograph and the development of many effective new drugs disclosed the essential neurological nature of epilepsy, putting an end to centuries of quasi-religious, metaphysical speculations about its causation. More recently, the discovery of niacin as a specific cure for pellagra brought to a roaring halt scores of tedious tomes and brochures attributing the disease to everything from the unusually warm springtimes in the South to the general malaise which followed upon the rigors of the Civil War and the Reconstruction Era.

In summing up some of these inexplicable resistances, Maisel writes:

". . . It is not easy to understand why many psychiatrists still insist upon adopting the attitude of Krafft-Ebing toward those mental maladies whose possible physical causes have not yet been fully explored. For most of the cures that psychiatrists are able to achieve against the remaining 'psychogenic' diseases are accomplished by physical treatments rather than by psychiatric means. The doctors who administer these treatments may be psychiatrists.

But their most effective weapons are not psychotherapy at all. They reach and correct the disorders of the mind through the channels of the body."

This predisposition toward psychological and cultural explanations for the major mental maladies also flies in the face of impressive anthropological evidence to the contrary. In a series of lectures in 1953 to the New York Academy of Medicine, Dr. Ralph Linton, Sterling Professor of Anthropology at Yale, pointed out that neuroses, psychoses, and hysterias are common to all people and all cultures. The fact that these mental diseases are prevalent in every culture known to anthropology is a strong argument for a biochemical basis for these diseases.

If upbringing were an important factor, Dr. Linton argued, some societies should be free of mental disease, since their free-and-easy ways of acculturating the young meet all the approved canons of modern psychiatry. In other societies, all the young go through rigid, striated periods of disciplined development, with no deviation from the tribal patterns. Yet these societies also produce their percentages of neurotics and psychotics. In sum, whatever the patterns, whatever the differences in psychological and cultural upbringing of the young, there is still a roughly comparable incidence of mental illness.

The accumulating evidence is showing signs of breaking down some of the resistances. Concluding his 1949 lecture, Dr. Terhune was able to strike an optimistic note.

"In stressing the importance of the organic basis of psychiatry, I am only expressing the belief of many of us," he told his colleagues. "However, it is high time we told our medical confreres that we are no longer working in a field apart. And, what is equally important, we should let the public know that rapid advances in physiological psychiatry may soon enable us to prevent and successfully treat many manifestations of mental disease which, up to this time, we have been powerless to ameliorate. We should tell the people of the world, sadly oppressed by the spectre of mental disease, that there is new reason to hope, and ask them to provide us with the means to make this hope a reality."

Concurrent with the growth of this new understanding of the importance of physiology in mental illness there has developed a powerful clinical and philosophical concept of physical and mental illness which many believe to be the most important and far-reaching since the pioneer work of Sigmund Freud.

This is the concept of stress. The development of the stress theory is largely the work of the German-trained Dr. Hans Selye, who for the past twelve years has headed the Institute of Experimental Medicine and Surgery at the University of Montreal. However, in his many writings, Selye traces the development of the stress concept back through Walter Cannon and ultimately to Louis Pasteur.

Selye's theory of disease holds that the body, under excessive external pressures of one sort or another, reacts chemically. The key roles in this chemical reaction are played by the pituitary and the adrenal glands. They provide the hormones which enable the body to fight off the disease. In his massive work, *Stress,* published in 1950, Dr. Selye describes this over-all marshaling of chemical fighters as the General Adaptation Syndrome (G-A-S). In a more recent treatment of the subject, in the January, 1954, issue of *The Practitioner,* Selye breaks this general adaptation down into three stages: (1) the alarm reaction, in which the body is alerted to the threat of disease or attack; (2) the stage of resistance, in which the glands produce excess hormones to ward off the attack; and (3) the stage of exhaustion, in which the defense mechanism breaks down, and stress produces any number and kind of diseases —hypertension, arthritis, ulcer, and so on.

Selye documented his revolutionary thesis in endless experiments upon animals. Injecting rats with two key hormones, STH from the pituitary and DCA (desoxycorticosterone) from the adrenals, he produced hardened arteries, swollen joints, and kidney disease. From these and other experiments, he reasoned that what some chemical hormones could destroy, other chemical hormones could counteract. With the development of ACTH, the progress of a number of diseases created by chemical imbalance was either arrested or reversed.

In recent publications, Selye has pointed up the role of STH in combating susceptibility to infections.

". . . Experiments on rats have already demonstrated the great influence of adaptive hormones upon resistance to the human type of tuberculosis," he wrote recently. "Normally, the rat is virtually resistant to tubercle bacilli; it may be rendered sensitive by ACTH or ACE and this sensitivity can in turn be abolished by STH. . . . It remains to be seen to what extent these actions of STH will prove to be of value in management of infections in man."

Selye, and scores of experimentalists in all parts of the world who are following his lead, agree that we are just on the threshold of a fundamental understanding of the workings of the glands. However, the enormous promise of continued work in this area is summed up in these words of Selye's:

"If I might venture a prediction, I should like to reiterate the opinion that research on stress will be most fruitful if it is guided by the theory that we must learn to imitate—and if necessary to correct and complement—the body's own auto-pharmacological efforts to combat the stress-factor in disease."

Along these lines, there are a few pioneer attempts now going on to develop measurement techniques for checking chemical balance in the body. When we develop a yardstick of normal chemical performance, we can devise methods of restoring chemical imbalances through the injection of selected hormones.

The concept of stress is gaining increasing acceptance in the field of psychiatry. Each year, additional psychiatric researchers are producing detailed evidence indicating the basic physiological impairments underlying many mental illnesses. Furthermore, significant comparative studies on the handling of stress are being suggested. For example, A and B are both business executives with fairly comparable psychological stresses. Both use alcohol as a means of relieving strain. However, A cannot handle alcohol, and his life and that of his family have been smashed by it. His counterpart, B, consumes an equal amount of alcohol, but his functions are little impaired. Why the differences? From this fairly simple point of departure, research must extend into more complex areas. C and D have seemingly comparable psychological loads, and both receive treatment for severe neuroses. C responds and is functioning again. D fails to respond and for the last six years has been in a mental hospital. Why the differences?

A number of the biggest names in American psychiatry are inching their way toward application of the stress concept to therapy. Dr. Lawrence Kubie has written some illuminating

articles in the past few years. One of the more recent converts
has been Dr. Karl Menninger, for a generation one of America's
leading Freudians.

In his famous lecture in 1953 before the Royal Medico-Psychologic
Association in London, Dr. Karl summarized for his British
colleagues the paper, "Regulatory Devices of the Ego under Major
Stress," which he had recently delivered to the International
Congress of Psychoanalysis:

"The essence of my thesis was that the principle of homeostasis,
or steady state maintenance, can be applied to psychological
phenomena and psychoanalytic theory. The functions of the ego in
receiving external and internal stimuli and in dealing with them
for the best interests of the organism can be viewed as those of
a homeostatic effector. The constructive and destructive drives
of the organism must be so directed and modified as to permit
the maintenance of a level of tension which is both tolerable and
conducive to safe, productive and satisfying living and continued
growth.

"Events constantly occur which tend to disturb the adjustments
and reconciliations achieved, and these stresses require the ego
to improvise adaptive expedients for maintaining the integrity of the
organism. Minor stresses are usually handled by relatively minor,
'normal,' 'healthy' devices. Greater stresses or prolonged stress
excite the ego to increasingly energetic and expensive activity in
the interests of homeostatic maintenance.

"In its effort to control dangerous impulses under such circumstances and thereby prevent or retard the disintegrative process
which threatens, the ego initiates emergency regulatory devices
which fall into five hierarchically arranged and specifically
characterized groups, representing increasingly greater degrees of
failure in integration.

"I believe that this conceptualization of the ego's regulatory
function provides us with a broader frame of reference for
understanding mental illness and will enable us to discard some of
our vague, many-faceted, traditional terms in exchange for more
definite and precise designation of process and stage. It also helps us
to align our psychoanalytic concepts with general organismic-
biologic theory."

THE NEW
DRUGS
AND
BEYOND

7. THE NEW FRONTIER IN CHEMOTHERAPY

IN THE entire history of the physiological attack upon mental illness, no development has been more significant than the recent introduction of new drugs in the treatment of a wide variety of mental illnesses.

The surface story of the remarkable achievements of these new drugs has been told in scores of technical and popular articles. Yet, beneath the surface, there is a deeper story which illustrates in a graphic manner the thesis of this entire book—that physiological treatments must still fight an uphill battle for recognition among the High Priests of Psychiatry. This writer has witnessed, during the past several years, a set of resistances to the new drugs running the scale from downright ignorance and bureaucratic apathy to vicious, bitter attacks upon every researcher reporting success in using them. And this resistance was not, and is not, confined to the psychoanalysts, many of whom were rushing to second-hand dealers with their sagging couches. In its initial phases, it included a number of tax-supported Federal and state mental health officials whose bounden duty it is to support any treatment which holds promise of alleviating the miseries of the mentally ill.

Rauwolfia serpentina, a snakeroot plant, has been used in India for centuries for a wide variety of illnesses—epilepsy, insomnia, diarrhea, headaches, fevers, mental illness, etc. In Bihar province, the powdered roots of the plant were used as a sleeping potion for infants. (At the 1955 New York Academy of Sciences Symposium on Rauwolfia, a Texas pediatrician reported that the drug was the most effective agent known in the treatment of hyperactive and irritable infants with bizarre sleeping patterns.)

Although known to European scientists as far back as the seventeenth century, it was relegated to an undeserved obscurity until a few decades ago. In 1931, two Indian chemists, Drs. Salimuzzaman Siddiqui and Rafat Hussain Siddiqui, obtained *Rauwolfia* roots from the bazaar at Patna and from them isolated five crystalline alkaloids. They reported in the *Journal of the Indian Chemical Society* that the purified substances extracted from the root were particularly effective in disturbed types of mental illness complicated by acute insomnia.

In the same year, two Indian physicians, Drs. Gananath Sen and Kartrick Chandra Bose, published an account of their clinical work with two of the new alkaloids. They had worked with experimental animals previously and had observed the remarkable ability of the new compounds in reducing high blood pressure. In a conservative report in the *Indian Medical Record,* they noted:

"The authors have used it in all types of insanity and have found out that it is effective only in a certain type of insanity which is common. Insanity with violent maniacal symptoms yields readily to it. . . . Doses of twenty to thirty grains of the powder twice daily produce not only a hypnotic effect, but also a reduction of blood-pressure and violent symptoms. . . . Usually, the treatment has to be continued for four to six weeks (sometimes more), the doses being reduced gradually. In the demented and morose types of insanity, *R. serpentina* is not effective; it is rather contraindicated. Such cases are usually characterized by low blood-pressure and asthenia and are difficult to cure."

This report, written twenty-five years ago, could be given at any scientific gathering in 1956, and it would be hailed as an amazingly precise delineation of the treatment potential of the *Rauwolfia* alkaloids.

Yet Drs. Sen and Bose perceived that the defenders of the familiar and the timeworn would look askance at anything new, even though it offered great hope in the fight against the world-wide scourge of mental illness. They concluded their report with a plea that "medical men all over the world would work out the effect of this remedy both pharmacologically and clinically as it promises to be a valuable addition to the armamentarium of the physician." But their plea was in vain. Those medical men who read their report discovered it had something new to say, so they retreated to the safe confines of existing knowledge. However, this did not discourage the use of the drug in India; in the early years of World War II, more than one million patients were given the drug for high blood pressure and related psychic disturbances.

The awakening of the Western world began with a paper written by Dr. Rustom Jal Vakil of the King Edward Memorial Hospital in Bombay. Starting in 1940 and for almost a decade thereafter, he used *Rauwolfia* on several thousand of his hypertensive patients. He found it remarkably successful but, being a cautious man, he decided to check his experience against that of his colleagues. He sent a questionnaire to fifty of India's best-known physicians, asking them to name the best agent they knew for reducing high blood pressure. Forty-six of the fifty selected *Rauwolfia*. He then conducted a series of very detailed experiments on fifty of his patients. He submitted the report of these experiments to the *British Heart Journal,* in which it was published in October, 1949.

Dr. Vakil's report would probably have gone the way of all previous Indian reports but for a fateful trip to a Boston library one night by Dr. Robert W. Wilkins, Director of the Hypertension Clinic at Massachusetts Memorial Hospital. Dr. Wilkins read the Vakil report, and his interest was whetted. He sent for, and studied, the Indian medical reports of the previous twenty-five years. Impressed, he sent for a supply of *Rauwolfia* tablets, which arrived in Occidental Boston in the summer of 1950.

Dr. Wilkins and his group tested the drug on fifty patients. They discovered that Dr. Vakil and his predecessors had been most conservative in their claims. It was not only remarkably effective against high blood pressure, but it calmed patients ridden with anxiety and worry. In 1952, in a report to the New England Cardiovascular Society, the Wilkins group stressed the psychiatric implications of the drug.

"It has a type of sedative action that we have not observed before," they reported. "Unlike barbiturates or other standard sedatives, it does not produce grogginess, stupor or lack of co-ordination. The patients appear to be relaxed, quiet and tranquil. . . . The drug makes them feel as if they simply don't have a worry in the world."

Encouraged by the reports of the Wilkins group, Dr. Raymond Harris of Albany Medical College began an investigation of the effects of Reserpine, a *Rauwolfia* derivative, upon twenty-six aged people who suffered from high blood pressure and related psychiatric complaints—nervousness, crying spells, extreme excitability, and insomnia. They were all residents of the Ann Lee Home in Albany, and their average age was sixty-seven years. The drug not only significantly reduced the blood pressure of 95 per cent of the oldsters, but it had a powerful impact upon their psychiatric symptoms. Most of them slept better and reported a feeling of well-being. Dr. Harris then extended the study to fifteen elderly patients living in their own homes while being treated in private practice. On the basis of these two studies, Dr. Harris reported in 1953:

"The sedative and tranquilizing effect of Reserpine is of value in reducing the mental strain of geriatric patients and permitting them to carry on more useful and comfortable lives."

The evidence began piling up. Successes in the cardiovascular and geriatric fields were followed by reports of its effectiveness in such gynecologic conditions as premenstrual tension, difficult menopause, frigidity, etc. But psychiatry still dragged a cautious foot. In "The Rauwolfia Story," a medical writer expressed his puzzlement in these words:

"Oddly, one of the last applications of Serpasil (Reserpine) to be tested by modern investigators was in the control of severe mental disease—the very field in which *Rauwolfia* has been widely hailed in India for at least five centuries."

One young psychiatric researcher finally broke the ice. Dr. Nathan S. Kline, thirty-seven-year-old Director of Research at New York's massive Rockland State Hospital, got interested, he said later, because of "the tremendous paucity of pharmalogical methods of treating mental disease." After a careful review of the literature, Dr. Kline decided to plunge in. He first tried the drug on himself and volunteers from his research staff. Then he moved on to a large-scale experiment. He tried the drug on one of the toughest wards at Rockland. Of the 411 patients who were given the drug over a period of a month, all were listed as severely disturbed and many as destructive and suicidal. All but 5 per cent were diagnosed as schizophrenic.

Dr. Kline reported the results of his experiment in February, 1954, at a New York Academy of Sciences symposium devoted mainly to reports of the successes of *Rauwolfia* in physical illnesses. His paper was an extremely cautious one. He reported that the drug had a generally calming effect on the ward; incidents of violence were reduced by a third, and much less restraint and seclusion were employed. But he leaned over backward in summarizing the results.

"A great deal more investigation is needed to insure that the improvement noted was not the result of 'psychological' factors," he warned. "Those cases reported on showed *improvement,* and the time elapsed has been too brief to know if there is not a rapid relapse unless other treatment is maintained. There is little doubt that in most people *Rauwolfia* brings about a change of psychic state. This in itself may be the 'effective' factor in conjunction with psychotherapy. . . .

"Considerable research is indicated: (1) to determine for which patients *Rauwolfia* is a satisfactory sedative; (2) to confirm the beneficial action of *Rauwolfia* in certain psychoneurotics; (3) to determine if other neurological and psychiatric conditions may be benefited; (4) to investigate the possible modes of action; and (5) to extend further the research on related Ayurvedic [native Indian] drugs."

What could be more cautious? Impressed with Dr. Kline's paper, and deeply convinced he had opened the door to a vast new chemical attack upon mental illness, I circulated his paper among some of my psychiatric and medical-writer friends. With a few notable exceptions, the responses were astonishing. I was solemnly warned that I had succumbed to "sensationalism," that Dr. Kline had plunged far beyond the pale of "responsible scientific behavior," that it was "barbaric" to suggest that a mere drug could alleviate anxieties, and so on. A number of the psychiatrists got up on their moral high horses and cried out that we were arousing "false hopes" in the mentally ill and their families, and that psychiatry had been through this business before with a lot of other therapies. As politely as possible, I replied that all we wanted was a fair trial for the new drug. Why didn't they try it before burning Kline at the stake? Furthermore, what was wrong with giving the mentally ill some hope, in whatever degree? What hope did the current state of knowledge in psychiatry offer them? To those in the high income brackets, five years of psychoanalysis at a cost of $10,000 or more so they could learn to live with their symptoms. To those of average income, years of misery and neglect in a public mental institution. What the hell is so wrong, I asked, with trying anything that offers some hope of breaking through the gloom, doom, and despair in which American psychiatry is wallowing? In my angrier moments, I suggested that the psychiatrists themselves take the drug to calm their ever-present anxieties and insecurities about anything which was a little off the beaten, weary track.

The Kline paper was pretty much ignored in the early months of 1954. Then, in June, 1954, *The Saturday Evening Post* broke out with a major article on Reserpine called "The Drug That Fooled The Doctors." It was written by Milton Silverman, a Ph.D. in chemistry and one of the nation's top science writers.

The Silverman article dealt, in part, with the use of Reserpine by Drs. Robert H. Noce and David B. Williams on seventy-four severely disturbed patients at the Modesto State Hospital in California. The Modesto doctors had begun using Reserpine in October, 1953, and the *Post* article reported on experience over a seven-month period. Of seventy-four patients to whom the drug was administered, eight were discharged and another twenty showed dramatic abatement of psychotic symptoms. Eighty per cent of the entire group showed marked improvement.

Just about the time the Silverman article appeared, I was working on two projects with the National Institute of Mental Health. The first was a brochure analyzing the current status of psychiatric research. In the draft sections prepared by the Institute, I noted the complete omission of even the slightest reference to the new drugs. I questioned this, particularly in view of the fact that the brochure was replete with descriptions of research projects still in the testing stage. The answer given me was the usual one: "sensational stuff" and "false hopes." Fortunately for the National Institute of Mental Health, our committee went ahead and included a couple of exceedingly conservative pages on the new drugs. By the time the brochure appeared, the drugs had proved themselves in scores of clinical trials.

The second project was a magazine article highlighting the new developments in psychiatric research. We submitted one draft to the Institute people which emphasized some of the dramatic results being obtained by the new drugs. They balked so determinedly that the co-operative project was dropped and the National Mental Health Committee assumed full responsibility for the summation, which finally appeared as a two-part series on the editorial pages of the conservative New York *Herald Tribune*.

The public information section of the Institute also began moaning to me about the flood of inquiries on the new drugs they were getting from the families of patients. They allowed as how this was a terrible thing: people in this democracy of ours writing letters to a tax-supported agency clamoring for information on the drugs! They were particularly bitter about the Silverman article, charging "sensational" handling of "sober" psychiatric material.

The ground was soon cut from under them. On October 30, 1954, the exceedingly sober *Journal of the American Medical Association* printed the scientific report of the Modesto group. In subdued, dispassionate prose, it told a remarkable story.

"At the time of this report," the authors wrote, "we have sixty-eight female and six male mentally ill patients taking Reserpine by mouth or injection or both. For this investigation we have selected only those mental patients who had the worst prognosis as far as recovery was concerned. They were the so-called back-ward patients who had been regarded as hopeless. A great majority had been mentally ill for a long period of time and had been entirely refractory to other methods of treatment. Three or four of this group had received over one hundred electroshock treatments each. In fact, all of the first nine patients were selected from our maximum security wards.

"Prior to this study these wards presented the usual picture of wards of this type, namely, ten to twelve patients in seclusion, some also in camisole or other types of restraint. In addition, heavy sedation and electroconvulsive therapy, as well as hydrotherapy and wet packs, were necessary and being utilized daily. Owing to the raucous, hyperactive, combative, sarcastic, resistive, uncooperative patients, the ward was in a continual turmoil. Necessary daily tasks, such as feeding, dressing, and bathing the patients, were arduous and had a depressing effect on the personnel assigned to these wards. Large numbers of physically strong technicians were needed to supervise and care for such patients, many of whom had to be spoon-fed because they were too uncooperative to go to the dining room. They kept other patients awake at night because of their noisy behavior, and some continually ran up and down the hallway. Although frequently attempted, the administration of electroconvulsive therapy was difficult because of the resistance of these patients to treatment and their intense fear reactions."

To anyone who has spent any length of time in the back wards of our mental hospitals, the above is a classic description of conditions which have gone on day after day, week after week, month after month, year after year, and decade after decade in the back pits of these dungeons of doom. And now a new therapy is introduced. What are the results?

"Since the advent of therapy with Reserpine by the oral and parenteral routes, changes in the patients' attitudes and behavior have been noted," the authors report. "The patients do not manifest a fear reaction to the alkaloid and gladly express a preference for this drug over electroconvulsive therapy. Patients have undergone a metamorphosis from raging, combative, unsociable persons to cooperative, friendly, cheerful, sociable, relatively quiet persons who are amenable to psychotherapy and rehabilitative measures. Most patients have shown favorable weight gains, and they have further expressed a desire to be assigned to work details. . . . At present on the wards where patients are receiving Reserpine, seclusion, restraint of all types, sedation, and electroconvulsive therapy have been almost eliminated. It seems incredible that a drug can replace electroconvulsive therapy in this manner, but apparently such a drug has been found, and we expect it to revolutionize and facilitate modern psychiatric treatment."

And how about the ward attendants, assigned the daily task of working in these pits of violence? Do the drugs raise "false hopes" in them?

"Not only the patients have benefited but the ward technicians have adopted hopeful, optimistic attitudes, which are required for a positive and effective approach to therapy," the authors conclude.

"They are overjoyed at the prospect of being converted from custodians to rehabilitation therapists. They are constantly requesting Reserpine for all types of disturbed patients and would be alarmed if such therapy were discontinued, because they know that their duties would again entail restraining combative patients."

On December 2, 1954, the Modesto doctors reported on additional work with Reserpine to the Eighth Clinical Meeting of the American Medical Association. Of 247 patients, mostly severely schizophrenic, treated for periods up to twelve months, 27 per cent left the hospital on either indefinite leave of absence or discharge. The authors concluded their report with an earnest plea for more research in chemotherapy:

"The use of Reserpine should result in annual savings to taxpayers by virtue of its decreasing admissions as well as making possible many leaves of absence and discharges. Many chronic mentally ill patients who were regarded as having a hopeless prognosis have gone, and others will continue to go on indefinite leave of absence from the hospital. . . . Further research in reference to chemical and physiological disturbances of the cerebrum in mental disorders should provide enlightening information about the effectiveness of Reserpine and other chemical therapies. . . . This period of chemical treatment of the mentally ill is in its infancy, and we believe that more specific drugs will be discovered in the future that will make it possible to treat specific symptoms or diagnostic categories."

As the months went by, the clinical evidence began to multiply. In February, 1955, the New York Academy of Sciences held a second symposium on Reserpine. The clinical evidence of the remarkable success of the drug had multiplied to such an extent that the entire two-day symposium was restricted to its use in neuropsychiatric and related disorders. The following summary of a few of the thirty scientific papers delivered by outstanding American and European investigators may convey some idea of the impact of the symposium upon current thinking in psychiatry:

1. The Use of Reserpine in Ambulatory and Hospitalized Geriatric Psychotics—Dr. Anthony Sainz, State Psychopathic Hospital, Iowa City, Iowa.

Reserpine was given to eighty-nine seniles, ranging in age from sixty-four to ninety-two years. Of the group, twenty-six were outpatients being seen at the Mental Health Institute in Cherokee, Iowa.

"In conclusion, it may be stated that the results produced by the use of Reserpine alone in these patients were most gratifying," Dr. Sainz reported. "Many ambulatory patients were able to remain at home while under treatment, and an analysis of the behavior of the sixty-three hospitalized patients included in our study showed that man-hours of work spent by psychiatric aides, nurses, and doctors in their care decreased an average of 50 per cent. This reduction should be of great interest to state hospitals in general which are surfeited, by and large, with patients in these categories."

2. Reserpine at Manteno State Hospital—Drs. Dean C. Tasher and Marianne Chermak.

Manteno is one of the largest mental hospitals in the country, with more than eight thousand patients. In February, 1953, Dr. Tasher had begun a bold program with prolonged maintenance electro-shock therapy on more than three hundred chronic schizophrenics in the back wards at Manteno. However, even among the group classified as "shock-reversible" (able to maintain some reality contact with one or two shock treatments a week), difficulties were practically insurmountable.

"The ward on which these patients resided was noted for frequent assaults, moderate to very severe injuries, and daily transfers to the hydrotherapy division," Dr. Tasher noted. "By the beginning of last year [1954], it was deemed necessary to project construction plans for hydrotherapy facilities on the ward because of the frequency of violent disturbances. Overcrowding and inadequate numbers of personnel presented an insurmountable hurdle to the realization of any further attempt to expand or even to continue long the maintenance shock ward. Therefore, we were on the alert for any type of easily administered, efficacious mass therapy which could supplant this program."

When Reserpine first became available at Manteno in the summer of 1954, Dr. Tasher tried it on eighty-two chronically disturbed women who were getting one or two shock treatments a week. The response was so dramatic that the electroshock treatment was discontinued. Of these first eighty-two women, fifty-nine were either discharged or referred to social service for home placement, and only eleven showed no significant improvement.

Then Dr. Tasher moved in on the toughest group, those resistant to all forms of therapy, including shock. As he describes it:

"Various groups of severely regressed, very long-term patients (five to thirty years of continuous hospitalization) were then surveyed to see whether this medication could be successfully administered in wholesale fashion to the typical 'back-ward' patient with any expectation of improvement. These patients had all received, at various times, different types of intensive treatment from the earliest methods, through the eras of metrazol and large-scale insulin therapy, then electric shock, and had shown a uniform lack of response. In addition, many of them had been subject to other types of treatment such as carbon-dioxide therapy, prolonged sleep-therapy, and varied new medications as they would appear and then disappear from the market. More subtle techniques had been tried on occasion. Whole wards would be shifted, personnel would be changed, and whole teams of the ancillary therapists would make sustained efforts through the media of occupational and recreational therapy to bring about some change in the schizophrenic withdrawal of these untidy, severely regressed patients. All such measures were to no avail. For the purposes of this paper, these patients are referred to as 'shock-resistant' and constitute the growing population of the hospital, for many enter at sixteen to eighteen years of age and remain fifty or sixty years."

This is the real hard core of the mental hospital load, and yet Dr. Tasher was able to report in February, 1955:

"The 'shock-resistant' group, including 104 women and 35 men, have been under treatment for only two months. Of these, nineteen are discharged or ready for discharge after hospitalizations up to thirteen years. Fifty-two show definite clinical improvement. The remainder have not yet shown response to therapy. . . . In view of these results, the authors believe Reserpine to be a valuable new adjunctive or even replacement therapy in the treatment of chronic schizophrenic patients who were formerly considered more or less permanently institutionalized."

> 3. Treatment of Chronic Schizophrenic Reactions with Re-
> serpine—Drs. Leo E. Hollister, George E. Krieger, Alan
> Kringle, and Richard H. Roberts, Veterans Administration
> Hospital, Palo Alto, California.

"We purposely chose patients with chronic schizophrenic reactions for evaluation, because this particular diagnostic category accounts for 47 per cent of mental hospital in-patients," the Palo Alto doctors reported. "Each year, at least $235,000,000 is spent caring for this group of 270,000, whose average hospitalization lasts thirteen years —usually during the most productive period of life. In terms of human misery, the cost of this illness is incalculable.

"Eight years ago, an analogous situation existed in patients with tuberculosis. Since the introduction of effective drugs in the treatment of that disease, the entire character of the treatment has changed. The necessity for hospital treatment of tuberculosis has diminished. The degree of disability has been lessened, and the mortality rate has been reduced. It is altogether possible that Reserpine, Chlorpromazine, and other drugs to follow may cause a similar revolution in the treatment of the mentally ill."

The Palo Alto doctors selected 127 chronic schizophrenics for a trial with Reserpine. These patients had been ill for periods of from six months to thirty-seven years.

"The main reasons these patients were selected for treatment," the authors reported, "were these: (1) they were so disturbed as to require frequent restraint, seclusion, or heavy sedation; (2) they were too anxious or hostile or too withdrawn and uncommunicative to be amenable to other psychiatric treatment; (3) they had not responded to any previous therapy."

Almost from the inception of the drug treatment, dramatic changes were noted by the authors:

"When patients showed marked improvement, the result was frequently astounding, even to psychiatrists of long clinical experience. Patients who had been clearly responding to hallucinations, or careless of personal habits, or hostile, destructive, and resistive, or completely withdrawn and mute became, within a short period of time, clean, co-operative, and communicative persons. Many of the patients who showed moderate improvement were better than they had been during most of their hospital course. In many cases, these patients were able, for the first time, to participate in some of the psychiatric rehabilitative programs which they had previously spurned. Often moderately or markedly improved patients demonstrated some evidence of increased understanding of the nature of their illness and the methods by which it might be treated. Previously insurmountable psychotic defenses often weakened considerably. Hallucinations either disappeared or were no longer troublesome. Slight degrees of improvement were often most appreciated by the hospital staff or the patients' relatives, both of whom were gratified to see these patients become more approachable and show greater interest in their surroundings."

Of the 127 patients treated, ninety-eight showed significant improvement. Twenty-five were granted passes from the hospital, and five were discharged. Four patients in the group had been scheduled for lobotomies, which were canceled because of favorable response to Reserpine. In a number of other cases, electroconvulsive therapy was discontinued.

4. Clinical Evaluation of Reserpine in a State Hospital—Drs. William L. Kirkpatrick and Foster Sanders, East Louisiana State Hospital, Jackson, La.

"Our study totaled 206 patients consisting of five groups," the Louisiana doctors reported. "These groups were as follows: (1) eleven acutely disturbed patients; (2) thirty-nine chronic epileptic patients; (3) twenty-two chronically ill patients residing in a violent ward; (4) twenty-four psychotic patients with pulmonary tuberculosis; and (5) a supplementary mixed group totaling 110, including (a) geriatric patients; (b) cases refractory to a large number of EST [electroshock] treatments; (c) deteriorated patients who were denudative, assaultive, destructive, and uncooperative; and (d) mental defective patients."

Of the 164 patients who received Reserpine—forty-five served as controls—sixty-seven patients either were able to leave the hospital on furlough or pass, or were transferred to better wards. There was a statistically significant reduction in seizure frequency among the epileptic group. There was an 83 per cent improvement in the TB group. Of those patients unable to leave the authors had this to report:

"Many patients who improved, but were unable to leave, became assets to the hospital and were able to take care of themselves. Some performed useful functions in the ward or worked in some productive capacity in other areas. The cost of the medication daily per

patient is negligible when one considers the savings resulting from
a reduction of (1) materials destroyed by violent patients; (2) number of attendants necessary to manage a violent, untidy, chronic, or
TB ward; and (3) the extra medical care necessary for patients in-
jured by assaults."

> 5. Clinical and Psychological Observations on Psychiatric
> Patients Treated with Reserpine: A Preliminary Report—
> Drs. Jay L. Hoffman and Leon Konchegul, St. Elizabeths
> Hospital, Washington, D. C.

Drs. Hoffman and Konchegul, staff psychiatrists at St. Elizabeths,
huge Federal mental hospital housing more than seven thousand
patients, frankly admitted they shared the resistance of many of
their colleagues to use of the new drugs.

"A considerable number of psychiatrists are prejudiced against
the use of drugs in the treatment of psychological illness," they reported. "In part, this prejudice is based on the widespread use, or
abuse, of the sedative and hypnotic drugs. These medicaments have
been aptly described as representing 'chemical restraint' and, when
they are so used, subject to all the objections made against mechanical restraint of the mentally ill.

"Sharing the prejudice above referred to, the authors were im-
pelled to determine for themselves, with as much objectivity as they
could muster, whether the drug Reserpine (Serpasil) is, in fact, a
generically different therapeutic agent than the hypnotic drugs and
whether it has the effects desired for our patients. Although this is
only a preliminary report of a seven-week period of observation, and
although there are still certain details regarding the use of this drug
about which we expect to learn more, we believe that we can properly answer both of these questions in the affirmative."

The drug was given to 108 patients, the majority of them disturbed schizophrenics.

"The patients here considered—before medication—were restless,
agitated, confused, assaultive, and combative," the doctors from
St. Elizabeths noted. "The number who required seclusion was
relatively high. Many were hostile, suspicious, tense, and threatening. They included the untidy, the incontinent, the markedly regressed patients who refused to wear clothing or who smeared

themselves and their surroundings with feces. They did not, as a rule, participate in the activities available to them, nor could they associate with their fellows without conflict. Many were hallucinated or delusional or both. They were noisy, destructive, resistive, angry, obscene, vulgar, vituperative.

"After receiving Reserpine, 27 per cent showed little or no change. This is itself a point of differentiation from the common hypnotic drugs. The latter, with a single dose of the appropriate drug, will almost always produce the expected effect promptly.

"For the 73 per cent who showed some degree of improvement, the most common observation was a reduction of motor hyperactivity, of tension, of hostility and aggressiveness. Seclusion became less frequent or was eliminated. Patients who had not previously worn clothes now did so. Those who had been untidy or careless in their dress now took more interest in their personal appearance. Communication with some of the patients became easier, and their speech became more coherent and less confused. They found it easier to talk about their delusions and hallucinations. While most, if not all, retained their abnormal content, they seemed to be made less anxious by it. Sometimes, if they were willing to discuss their delusions or hallucinations at all, they gave the impression that their abnormal ideas were actually not their own, but rather those of a third person.

"Those who showed the most marked degree of improvement became affable, bland, friendly. They asked to be given ward work to do, and began talking about when they could go home. They participated again in recreational activities, played checkers and cards, took part in ball games, went for walks, watched television programs, and read newspapers and books.

"The effect of such patient improvement on the morale of the ward personnel was noteworthy. In one ward, where the Reserpine was reserved for the patients included in this study, an overactive boy had been given some of the drug by a physician who had begged of his colleagues all the samples they had. When no more samples were forthcoming and the boy was again becoming disturbed, the nurses agreed among themselves to take up a collection to buy more of the drug for this patient. Needless to say, the hospital took appropriate action to make this action unnecessary."

The 1955 New York Academy of Sciences symposium also included several excellent papers on the use of Reserpine in the private practice of psychiatry. Patients beset with anxieties were calmed down and kept at a functioning level through the oral use of the drugs on an out-patient basis. Summing up the point of view of the private practitioner, Dr. Sydney Kinnear Smith of Berkeley, California, suggested the enormous potential of Reserpine and other drugs in bringing psychiatry back into the mainstream of medicine.

"The results of diminished tension and anxiety, associated with an improved accessibility of psychotherapy, is of particular significance in private practice," Dr. Smith noted. "In its final evaluation, this may be the dominant contribution of Reserpine to psychiatry. We may be entering a New Era because of a better integration between the several schools that constitute our speciality. The Couch may yet be moved from the Ivory Tower to the Temple of Aesculapius."

During the remainder of 1955, the clinical evidence poured in. *The Journal of the American Medical Association* published a sheaf of significant studies, as did *The American Journal of Psychiatry* and numerous other technical journals. The regional research conferences of the American Psychiatric Association, and the APA annual convention in Atlantic City in May, were dominated by papers on the drugs.

Finally, even the National Institute of Mental Health saw the light. During the 1955 Congressional hearings, the Director of the Institute had some kind things to say about the new drugs, although not until he was pressed by Senator Hill as to what he would do if he were allocated additional money.

There were plenty of resistances still kicking around, though. I went into a Southern state late in February, 1955, to address a state mental health association meeting to which a number of key legislators had been invited. Prior to coming into the state, I had been informed that several of the state hospital superintendents were dragging their feet on the drugs—to the point where the families of patients who could afford to were buying drugs for them. I ripped into this practice as unconscionable, since it discriminated against those patients who had no outside resources. Several of the hospital superintendents, under the baleful glance of the legislators in the audience, rose and begged off the hook on the grounds they didn't have enough technical and clinical information on the drugs. In reply, I pointed out that New York had more than five thousand patients on treatment, other neighboring states had additional thousands, and the Veterans' Administration was doing a large testing on thousands of patients. The reply must have convinced the legislators, because money for the new drugs was soon forthcoming.

8. MORE DRUGS

AND MORE

CLINICAL

EVIDENCE

WHILE Reserpine was daily demonstrating—even to the most die-hard skeptics —its right to a pre-eminent place in the armamentarium of both the hospital and the private psychiatrist, an even more remarkable drug was having trouble gaining entry into this country.

Chlorpromazine was first discovered by basic scientists in the Rhone-Poulenc Laboratories in France early in 1951. They were actually hunting for a new kind of antihistamine which wouldn't induce so much drowsiness in patients. One day they mixed up a chemical compound — R. P. 4560 — which acted strangely on a group of test animals. Given the new compound in large amounts, the animals quickly went to sleep. But the drug differed from the ordinary run of sedatives in that it did not "slug" the dogs— they could be easily aroused for feeding or other purposes.

Further animal experiments were then run with the new compound in other chemical laboratories. Madame Courvoisier and her associates reported late in 1951 that the new drug, used on experimental rats, completely calmed their anxieties during conditioned reflex experiments. Other experiments, reported in the French literature both in late 1951 and early 1952, confirmed these observations.

On January 26, 1952, Dr. Henri Laborit reported the successful use of Chlorpromazine on the common nauseas of pregnancy. He noted that it not only controlled physical disturbances in expectant mothers but had a remarkable effect in practically eliminating their anxieties and apprehensions about the coming event.

In the summer of 1952, a French psychiatrist, Dr. Jean Delay, and his colleagues reported in a number of issues of authoritative medical publications on its successful use in treating a wide variety of mental illnesses. Of the first thirty-eight patients on whom they tried it, all but three showed remarkable improvement.

In the next year and a half, European medical journals were filled with enthusiastic clinical reports on the effectiveness of Chlorpromazine. In addition to scores of articles in French medical journals, there were numerous reports of investigations in Italy, Austria, Germany, Switzerland, and England. There were strong editorials in such distinguished British medical publications as the *Lancet* and *The British Medical Journal*.

As early as 1952 American physicians were being supplied with bibliographies of the European literature and translations of the more important studies.

In May, 1953, there came to my desk a translation of an article by Drs. J. Sigwald and D. Bouttier which had appeared in a recent issue of the French *Annals of Medicine*. It was a superb description of French experience with the drug since 1951. In addition to a summary of the literature, the authors detailed, with Gallic meticulousness, the case histories of sixty-six patients on whom the drugs had been used. They reported the successes and they reported the failures. Of the forty-eight patients with psychiatric disabilities, most of whom had been treated on an ambulatory basis, they noted:

"A study based on the treatment of forty-eight cases of practical, everyday psychiatry shows that R.P. 4560—Chlorpromazine—is a drug which has a very good action, superior to other therapeutic agents, on anxiety states, depression, obsessions, cenesthopathias, serious forms of psychasthenia, and psychic hyperexcitability. Favorable results have been obtained in chronic interpretive psychoses. The therapeutic effect is more suspensive than curative, but prolonged treatment does not appear to be dangerous. There is no serious disadvantage in using this compound. . . . The neuroplegic effects of Chlorpromazine can be put to use widely in therapy and the results obtained are characterized by a considerable percentage of success."

The French authors concluded their twenty-nine-page paper with a critique of the metabolic action of the drug which has not been excelled in any of the papers that have appeared in America and Canada since then, even though such brilliant investigators as Drs. Heinz Lehmann, Harold Himwich, Frank Ayd, Jr., Vernon Kinross-Wright, and others had the advantage of much subsequent experience before publishing their findings on the possible mode of action of the drug.

"Experimentation on rats shows that Chlorpromazine has the property of deconditioning an animal in which a conditioned reflex has previously been established," the French authors wrote early in 1953. "This experiment enables an understanding of the mode of action of this compound. By analogy, one can suppose that in pathology it creates a disconnection between the excitations originating from outside the body—or developed within it—and conscious perception. There is produced, according to the expression of Laborit, a synaptic interception between cortical processes and the diencephalon, which permits a deconditioning. It acts in this way on the obsessions, cenesthesias, pains, and also on thymic dysfunction. One understands by this hypothesis its seemingly so complex action, in particular the property of acting on anxiety and melancholic depression, or on hyperexcitability and hypomania or mania. . . .

"The therapeutic application of Chlorpromazine shows that its neuroplegic action, so useful in the treatment of shock and in the application of therapeutic hibernation, is not its only value. Its activity on the higher nerve structures is also very important. One speaks of 'functional lobotomy'; the expression is perhaps unsuitable because it does not seem that the personality of the patients treated is affected, even temporarily, as it can be in lobotomy, but often the result suggests such a comparison."

As in the instance of Dr. Nathan Kline's pioneer paper on Reserpine, I called the Sigwald-Bouttier paper to the attention of a number of prominent psychiatrists, including two state mental health commissioners and a few state hospital superintendents. They patted me kindly in the area of the midbrain, generally regarded as the seat of the emotions, and warned me about French scientists—"so sensational, so dramatic." I guess they were right. After all, Louis Pasteur was so "sensational" he shocked the French Academy of Sciences. And, of course, there were the Curies.

However, there were a number of adventurous spirits still alive and kicking in this great land of ours. Like Dr. Kline, they were pretty fed up with the feeble armamentarium of the latter-day psychiatrist. When the Smith, Kline, and French Laboratories imported a shipment of Chlorpromazine, they jumped at the opportunity of testing it in clinical trials.

The first North American report of the remarkable therapeutic properties of the new drug came from Canada. In the February, 1954, issue of the *Archives of Neurology and Psychiatry,* Dr. Heinz Lehmann of the Verdun Protestant Hospital in Montreal reported on the success of the drug in the treatment of seventy-one psychotic patients.

"We are particularly impressed," Dr. Lehmann reported, "with the favorable results in our manic-depressive patients in a chronic manic state, all of whom had been continuously manic or hypomanic for more than a year and had previously failed to respond to standard therapeutic procedures or had had only brief remissions. In some of these long-standing cases recovery with Chlorpromazine may not be immediate, the improvement gradually progressing for a month or two after termination of therapy. In acute manic states Chlorpromazine therapy usually leads to recovery in a shorter time than is required with other, established treatment procedures. It is generally known that the rapid remissions that follow electroshock therapy often are short-lived, while relapses following Chlorpromazine therapy are not frequent. . . .

"One manic patient stated after her recovery that with the drug she soon lost the feeling: 'I had to live my whole life in one day.' Another patient suffering from long-standing anxiety described thus the effect of small doses of Chlorpromazine on her feelings: 'It was like a chairman taking control of a meeting where everybody previously had been shouting at once.' Although a patient under the influence of Chlorpromazine at first glance presents the aspect of a heavily drugged person, one is surprised at the absence of clouding of consciousness. The higher psychic functions are preserved to a remarkable degree, and the patients are capable of sustained attention, reflection and concentration."

A few months went by, and then in May the American medical and technical journals burst forth with a rash of papers substantiating the clinical claims which had been advanced two and three years previously by European scientists.

The May 1, 1954, issue of *The Journal of the American Medical Association* carried a remarkably complete paper by the distinguished neuropathologist Dr. N. W. Winkelman on the use of Chlorpromazine on a wide variety of mental illnesses. Dr. Winkelman tried the new compound on a roster of 142 cases: patients suffering from anxieties and tensions, patients who had endured obsessions and phobias for years, seniles, epileptics, etc. He found the drug particularly effective in two areas: obsessions and senile agitations. In a matter of a few short weeks, the drug cleared up phobias and obsessions in a number of patients who had been subject, over a period of years, to every form of treatment from intensive psychotherapy to frontal lobotomy. The drug was also used on twenty-seven senile patients who exhibited continual agitation, severe anxiety, and belligerence. Of the group, twenty-one were relieved of their agitation after a two-month course of treatment with the drug.

In his summation of the clinical experiment, Dr. Winkelman pointed up the incredibly wide therapeutic spectrum of the drug:

"Chlorpromazine is especially remarkable in that it can greatly reduce severe anxiety, suppress the intensity of phobias and obsessions, reverse or modify paranoid psychosis, quiet manic or extremely agitated patients, and can change the hostile, belligerent, agitated, senile patient into a quiet, easily managed patient."

Just about the time doctors all over the country were picking up their AMA *Journals* and reading of the work of Dr. Winkelman, the 1954 convention of the American Psychiatric Association heard a remarkable report on Chlorpromazine from Dr. Vernon Kinross-Wright of Houston, Texas. Dr. Kinross-Wright, an English-trained psychiatrist who had come to the United States only a few years before, gave his colleagues the first of what were to become a series of beautifully detailed reports quickly establishing him as a researcher of the first rank.

Dr. Kinross-Wright reported on use of the drug on ninety-five patients in a general hospital affiliated with the Baylor University College of Medicine. The majority of the group were suffering from mania and were unselected admissions to the psychiatric service of the hospital. Of the ninety-five, thirty-two were completely freed of their symptoms, while another thirty-five were in the "much improved" category. Only nine of the patients treated with the drug failed to show any improvement.

In that same productive month of May, two independent reports appeared in the medical literature on the effectiveness of Chlorpromazine in treating alcoholics, particularly acute cases with delirium tremens. Dr. James F. Cummins and Dale G. Friend of Peter Bent Brigham Hospital in Boston reported in *The American Journal of the Medical Sciences* that they had been using Antabuse to aid in cutting alcoholics off the liquor. However, unless the patient was kept free of alcohol for at least six days prior to the administration of Antabuse, a severe, nauseating reaction set in. Many patients could not stand this withdrawal period; they shook so badly and were so agitated that they had to be taken off the therapy. Having tried countless remedies, Drs. Cummins and Friend took a "flyer" on Chlorpromazine, having little real hope that it would bring results. To their gratified surprise, it worked wonders. It calmed the patients down, reduced their craving for liquor, and got them over the dreaded withdrawal period in miraculous fashion.

Almost simultaneously, there appeared in *The Medical Annals of the District of Columbia* corroborative evidence of the effectiveness of Chlorpromazine in the treatment of alcoholism. Dr. Joseph Fazekas and his colleagues at the District of Columbia General Hospital reported on its use with sixty-four patients, twenty-one with delirium tremens and the remainder with severe psychomotor agitation.

"Many of our patients were chronic alcoholics," the Washington doctors wrote, "and their reaction to the drug may be of interest, since most of them have previously received either barbiturates, paraldehyde, or both. The impressions of the patients were very favorable, and probably most important was the comment that 'you are not nervous after you come out of it the way you are with paraldehyde.' . . . It was found to be highly effective in controlling the acute mental and physical aberrations associated with these states, the drug inducing a sleeplike state from which the patient could be easily aroused to take required nourishment and fluids."

A few months later, in the October issue of *Postgraduate Medicine,* Dr. Kinross-Wright added important clinical evidence of the effectiveness of the drug in the various deliriums.

"The deliriums, or toxic confusional psychoses, respond rapidly to the drug," he noted. "A few 50 mg. injections usually suffice to clear confusion, hyperactivity, and hallucinations. Further, the systemic toxicity characteristic of these states is quickly alleviated, too. Whether the confusion is associated with senility, a brain lesion, fever, or chemical poisons is immaterial. Alcoholic delirium tremens is very satisfactorily treated by this means. Two alcoholic patients I had treated for delirium by this means, when brought into the emergency room during subsequent attacks, surprised the intern by demanding Chlorpromazine. Unhappily, he dismissed their requests as hallucinations!"

In that same paper, Dr. Kinross-Wright reported his first observations on the use of the drug with schizophrenics.

"Schizophrenia, the most crippling and chronic of mental disorders, is the greatest challenge to psychiatric methods of treatment," he wrote. "About one-half of all schizophrenic patients were not substantially benefited by any combination of treatments hitherto available. In one series of thirty schizophrenic patients I reported, the situation two months after the conclusion of treatment was as follows: eight were at home and symptom-free; thirteen were much improved, with most of them living at home; five were somewhat improved, and four were no better. With so small a number of patients, conclusions must be limited. The results are highly provocative, however. It should be noted here that most patients on Chlorpromazine are more accessible to psychotherapy; indeed, patients often discuss their deep-seated emotional problems spontaneously."

In the early months of 1955, as some of the bigger state mental hospitals began to use the drug, the evidence began to flood the medical journals and the scientific meetings.

In an article in the April 9 issue of *The Journal of the American Medical Association* and in a subsequent paper of broader scope delivered at the 1955 American Psychiatric Association convention, Dr. Douglas Goldman, Clinical Director of the Longview State Hospital in Cincinnati, foreshadowed the revolution the drug was to foster in the treatment of chronic patients in the back wards of mental institutions all over the land.

"Chronic psychotic illness presents the largest per capita patient load for any illness in the United States and probably in the entire civilized world," Dr. Goldman told his colleagues at the 1955 convention. "At the beginning of the year 1950 there were 656,061 patients under jurisdiction of 'prolonged care' in hospitals devoted to care of the mentally ill.

"Numbers, however, do not indicate adequately the nature of the problem of the chronically mentally ill, particularly in the state hospital setting. There are well over one-half million human beings whose hope of ever being able to take an active and interested part in the life of their families and communities dwindles year by year in accelerating fashion. Some of these patients are suffering from degenerative infections and other organic illnesses which are not particularly or specifically susceptible to any known form of treatment. However, more than one-half of the residual patients, more than one-quarter of a million human beings, are suffering from what we have for many years called 'functional psychoses,' which in the last two decades have been found to be susceptible, in the early stages particularly, to treatment by physical and pharmacologic methods such as electric shock and its variants, insulin coma and psychosurgery. This quarter of a million residual patients are now largely residual after failure of treatment by these methods. There are, in addition, in all of our state hospitals quite a number of patients who were, even at the time of introduction of insulin and electric shock treatment, already in the chronic and so-called deteriorating stages of their illness. It is to this chronic and thus far treatment-resistant group of patients that we give our attention in this report."

Tackling the hard core of the state mental hospital load, Dr. Goldman and his colleagues gave Chlorpromazine to more than 600 patients—439 schizophrenics, 80 manic-depressives, and 160 patients in miscellaneous categories.

"These patients represented at the time of present admission chronic, heavily pre-treated psychotic illness, or had been in the hospital for periods up to thirty years," Dr. Goldman noted. "All of the patients who form the bulk of the material had been subjected to vigorous treatment with electric shock, with insulin coma, or both, and a considerable number had had, in addition to one or the other or both of these forms of treatment, psychosurgery in the form of prefrontal or transorbital lobotomies with no enduring improvement. . . . Although almost twice as many patients have been under drug treatment in the last year at Longview State Hospital, the material was chosen for this report because the patients represented the least favorable prognostic criteria as well as the worst management problems, medically and administratively, in the state hospital, on 'violent', 'deteriorated' or 'chronic' wards. . . . In a sense, such patients represented a sort of acid test for the effectiveness of Chlorpromazine and, indeed, any other method of treatment. Enduring response to treatment in psychotic conditions at this stage of development has heretofore been at the very most extremely rare, and for many psychiatrists of long experience, unheard of."

In tabulating the results of his lengthy clinical trials, Dr. Goldman used four classifications:

a. Patients who had recovered from all active psychotic manifestations.

b. Individuals who had recovered from most psychotic manifestations, and whose improvement might be summarized as "a good social remission."

c. Patients who had improved from their initial illness in significant ways.

d. Patients who had improved slightly or not at all.

"In the manic-depressive group," Dr. Goldman summarized, "even among the patients who have been in the hospital continuously for from 5 to more than 20 years, 5 of 32 achieve *a* and *b* remissions, and of the total group of 80 patients, 29 achieve such levels of improvement. . . . In the schizophrenic group of over 10 years continuous hospitalization, we see that 8 of 136, about 5 per cent, achieve *a* or *b* grades of remission and in the total group 146 out of 439, or roughly one-third, achieve this amazing level of improvement. In all instances, such improvement has been of at least two months duration, and in many cases a great deal longer, and gives every indication of being maintained or further favorably developed. . . .

"The group of patients graded as having achieved c improvement represents from the point of view of institutional administration and clinical management a result almost as important as the group which achieves 'social remission' and 'recovery,' particularly since more than one-half the patients in the extremely chronic group achieve results at this level. It is in this group that such important changes take place as the cessation of physical assaults, destructiveness of the physical plant, and the need for physical restraint; and the beginning of adequate communication after long episodes of muteness, and co-operative helpfulness instead of hostile resistance to discipline. It is the marked palliative effect of treatment in this group which has made it possible to discontinue the use of restraints in wards formerly labelled 'violent,' which has made it possible at times to keep previously denudative patients clothed, incontinent patients neat. In contrast to the effect of electric shock, which has long been used as a palliative measure, is the effect of Chlorpromozine which serves in a much more continuous and lasting fashion to achieve the palliative results. The improvement produced by Chlorpromazine is not, with rare exceptions, fluctuant, but is steadily maintained while the patient is receiving treatment so that behavior, instead of being unpredictable and impulsive, becomes in many important ways dependable. Even the patients who are considered to be failures from the use of Chlorpromazine in the statistical formulation in many instances present changes in behavior which make ward management a much less hazardous chore than before."

Concluding, Dr. Goldman spelled out some generalized results which have been thoroughly substantiated during the past six months as large Federal and state mental hospital systems have reported on their experience with Chlorpromazine:

"The experience in treating over six hundred chronic patients with Chlorpromazine over a period of almost a year has been reported in some detail, indicating, (1) that a significant number of such patients are susceptible to improvement of marked degree, which can be described as social remission or recovery; (2) that another group of more than half the patients showed what may be described as a palliative effect so that the psychotic behavior which presented the greatest difficulty in management was markedly ameliorated; (3) that continuation of treatment with Chlorpromazine over long periods of time produces progressive improvement with the increased duration of the treatment, with no limiting time factor as yet evident; (4) that the side-effects and toxic complications of the treatment are themselves susceptible to adequate management and do not present any undue hazard in carrying out the treatment; (5) that the theoretical implications of the results of this new organic method of treatment of psychotic illness represent the probable key to the development of a new body of knowledge of psychotic illness with firm roots in anatomy, physiology and pathology."

In the light of subsequent evidence, Dr. Goldman understated the case for Chlorpromazine at the APA convention. Reporting on further experience with the drug to the October, 1955, APA Mental Hospital Institute, he described a control study initiated to determine how effective the drug is in keeping released patients from returning to the hospital. In the period from August, 1954, to August, 1955, of ninety-three patients who were treated with Chlorpromazine and then sent home on convalescent leave, only six returned to the hospital. This is a remarkably low return rate. Over the same period of time, of 124 patients at Longview who received treatments other than drug therapy and were then released on trial leave, fifty-seven returned to the hospital.

In the floor discussion following Dr. Goldman's report, a number of state hospital doctors confirmed the low relapse figures following drug therapy. For example, Dr. Benjamin Pollack of Rochester State Hospital reported on a lengthy study of 250 patients who had received drug therapy at that institution and then been released to their homes. Over a period of a year, only 5 per cent had returned to the hospital. This is a dramatic contrast to the depressingly high percentage of former mental patients—the national average runs from 35 to 40 per cent—who eventually must return to institutions for further treatment.

In an even larger series of trials than those of Dr. Goldman, Dr. Herman C. B. Denber and his associates at New York's huge Manhattan State Hospital reported on the use of Chlorpromazine on 750 patients. Of this group, 494 patients had been hospitalized for from three to ten years. Electroconvulsive therapy, insulin coma treatment, and lobotomy, alone or in combination, were "the previous unsuccessful treatments administered to 493 patients." The majority of the 750 patients were given relatively low dosages—300 milligrams

—of Chlorpromazine daily for from two to five months. In a preliminary clinical tabulation published in *The American Journal of Psychiatry,* Dr. Denber and his colleagues reported the following remarkable results:

"Forty-eight patients have been discharged, and 5 are ready for discharge; 48 patients were markedly improved; 475 improved; 174 patients showed no change. At the present time, electroconvulsive treatment has been discontinued on the female wards, and is rarely used in the male services. Insulin coma treatment is only occasionally used. . . . Physical restraint has been decreased 74 per cent and accidents by 75 per cent in the female wards. This change has been slower on the male services where patients have been under treatment for a shorter time. . . . The effects of Chlorpromazine medication vary inversely with the duration of hospitalization. Nevertheless, it was still possible to discharge 17 patients ill from five to ten years, 3 of whom had been unsuccessfully treated previously with electroshock, insulin coma, and lobotomy."

The evidence also began to roll in on the effectiveness of the new drugs in treating hyperactive, emotionally disturbed children. At an American Psychiatric Association regional research conference in Galveston in February, 1955, Drs. Nathan Kline and George T. Nicolaou of Rockland State Hospital, New York, reported on preliminary work with Reserpine on a group of twenty-five adolescents hospitalized at their institution. Of the eleven young schizophrenics, all of whom had been psychotic for at least five years, only three showed marked improvement. However, of the fourteen in the nonschizophrenic group—overactive, aggressive, and deeply disturbed—eight improved so remarkably that they were either discharged or readied for discharge as soon as a suitable placement could be found.

"The same patients who showed a sustained improvement in behavior also demonstrated significant changes in their mental status," Drs. Kline and Nicolaou reported at Galveston. "Overt hostility and aggressive attitudes were no longer the prominent features which characterized these patients. Invariably they showed a desire to relate and to enter into co-operative activity. There was greater willingness to talk about their problems and to take advice and guidance. Comments such as 'I feel content and happy inside and don't feel like fighting any more' were not uncommon. One of the patients appraised his status rather appropriately in the following manner: 'I know I have improved and want to go home, but I'd rather stay longer to help myself more, go to school and make up my grades before I go home for good.' Another youngster expressed himself as follows: 'Before I felt bad all the time, so I would fight a lot; now I feel good and don't have to fight.' "

At the 1955 APA convention, Dr. Herbert Freed, Chief of the Child Psychiatry Clinic of the Philadelphia General Hospital, reported on the use of Chlorpromazine on twenty-five children ranging in age from seven to fifteen years. All of them had been referred to the Clinic by the school authorities; a number of them were so assaultive and destructive they had been excluded from school. Because of their disturbed condition, and because most of them came from broken homes, psychotherapy with either the children or the parents was practically impossible. The drug was therefore tried as a sort of last resort, and it was given over periods varying from four to sixteen months.

The Clinic staff, the school counselor, and a battery of psychological studies all testified to significant improvement in twenty-one of the children. The outstanding manifestation was a lessening of nervous overactivity. Many of the children spontaneously commented that they didn't feel the urge to fight any more. This was gratefully confirmed by their teachers.

There was an appreciable increase in learning ability, although the IQ's remained the same. With a decrease in hyperexcitability, the children seemed able to tackle the learning process in calm fashion. Memory span increased, and previously insuperable chores such as the multiplication tables succumbed to a quieter, more controlled approach. In five cases, the learning improvement was spectacular, and two children who had been excluded from school returned and made a satisfactory adjustment.

"It is suggested that the children are helped by this drug because the primitive animal-like response when encountering a new situation—to fight it or seek flight from it—is controlled so that the child faces previously disturbing situations and learns how to control them," Dr. Freed concluded.

In assessing the remarkable therapeutic range of Chlorpromazine, there is considerable agreement that its most exciting potential lies in its use in the private practice of psychiatry. In November, 1954, a young Baltimore psychiatrist, Dr. Frank Ayd, Jr. reported to the Southern Medical Association on the use of the drug on one hundred patients seen in his private practice. He followed this with a more extensive report at the Galveston conference, and at the 1955 APA Convention he reported on the use of Chlorpromazine with 150 patients and Reserpine with another 150 patients.

In Dr. Ayd's experience, as in that of most of his colleagues, Chlorpromazine proved slightly more effective. Of the 150 patients who used Chlorpromazine, ninety-nine showed significant improvement, while of the 150 who used Reserpine, eighty-four showed like improvement. In a smaller number of cases, therapeutic failures with Chlorpromazine were treated with Reserpine, and vice versa. Again Chlorpromazine had a slight edge.

In summarizing the results of his work with the drugs over a sixteen-month period, Dr. Ayd stressed the vital role of these drugs in giving both the private psychiatrist and the general practitioner really effective weapons against acute mental illness.

"Chlorpromazine and Reserpine make it possible to treat on an ambulatory basis many patients who would have had to be hospitalized," Dr. Ayd told his colleagues. "In the few instances that hospitalization was necessary, patients could be adequately treated in a general hospital or a regular nursing home. After a week or two of hospitalization, these patients were treated in the office. Only in severe manic or schizophrenic reactions was commitment to a psychiatric hospital necessary for a few weeks. . . . Geriatric patients made satisfactory home adjustments while taking Chlorpromazine or Reserpine. Without these drugs these senile individuals would have been placed in nursing homes, or state or private psychiatric hospitals. When treated with Chlorpromazine or Reserpine, geriatric patients in nursing homes were able to remain there or return home instead of entering a psychiatric hospital. . . .

"Chlorpromazine and Reserpine are valuable additions to the therapeutic armamentarium of the private practicing psychiatrist. Properly utilized, these drugs can: (1) increase the number of patients who may be treated in the office; (2) shorten the period of hospitalization, or make hospitalization unnecessary, thereby reducing the admissions to our overcrowded state psychiatric hospitals; (3) replace or reduce the need for electroconvulsive therapy, and (4) reduce the cost of psychiatric care."

The importance of Dr. Ayd's viewpoint cannot be exaggerated. Over the past few decades, a wall has grown up between the general practitioner and the psychiatrist. When the family doctor today encounters a patient with a severe mental disturbance, he is, in most cases, reluctant to refer the case to a private psychiatrist. He feels that any treatment program undertaken will be prolonged and expensive, with the end result quite uncertain. On the other hand, the general practitioner feels that his own medical training does not qualify him to handle routine cases of anxiety or other acute emotional disturbances.

With the advent of the new drugs, this picture has changed dramatically. The prominent British psychiatrist Dr. Thomas P. Rees, Superintendent of the famed Warlingham Park Hospital, capsuled this change in these words, delivered on a closed-circuit television broadcast during the 1955 APA convention:

"I believe," Dr. Rees told his American colleagues, "that the future of psychiatry lies not in the mental hospital, but outside the mental hospital, and that our first task should be to educate the general practitioner so that he can become a better psychiatrist and eventually, I hope, put us all out of a job."

At the conclusion of Dr. Rees' talk, the couch market dropped four points.

9. THE OLD GUARD GOES DOWN

THERE is a revolution in psychiatry: a change of emphasis from psychology to biology. And the biological approach seems to be working."

So wrote astute Earl Ubell, science editor of the New York *Herald Tribune* in a Sunday feature summarizing developments at the 1955 convention of the American Psychiatric Association.

"The program of the American Psychiatric Association meeting last week reflected this drastic change," Ubell continued. "A few years ago the only papers on the biology of mental diseases dealt with electrical patterns of the brain, and there were only one or two presentations. Last week, a score of scientists reported on biochemistry, hormones, biological electricity and the physiology of normal and abnormal states. Most dramatic were the descriptions of two drugs which, in the words of one scientist, have ushered in a new era in psychiatry."

The new era wasn't ushered in without a scrap. On the second night of the convention, a panel discussion was held on the new drugs. It opened with the reports of top Canadian and American researchers on their clinical experiences with the drugs. One was struck with the youthfulness of the scientists on the panel and with both the precision and enthusiasm of their papers. The Canadians—Drs. Heinz Lehmann and Gorman Hanrahan—were wondrously meticulous in their descriptions of both the clinical and metabolic effects of the drugs, and their American confreres—Drs. Vernon Kinross-Wright, Nathan Kline, Veronica Pennington, Harold Himwich, *et al.*—were equal to the technical pace set.

Then the meeting was thrown open for questions, and the jam-packed room seethed with excitement. After about fifteen minutes of polite sparring, the lines were sharply drawn. The Elder Statesmen began peppering the Young Turks with "questions"—usually in the form of statements raising doubts about the efficacy of the new drugs.

The first line of attack pictured the drugs as "merely palliative." This one didn't get very far. Dr. Lehmann agreed that the drugs were largely palliative, but what drugs weren't? Was insulin not palliative? Was digitalis not palliative? Was cortisone not palliative? Dr. Lehmann then challenged his critics to name any medical procedure, other than the excision of a diseased organ, which was not, in essence, palliative. How could one speak in terms of "absolute cure" of a mental illness? Conversely, what was wrong with palliation or alleviation of anxieties which were crippling thousands of patients?

The Old Guard then fell back upon a line of attack similar to that used by the Russian tourist who, having all the usual criticisms of American democracy cut out from under him, cried out: "But what about the lynchings in the South?" So now the Elder Statesmen cried out: "But what about the side-effects?"

The panelists answered this one with a wealth of documentation. They pointed out that the drugs were remarkably low in toxicity. Furthermore, the major side-effects were easily manageable. In the small percentage of cases where the side-effects were severe, cessation of administration of the drugs cleared the condition. They cited an elaborate study of the side-effects of Chlorpromazine done over a fourteen-month period upon twelve hundred patients at the University of Texas Medical Branch at Galveston. Dr. Irvin M. Cohen, who headed the study, reported that Chlorpromazine is a remarkably safe drug and that even the most severe complications occurring in a small percentage of patients cleared completely when the drug was withdrawn. Several state hospital superintendents joined the fray at this point. They agreed that both drugs had some bothersome side-effects; however, they admitted that the complications worried the doctors more than the patients. The patients realized the enormous benefits they were gaining from the drugs, so their attitude was: "Damn the side-effects—Full Speed Ahead!"

As the drug panel staggered on toward midnight, the metabolic malfunctionings of the Elder Statesmen took their toll in an increasing verbal irascibility. At one point, the revered superintendent of a New England hospital got to his feet and, with the typical Yankee aversion to the new and challenging, cried out in warning: "You had better use these new drugs while they work." This was a fairly ungracious remark, and he got his comeuppance from a number of indignant state hospital men who documented the transformation the drugs had brought to their hospitals.

The revolution could not be stemmed, and it was in evidence everywhere at the 1955 convention. For the first time since I had started covering national psychiatric conventions a decade ago, I felt that I was at an honest-to-goodness medical meeting. There were a number of excellent physiological exhibits. The drug houses had their medical men and their detail men out in full force. The scientific sessions were liberally sprinkled with neurologists, chemists, anatomists, physiologists, and even a couple of very brainy mathematicians.

The new era brought on some amusing side-effects, and I doubt whether they are reversible. In years past, the big theoreticians—both analytic and otherwise—had attracted large audiences as they went through the "Sturm und Drang" of ballooning their one case history into a new metaphysical concept of schizophrenia. At the 1955 convention, the delegates stayed away from them in droves. The drug and physiological seminars consistently outdrew the old metaphysical spellbinders, some of whom had to render their one case history in what almost amounted to privacy.

There were more pleasant side-effects, too. For the first time in ages, the state hospital men came into their own. For years they had shuffled from one "scientific" session to another, listening to the private psychiatrists propound theories which had little or no clinical application. Now, in 1955, they were in the very thick of things. Their masses of patients, ignored in the past as unimportant globs of humanity, were now fascinating clinical material. For those of us who had insisted for many years that the state mental hospital offered the most valuable clinical material for psychiatric research, it was a wonderful day.

Some of the Young Turks in the American Psychiatric Association made little effort to conceal their pleasure at this turn of events, this new emphasis upon clinical practice rather than empyrean theory. As Dr. Vernon Kinross-Wright put it: "Perhaps we, as psychiatrists, can get back to the little black bag and be doctors of medicine again."

Although there was a wide and understandable enthusiasm for the new drugs, there was a modest realization on the part of all who used them that much more knowledge had to be acquired about them. Those critics of the new drugs who charged that they were being accepted and used with little effort at evaluation obviously made no effort to familiarize themselves with the literature on the subject. In practically every scientific paper on the drugs, there was a plea for intensive research on a number of important fronts: the metabolic action of the drugs, optimal dosage and length of administration, comparative value of the drugs in relation to other therapies, and so on.

In the fall of 1954, the massive Veterans' Administration mental hospital system began the task of accumulating comparative data on the value of the drugs. A two-day conference was held in April, 1955, at which representatives of thirty VA hospitals reported on their experiences with use of the drugs on more than nine thousand patients. There was practically unanimous agreement that Chlorpromazine and Reserpine were invaluable in the treatment of mental patients in large hospital situations, and all hospitals reported dramatic reductions in restraint, hydrotherapy, shock therapy, and lobotomy over and above the discharge of significant numbers of long-term psychotics. However, the summary report of the VA experience was couched in words of caution.

"There is general agreement that Chlorpromazine and Reserpine are of value in the treatment of many psychotic patients," the report pointed out. "They appear to have value particularly in rendering disturbed, assaultive, destructive patients more co-operative, quiet, relaxed and accessible. They reduce hyperactivity and agitation, tension and irritability. . . . Both drugs, when used with disturbed schizophrenic patients, reduce disorganization. . . . Chlorpromazine appears to be more effective than Reserpine in reducing resistive isolation. . . . There is considerable opinion and some evidence that Chlorpromazine is, in general, more effective than Reserpine, and some opinion that Chlorpromazine leaves patients more alert. . . . There was agreement that there is a need for further experience and particularly for more definitive studies to establish the place of these drugs in the tool kit of the physician."

Upon returning from the American Psychiatric Association convention, and after a careful analysis of the data accumulated by the Veterans' Administration, I became convinced that a way had to be found to finance a nation-wide, careful evaluation of the new drugs. Too much of the data coming in had not been subjected to rigorous, controlled experimentation. However, the New York State system was the exception to the rule. Possessing a strongly staffed central office and an excellent statistical department, it had held several conferences on the drugs and was moving in the direction of broad-scale evaluation. I therefore asked Drs. Henry Brill, Nathan Kline, and T. M. Stanley of the New York system if they would be willing to testify before a U. S. Senate committee on the need for a large evaluation project. They readily consented. In preparing our formal testimony for the Senate hearings, we all agreed that the major emphasis should center on how little we really knew about the new drugs. Our job was to convince the senators that we were just at the beginning of the chemotherapeutic era—that financial support was needed immediately to explore scores of new biochemical leads.

We testified on the morning of May 17, 1955. As the lead-off witness, I gave a brief summary of the literature on the new drugs, then described the kind of large-scale project we thought the Congress should support.

"But now we come to the real question—how to exploit and extend the usefulness of these drugs," I testified. "The first step, it seems to me, is a precise study in depth of the physiological results of these drugs upon various types of mental illness. . . . We have only a scattering of technical information on these new drugs, and most of this information is not centrally co-ordinated and readily available. For example, we know some of the clinical results of these drugs, but little about how these drugs work in the human metabolism. What effects do these drugs have upon the hormones? What part or parts of the brain do they influence, and how?"

After a review of prior Congressional appropriations for the evaluation of drugs in other fields, I made this direct request of the Senate committee:

"In the light of these prior appropriations for the development of important drugs which have saved thousands of American lives, the National Mental Health Committee requests the Congress to appropriate $1,500,000 for research work on all new drugs having a beneficial effect upon mental illness.

"We suggest that this $1,500,000 special drug research sum be broken down into two major items:

"1. $500,000 for a broad-scale technical evaluation and study of both the adequacies and inadequacies of the new drugs in their effect on mental illness. These studies would cover not only Chlorpromazine and Reserpine but also LSD-25, Meratran, Frenquel, Mescaline, and any other of the exciting new chemical discoveries which are being used in the psychiatric field.

"It is our feeling that the National Institute of Mental Health should administer the over-all drug study, and that the best mechanism for the administration of the grant would lie in the setting up of a special study committee on chemotherapy within the Institute. We believe that the procedure followed in the excellent National Heart Institute evaluation of Reserpine on hypertension should be followed. This would include grants-in-aid to institutions and agencies capable of participating in such a study. Evaluation projects should be conducted in a number of states, cover all types of major illness, and cover all the age ranges in which mental illness occurs.

"2. . . . The remaining $1,000,000 of the specific allocation for drug research should go in grants-in-aid to researchers in all parts of the country willing to conduct further experimentation with existing drugs, or development of new and more effective drugs. It is our considered opinion that chemotherapy has been the low man in the mental health totem pole. Over the past several years, the National Institute of Mental Health has given very little support to drug research."

In support of our drug research project request, Dr. Brill, Assistant Commissioner in charge of research and training for the New York State Department of Mental Hygiene, described his state's preliminary attempts to evaluate the effects of the drugs.

"About a year ago we became interested in the use of these drugs," Dr. Brill testified, "and after a month or two, it was quite obvious that the drugs really had the psychiatric effects which you have heard described here; that they were therapeutically effective. The next step was to get them into use in a large group of patients so that we could tell something about the broad expanse of effect. Starting in January, we had 4,200 patients on treatment. In February it rose to 5,500; the next month 6,900; the last month it was 8,300. That is 8,300 patients on drug therapy of a total of 93,000 patients in the Department of Mental Hygiene in New York State. . . .

"But in spite of the fact that we have applied these drugs broadly now for about five months, and we have applied them in a number of different settings, there are lots of questions that remain to be answered. We have applied them, for example, in the treatment of delinquents and antisocial behavior—people who are in correctional institutions. That is one field where it should be tried. We have applied the drugs in the treatment of epileptics who are disturbed and in hospitals because of their behavior. We have also used them in the case of mental retardation with disturbed behavior—this all in addition to the mentally ill that we have just described."

But, as Dr. Brill then modestly and cautiously pointed out to the Senators, these early experiences raised more questions than they answered.

"Now, the evaluation of the drugs in all these settings has given us a qualitative answer, not a quantitative answer," he warned. "We know that both drugs are useful. We know that we can get certain results. But we do not know how good they are; that is, we do not know how much better the results of treatment are than the results of spontaneous evolution of illness. We do not know how these drugs compare with each other really, or with other standard methods of treatment. We are not at all sure as to the gross effect on release from the institution. We are not positive what types of cases are best treated, what the best dosages are; the types of combination, the methods of combination with other methods of treatment, for instance, insulin, electric shock, psychosurgery, and so on.

"And to wait for the normal evolution of scientific investigation to go on might seem to answer the question; but our experience in the past has not been very favorable. We have been using insulin

since 1935 and electric shock since 1940. We have been using lobotomy now quite extensively since 1942 or 1943. And these facts, the
type of material, the type of question I have just raised about the
new drugs, have also been raised about these methods of treatment,
and we do not have fixed answers, probably in part because of a lack
of a well-organized, well-controlled, broad-scale evaluation program.
. . . We have a fairly well-defined question to be answered now
which we did not have in psychiatry before, and this seems to be an
excellent method for answering it without further loss of time. We
are losing a great many valuable lives as the years go on."

In concluding our testimony, I again emphasized that the drugs
were not panaceas; they were but the crude beginning of a new line
of endeavor.

". . . These drugs only begin to open something up," I pointed
out. "They really open up a tremendous biochemical vista. They are
just the beginning. They are not perfect; they have side-effects.
We do not know too much about their duration of potency, or
anything else; but for the first time they get us back into an area
where, if we do go into the biochemical and neurological areas, we
can, we think, bring a workable psychiatry into the community
and into the office of the general practitioner—where it belongs—
rather than in the isolated mental hospital, which I have known for
too many years. This I regard as a return to medicine. . . . I think
this is a happy thing, and if the Congress can only, in its wisdom,
in a small way support the many leads that are not being pursued
—and I say this very honestly, Senator Hill—there are 100 to 150
biochemical leads that I heard of last week in Atlantic City that
could be pursued if we had the money and supported the trained
men in the field. So therefore I think it is terribly important."

Consequent upon the successful clinical application of Reserpine
and Chlorpromazine, the quest for additional drugs has been
intensified.

A new antidepressant drug, Meratran, has evoked considerable
interest after clinical trials by several of the country's top researchers.
At the 1954 convention of the American Psychiatric Association, the
distinguished neurologist Dr. Howard Fabing and his associates at
the University of Cincinnati reported considerable success with the
drug in the treatment of out-patients with acute depressions. In the
course of administering the synthetic compound to 320 patients

over a sixteen-month period, Dr. Fabing found that it benefited 90 per cent of patients with mild depressive reactions. In the more severe depressive conditions in which the patients were morbidly melancholy, sometimes to the point of contemplating suicide, the drug was effective in 65 per cent of a trial group. However, it failed to help those patients who had agitated melancholia, because it increased the agitation along with the elevation of mood.

The importance of the new drug lies largely in the fact that it does not seem to produce the serious side-effects characteristic of most stimulant drugs, such as the more commonly used amphetamines.

"The drug has proved valuable in office practice because the appetite loss and the cardiovascular pressor reactions sometimes observed after the administration of amphetamines are not encountered," Dr. Fabing reported in the May, 1955, issue of *The American Journal of Psychiatry*. "In addition, the drug seldom interferes with nocturnal sleep, and when it produces anxiety side reactions, these are less severe and less disturbing subjectively than those encountered with the amphetamines."

In a much tougher test of Meratran, Dr. Harold E. Himwich and his colleagues at Galesburg State Hospital in Illinois tried it over a seven-month period on twenty-five deteriorated patients whose average hospital stay was over ten years. They were selected from the hospital population because "they exhibited depressive features, regression, or were feeding problems."

Fourteen of the twenty-five patients snapped out of their depressive states to a remarkable degree. They participated actively in occupational and recreational therapy. They seemed quite happy, and their fields of interest widened perceptibly. As had Fabing, Himwich also noted the superiority of Meratran over more commonly used stimulants, pointing out that "it does not characteristically evoke the overactivity of the sympathetic nervous system characterized by dilated pupils, sweating, fast heart rate, and increased blood pressure."

Dr. Julius Pomeranze of New York Medical College has also reported on the effectiveness of Meratran when used on old people suffering from depression.

"Retirement and the fear of impending deterioration and death often creates a serious mental depression in the older but otherwise organically fit individual," Dr. Pomeranze reported in *The Journal of Gerontology*. "It is difficult to inspire them to continue normal activities. A new drug, Meratran, has suggested itself as valuable for stimulating a greater zest for living in the older depressed patient. Meratran is effective in small doses (2 mg.) and its duration of activity is at least twenty-four hours. The necessity for repeated doses and constant observation of drug-taking is obviated. In therapeutic doses there are few side effects when its use is limited to the depressed or tired patient. . . . The depressed subject displayed an increased alertness and a better interest in routine activities. This was quickly apparent and was well maintained throughout the day without any apparent interference with sleep."

A chemical relative of Meratran—Frenquel—has also created quite a stir of late. Despite strong structural resemblances between the two drugs, their pharmacologic actions are at opposite poles. Frenquel belongs to the Reserpine-Chlorpromazine school; it diminishes spontaneous activity and quiets central nervous system activity.

The first preliminary report on the action of the new drug in a state hospital situation was presented at the 1955 convention of the American Psychiatric Association by Dr. Himwich and the Galesburg group. Dr. Himwich and his associates tried it on thirty-nine chronically disturbed psychotics whose average hospital stay exceeded seventeen years.

Of the hard-core group, twenty-one of the thirty-nine showed significant improvement, while another seven showed appreciable improvement. However, the most remarkable property of Frenquel is a negative one; it produces no appreciable side-effects. In this, it is superior to its sister calming drugs, Reserpine and Chlorpromazine.

"This drug is good not only for what it does, but also for what it does not do," Dr. Himwich noted. "So far it has produced no deleterious side reactions. There are no apparent effects other than those on behavior. Frenquel did not display any hypnotic action to account for its tranquilizing effect, nor did it cause a fall in blood pressure nor alteration in heart rate."

Dr. Fabing has also done considerable experimental work with Frenquel. Noting "the dramatic way in which it has cleared up hallucinated, deluded and dissociated patients on occasion," he reported in the February 11, 1955, issue of *Science* on the remarkable blocking action of Frenquel when used to clear up an induced psychosis produced by LSD-25. When it is used in an LSD-induced situation, Frenquel exhibits remarkable power in ameliorating schizophrenic symptoms and wiping out psychotic manifestations.

Each major annual conclave of basic scientists seems to feature an exciting report on some new drug or compound being experimentally used to reverse the course of mental disorder. At the ninety-first annual meeting of the National Academy of Sciences in the spring of 1954, Drs. Dilworth W. Woolley and Elliott Shaw, both biochemists with the Rockefeller Institute for Medical Research, reported on serotonin, a substance which may be lacking in the disordered brain.

Serotonin, isolated about five years ago from beef tissues, was studied extensively in animal tests. Present in the brain of animals, it proved chemically active against drugs which stimulate mental disturbances. Drs. Woolley and Shaw also noted that the presence in animal brains of chemical analogs which prevented proper utilization of the natural serotonin led to mental aberrations.

At the 126th annual meeting of the American Chemical Society in the fall of 1954, Dr. Merrill E. Speeter, head of the Department of Biochemistry of the Upjohn Company, reported that a process had been developed for the production of cheap and plentiful supplies of serotonin. Extensive additional tests are now under way on animals, and the new substance will be eventually tested on humans. Scientists are excited about the potential of serotonin, not only as a possible therapeutic agent, but as a valuable chemical tool for the study of various mental disorders.

In the battle against epilepsy, centuries-old scourge of mankind, drugs and biologic substances have made more inroads in the past few years than all other treatments used since the beginning of recorded medical history. Describing this progress to a Congressional committee, Dr. Pearce Bailey, Director of the National Institute of Neurological Diseases and Blindness, remarked:

"Neurological research has produced the electroencephalograph and demonstrated the essential nature of epilepsy as a disorder of the energy and economy of brain cells which is controllable by chemical means. The result is that 85 per cent of all epileptics can now lead normal lives. The need for epileptic institutions is decreasing; the State institution in Ohio has closed and other states are following suit."

In the past few years, drugs such as dilantin and mesantoin have been used to hold down or control epileptic seizures. However, their action is essentially palliative; they are unable to restore normal brain-wave patterns. Besides, these and other drugs have a strong sedative and inhibiting effect on normal brain activities.

However, Dr. Bailey reported to Congressional committees in 1954 on a biologic substance—glutamine—which has, for the first time in the history of epilepsy, reversed brain waves from abnormal epileptic types to normal ones in a limited number of patients tested. Studies at the National Institute of Neurological Diseases and Blindness indicated that the epileptic brain was lacking in glutamic acid in a manner similar to the diabetic's lack of insulin. However, up until recently it had been impossible to correct this deficiency because glutamic acid, given as a medicine, would not pass from the blood to the brain. The problem was to find some compound of glutamic acid and another substance that would pass into the brain and break down into glutamic acid. This led to the development of glutamine, a compound manufactured from beets, which Dr. Bailey describes as "the first brain vitamin ever produced."

Initially, glutamine was prohibitively expensive, costing about $200 for a single day's oral administration to a patient. The 1954 Congress appropriated $750,000 to further the mass production of glutamine at a fraction of its present cost.

Scientists who have done preliminary work with glutamine are convinced that the drug will be more effective against epilepsy than insulin is against diabetes, since it can be taken orally as against the injective method now mandatory in diabetes.

In summarizing the importance of present research on glutamine in testimony to a House Appropriations subcommittee in April, 1954, Dr. Bailey commented:

"I think that we have broken the mysterious barrier which has prevented a scientific explanation of epileptic seizure and I think that this research will go away beyond the control of epilepsy."

PERSONNEL SHORTAGES AND THE STATE GOVERNORS

10. SHORTAGES OF PSYCHIATRIC PERSONNEL

On MARCH 10, 1955, Dr. Daniel Blain, Medical Director of the American Psychiatric Association, and I testified before the House Interstate Commerce Committee in favor of a Congressional resolution for a three-year nationwide study and re-evaluation of the human and economic problems of mental illness. In the preamble to the resolution, buried deep among all the "whereases," there was this strong statement which provoked an hour-long battery of Congressional questions:

"Whereas, there seems to be a discouraging lag between the discovery of new knowledge and skills in treating mental illness and their widespread application, as is evidenced by the fact that only about one-third of newly admitted mental patients are on the average discharged from State hospitals in the course of the year, whereas in a few outstanding institutions the recovery rate is 75 per centum or more."

What was common and somewhat bitter knowledge to Dr. Blain and myself seemed astounding to the congressmen. Here we were talking about the remarkable new drugs, Chlorpromazine and Reserpine, and yet we were forced to admit that their application was being severely limited because of shortages of psychiatric personnel in the state hospital systems.

Congressman John Heselton of Massachusetts, a keen lawyer and an expert on health legislation, pursued the point. He asked me to document differences in the quality of state mental hospitals. I respectfully referred him to page 274 of the 1953 Council of State Governments study, "Training and Research in State Mental Health Programs." On that page, there was a listing of personnel-patient ratios for all the state hospitals in the Commonwealth of Massachusetts. At Boston Psychopathic, an intensive treatment unit of 109 beds, there was a psychiatrist for every fourteen patients. Did this pay off? A recent cost study of treatment results over a five-year period at Boston Psychopathic showed that an intensive treatment facility sent many more patients back to the community than the traditional state hospital did, cost three-fourths as much over the patient's life-span, and, because of increased patient turnover, required one-seventh the number of hospital beds for the same number of patients.

I gave the able congressman further documentation. At Boston State Hospital, with more than three thousand patients, there were nineteen psychiatrists—one psychiatrist for every 160 patients, fairly close to American Psychiatric Association standards. Yet, less than a hundred miles away, at Gardner State Hospital, there were only four psychiatrists to care for 1,367 patients—an impossible ratio of one psychiatrist for every 342 patients. I asked the congressman a hypothetical question: If he had a loved one in need of hospitalization for an emotional disturbance, to which hospital would he send that person—Boston State or Gardner State?

Then Mr. Heselton got to the nub of the issue; he wanted an example of a state hospital which took all comers and yet discharged more than 75 per cent of its first admissions. Furthermore, he wanted to know how they did it.

I told him about Topeka State Hospital. In 1946 and 1947, I had toured a number of state hospital systems in an effort to get at the common denominators involved in creating a good public hospital. I had gone up to Kansas a number of times and, late in 1947, wrote "If We Can Love," a study of the dynamic psychiatric programs at the Menninger Foundation and the Winter Veterans' Administration Hospital in Topeka. Subsequent to that, I toured the Topeka State Hospital. I was deeply shocked at the contrast between this state hospital and the Veterans' Administration hospital just two miles away. Both were supported by public moneys, yet Topeka

State was a nineteenth-century dungeon engulfed in a swamp of lethargy and hopelessness.

I expressed my indignation to Dr. Karl Menninger. He agreed and said something had to be done about it, but this something involved an enormous increase in appropriations by a Kansas legislature noted for its reverent attitude toward a tightened public purse. We went up to see Governor Frank Carlson, and we gave him both barrels. Dr. Karl continued to work on Governor Carlson, and the Governor asked for, and got, a 60 per cent increase in the mental hospital budget.

With this start, and subsequent actions by the 1951 and 1953 Kansas legislatures, Topeka State moved rapidly into the twentieth century. A flock of young psychiatrists moved into the dungeon, accompanied by eight social workers and scores of nurses. They began the massive job of almost literally restoring these patients to life; they had lost identity, family, hope. I remember asking one of the patients in 1951 what he liked best about the revolution at Topeka State.

"The social workers," he replied without hesitation. "Sure, I like the doctors, but the social workers really get you out of here. They find out who you are, they find your family, and they get you a job."

Over the past six years, the number of patients has dropped from eighteen hundred to fourteen hundred, almost unbelievable when compared with national figures, which show a continually rising patient population in practically every state hospital in the country. And this drop at Topeka State is not due to a decrease in demand for hospital beds. In 1948, when the revolution began, 331 patients were admitted to Topeka State and there was a waiting list of more than 200; in 1953, 458 were admitted, but there was no waiting list.

"About 80 per cent of those who today enter [Topeka State] for the first time will get well enough to leave here," Dr. Karl said recently. "And I think we're going to push that figure up to 85 per cent."

How does Topeka State do it? Very simple. Adequate psychiatric personnel intensively applying new research knowledge to the treatment of patients. Nothing more complex than that. During the past three years, Oklahoma, under a new and dynamic mental health commissioner, has started to do pretty much the same thing, with a resultant drop in total patient population for the first time in the history of that state.

However, when you look at the national figures on psychiatric personnel, you see what a rarity Topeka State really is.

Over the past several decades, the American Psychiatric Association has established and published a set of minimum standards on the number of personnel needed to care for mental patients. For example, it recommends one physician for every 30 patients who are acutely ill, and one physician for every 150 patients on the "continued treatment services," a euphemism for the chronics who are relegated to the back wards. Applying these standards on a national basis, the 1953 study by the Council of State Governments found that the average ratio of physicians to patients in state mental hospitals was 1 to 228. However, as the Council study pointed out, many of these physicians had no formal psychiatric training. In fact, the actual ratio of psychiatrists to patients in state mental hospitals was 1 to 311. In documenting its figures, the Council report states:

"In 1951, there were slightly over 7,000 psychiatrists in the entire United States, of whom about one-fifth held full-time positions in state mental hospitals. The number of psychiatrists—1,578—and other physicians—578—in state hospital service obviously is extremely small considering the almost half-million patients now dependent upon their services. . . .

"In 1951, only ten state mental hospitals in the country were able to report a complement of physicians adequate to provide the standards of care recommended by the American Psychiatric Association. Most of these ten were special psychiatric institutes, involved primarily in research. Their combined patient population does not number more than a few hundred. . . . Although the average ratio of patients to psychiatrists in state institutions was 311 to 1, about one-fourth of all state hospitals still had fewer than 1 psychiatrist for every 500 patients. Such a spread permits a psychiatrist—even if he neglected all other duties—to provide only fifteen minutes of treatment a month to each patient in his care."

In analyzing the major causes underlying the inability of the state mental hospital system to attract psychiatrists to its ranks, the Council report ripped through to the nub of the issue in these words:

"A major factor in the shortage of mental hospital psychiatrists is the increase of private psychiatric practice. The public has come to recognize that many mild mental disorders, particularly those of a neurotic character, are susceptible of amelioration in the community and do not require rospitalization. As a result, the young psychiatrist who has just completed his training finds no difficulty in setting himself up in a very active practice. At present, the comparative financial attractions of private practice are such that public hospitals compete at a handicap in the market. State hospitals are able to attract residents for training, but many residents leave as soon as they complete the requirements for certification by the American Board of Psychiatry and Neurology.

"Through the country, not more than 450 psychiatrists complete the three-year residency annually. With the current need for psychiatrists estimated at between 10,000 and 20,000, it is evident that the states must seek ways of competing with private practice for the services of existing psychiatrists, and at the same time seek other means of providing for improved patient treatment."

The situation is no better with relation to auxiliary psychiatric workers. Although these professionals—psychologists, psychiatric social workers, nurses—are in far greater supply than psychiatrists, only a relatively small percentage work in state mental hospitals.

There are 13,500 members of the American Psychological Association. Of this number, several thousand are especially trained for clinical work with patients, yet only 396 are on mental hospital staffs. The majority of psychological internships in public institutions are going begging at the present time.

About eight hundred psychiatric social workers are employed in these same state institutions—one social worker for every six hundred patients. These eight hundred are only a very small percentage of the number of trained social workers in this country. Surveyed by their own professional organizations as to their reasons for not entering state hospital work, the social workers answered that public hospitals "offered the least attractive opportunities in the field of psychiatric social work."

Although mental hospitals care for approximately 50 per cent of all hospitalized patients, they have the services of less than 5 per cent of the 390,000 registered nurses in active practice. In a 1952 survey conducted by professional nursing organizations, nurses themselves severely criticized employment opportunities in state hospitals on the grounds of lack of educational and intellectual stimulation, insufficient opportunity for professional growth, and little recognition and status for the nursing profession.

An even more devastating picture of the manner in which severe shortages of psychiatric personnel are hamstringing the application of new research findings to patients is contained in the voluminous reports of two regional mental health surveys which were completed in 1954.

At the Southern Governors' Conference at Hot Springs, Virginia, in November, 1953, the sixteen Governors of the Conference spent the better part of a day brooding about the best way in which to initiate a revolution in the treatment of the mentally ill in the South. They had one tremendous advantage over the other regions of the country. In 1948, they had brought into being a Southern Regional Education Board which had, in the ensuing five years, initiated a number of successful programs of regional co-operation in higher education. With this in mind, the Southern governors voted unanimously that the SREB be charged with the task of making a year-long survey of the needs and resources of the South in the field of mental health, with particular emphasis upon the training of psychiatric personnel and the development of new research programs.

The professional staff of the SREB, composed of a group of superbly trained technicians who had come off the campuses of the South to staff this pioneer effort in regional co-operation, whipped into action in no time flat. Realizing the enormousness of the task, the Board persuaded each Governor to appoint a state research and training committee to gather basic data for transmittal to regional headquarters.

On four steaming hot days in late July, 1954, in Atlanta, 170 delegates from the sixteen Southern states gathered together to screen the data accumulated as a result of the dedicated work of more than two thousand individuals. Even the most hardened of the professionals were shaken by the first few paragraphs of the official report.

"Mental hospitals, institutions for mentally deficient, and mental health clinics are all grossly understaffed because personnel cannot be obtained," the report stated.

"The Southern states have 3,700 psychiatrists, clinical psychologists, psychiatric social workers, and psychiatric nurses in their mental health programs. Funds are available for about 750 additional positions which cannot be filled. But the South needs almost 24,000 trained persons, or about six times as many as it now has, to meet recommended standards in its mental health program.

"The Southern states do not train anywhere near enough personnel to meet the needs of their mental health programs. Their universities and institutions train about 75 psychiatrists, 60 clinical psychologists, 70 psychiatric social workers, and 60 psychiatric nursing specialists a year. At this rate, the South can never catch up with its needs. It must train five times as many persons as it now does to meet its needs within ten to fifteen years. The universities, mental hospitals, and mental health clinics of the South have facilities to train larger numbers of students for the mental health professions. If present training opportunities are used to capacity, the production of mental health personnel can probably be doubled."

However, in order to double the production of mental health personnel, the quality of the training courses must be improved tremendously. For example, the prime need in the South is more psychiatrists. The psychiatrist is, and must be, the key individual in any expanded treatment regime. Yet in 1954 there were only 795 psychiatrists in all the tax-supported mental health agencies of the sixteen Southern states. There were 247 budgeted psychiatric vacancies in the state mental hospital systems and, over and above this, a need for 608 more psychiatrists to meet minimum staffing standards. When to this is added the number of psychiatrists needed in private practice, the total number of psychiatrists required in the South today is 4,260. As against this, the entire Southland will graduate only 272 psychiatrists in the period 1954–56.

Why? In the first place, the South offers only 289 training residencies in psychiatry scattered among fifty state and private institutions. Less than half of these residencies are for the full three years required for the training of a psychiatrist in his speciality. One- and two-year residencies are of little help, because the trainee must go elsewhere to complete his course, and he usually doesn't come back. Furthermore, each year many of the residencies offered in state mental hospitals are unfilled; there are just no takers. The reason: "Only a few are recognized as really top-flight training centers in

psychiatry," the SREB report concludes. So many a Southern boy
hies off to New York, Chicago, Boston, Topeka, or San Francisco
for the top-quality training he can't get in his native region. He
usually remains where he gets his training, and eventually he forgets
to take his hat off when the band plays "Dixie."

These shortages of psychiatric personnel are not maladies pecu-
liarly indigenous to the gallant land once governed by the Con-
federacy. In the summer and fall of 1954, ten Midwestern states—
Illinois, Indiana, Iowa, Kansas, Michigan, Minnesota, Nebraska,
Ohio, South Dakota and Wisconsin—got a rude awakening after
a series of surveys ordered by their Governors.

At a Midwestern Governors' Conference on Mental Health held
in Chicago in November, 1954, the official report documented conditions little better than those found in the South.

"The ten states involved in this survey have a population of
around 41.5 million people, or 26.4 per cent of the nation," the
report noted. ". . . The ten states spent a total of $124,300,000 for
the care and treatment of 121,300 mental patients in 1953, approximately one-fourth of total state expenditures. . . . Overcrowding
of existing facilities is evident in each state and it is estimated that a
total of about 100,000 beds, at a cost of a billion dollars, are required
to meet immediate needs. But even if there were a sufficient number
of beds and other facilities, the Midwest cannot secure at present
enough mental health personnel to give adequate care to its mental
patients."

In a statistical volume accompanying the summary report, psychiatric personnel-to-patient ratios were described as follows:

Psychiatrists. The ten states in the survey group employed a total
of 397 psychiatrists in state mental hospitals, one psychiatrist for
every 307 patients.

Psychologists. They employed a total of 192 psychologists, an impossible ratio of one psychologist for every 626 patients.

Psychiatric Social Workers. They employed 237 social workers, a
patient load of 507 for each social worker.

Nurses. They employed 955 nurses, each of whom was supposed
to take care of 126 patients.

The Midwestern report concluded that, to meet minimum
standards, the mental hospitals of the ten states required:

     1,010 additional psychiatrists
       338 additional clinical psychologists
       589 additional psychiatric social workers
     8,365 additional nurses
     9,104 additional aides and attendants.

To achieve this, the rate of production for these professions would have to be stepped up to provide:

     Four times as many psychiatrists
     Six times as many clinical psychologists
     Four times as many psychiatric social workers
     Ten times as many graduate nurses
     Twice as many aides and attendants.

More significant than these figures, however, is the gap between the number of institutions offering training programs and the actual output of trained personnel. For example, there are sixty-three facilities—state hospitals, Veterans' Administration hospitals, general hospitals, and foundations—offering a total of 647 residencies in psychiatry. Yet in 1954 only a little better than 50 per cent, or 394, were filled.

The whole question of the inability of the state mental hospitals to attract psychiatric residents came up for heated discussion at several of the Midwestern conferences. Illinois, the most populous state in the region and one of the wealthiest in the country, was cited as an illustration of the incredible discrepancy between the number of training centers and the actual number of people trained.

Illinois is one of the nation's great training centers in the mental health field, with five medical schools, nine three-year residency programs in psychiatry, one of the world's most famous psycho-analytic institutes, and a host of other resources. Yet in 1954, Illinois offered only 105 psychiatric residencies, of which only fifty-seven were filled. Closer analysis reveals an even darker picture. Practically all of the unfilled residencies were in the state hospital system. For example, Elgin State Hospital offered twelve residencies, with not one taker; Jacksonville State, four with no takers; Manteno, six with one taker, and so on.

The really important residencies are those which offer the full three years of psychiatric training. Illinois, with more than thirty-eight thousand mental patients costing the state more than $40,000,000 annually, offered only seventeen of these three-year residencies. Even more discouraging, none of the seventeen was in a state mental hospital.

Dr. Paul Hletko, Assistant Medical Director of the Illinois Department of Public Welfare, spoke frankly and feelingly about the failure of the state to establish more high-quality psychiatric residencies. He cited an example which pictured the entire national dilemma in a nutshell.

In the city of Chicago, there is a state mental hospital which houses more than five thousand patients. Yet it offers no full three-year residencies. In canvassing prospective applicants for training in the Chicago area, Dr. Hletko found that most of them desired a training situation providing some instruction in psychoanalysis. Dr. Hletko thought he could do something about this. There are more than fifty analysts in the Chicago area, all within a short distance of the state hospital. Yet, after an intensive personal canvass, Dr. Hletko was unable to get even one of them to take the state's money in return for giving a few hours of instruction at Chicago State.

This tragic isolation between the private practitioner of psychiatry and the state mental hospitals which house 90 per cent of the mentally ill is at the heart of the problem of personnel shortages. It is not restricted to the State of Illinois. The neighboring states of Indiana and Nebraska do not have a single resident in a full three-year psychiatric training program, and the two residencies in Wisconsin are in a general hospital.

Describing the national situation in its 1953 survey, the Council of State Governments reported:

"Of the 212 state mental hospitals, ninety-three—44 per cent—are accredited for training psychiatrists (twenty-four for one year of training, forty-four for two years, and twenty-five for full three-year residencies). Twenty-one of the accredited state hospitals were unable to obtain residents to fill the positions available in 1952. . . . The following states were able to provide no residency training in 1952 for psychiatrists in either state medical schools or state hospitals for the mentally ill: Alabama, Florida, Idaho, Mississippi, Montana, Nevada, New Mexico, North Dakota, South Carolina, South Dakota, Utah, West Virginia, and Wyoming."

In a lead editorial in the March 5, 1955, issue of *The Journal of the*

American Medical Association, Dr. Winfred Overholser, Superintendent of St. Elizabeths Hospital in Washington, D.C., and a former President of the American Psychiatric Association, took off the gloves and told some plain truths. He pointed out that of 2,482 psychiatric residencies offered by state, Federal, and private hospitals in 1954, only 1,632, or 70 per cent, were filled. He expressed particular concern at the high number of vacancies among first-year appointments; while 649 first-year appointments were made, there were 336 for which there were no takers.

"This tends to suggest, if anything, a falling off in recruitment, since 40 per cent of all of the vacancies were in the first-year appointments," Dr. Overholser wrote. ". . . The intention of this editorial is not to urge more residency positions but rather to emphasize the importance of developing the existing psychiatric residencies, of which those in state hospitals are often unfilled."

Deploring the drift of the psychiatric profession away from the state mental hospital, Dr. Overholser cited his own St. Elizabeths as an example of a large public mental hospital—it houses 7,000 patients—where this isolation had not occurred.

"Formerly, the public mental hospital was practically the only place in which psychiatrists were trained, or at least in which they learned basic psychiatry. Indeed, it is the opinion of many that even today it is in the state hospital that basic psychiatry is to be learned. . . . In these days of rapid development of various psychiatric techniques of treatment, a basically eclectic approach, such as is best obtained in the state hospital, furnishes the soundest foundation. . . . In these various functions, St. Elizabeths Hospital is typical of what can be done in any state mental hospital, provided there is an adequate staff of physicians and related personnel and a program designed to give them an orderly training in the basic principles of clinical psychiatry. The advantages of such a program in stimulating better standards of care for the patients need hardly be argued. The program thus serves to establish a beneficial circle: better instruction of residents, better care of patients, more attractive opportunities for professional work by the staff, and to the residents greater attractiveness of hospital work as a career."

Dr. Overholser concluded by pointing a knowing finger at the medical profession for its ostrich-in-the-sand attitude toward state mental hospitals.

"Physicians—psychiatrists and nonpsychiatrists alike—have an obligation to the profession and their fellow citizens to aid such public mental hospitals as may be found in their vicinity, to supplement the efforts of the staffs of those hospitals in developing their training facilities. If the state hospitals are found wanting in the fulfillment of their professional training function, the medical profession—of which the members of the staff of the state hospitals are a part—should rightfully share in some measure the responsibility for that delinquency."

Private psychiatry has been very slow to assume that responsibility, and its diffidence has had some mighty unhappy consequences. In the past few years, the people have become aroused about the need for better state mental hospitals. Since the end of World War II, they have supported bond issues aggregating close to two billion dollars for the improvement of physical facilities. Even more important, they have supported a number of successful efforts to take the mental hospitals out of politics and place them in separate departments administered by medical men.

Heeding the insistent cry of the people, a number of Governors have shaken off the shackles of the past and sought out top psychiatrists to head up their state programs. In only a few cases have they succeeded. For the most part, the leading psychiatrists have turned down challenging opportunities to spearhead revolutionary state mental health programs. I know, and bitterly, whereof I speak. With the election of a new group of Governors in November, 1954, the National Mental Health Committee was asked to lend its efforts in obtaining top psychiatrists to head programs in several of the key states in the country.

The procedure was a disheartening one. We would comb through the same handful of people we thought might be interested. Even though the salaries offered were high—in a number of cases, $20,000 to $25,000, usually far more than the Governor's salary—we were invariably turned down.

The Governors were deeply disturbed and puzzled by this reluctance. In a private conversation, a Governor of one of the large Eastern states expressed his deep disappointment in these words:

"The people of my state have given more than their share of sweat, blood and tears to pressure the state legislature into setting up a new, adequately financed mental health program. But when I turn to the psychiatric profession to find just one person to head up this revolution, I am met with one excuse after another. There are several hundred psychiatrists in private practice in this state. Is it really true that not one of them is willing to answer this great challenge? To me, this is a betrayal of the wishes of the electorate."

This is no exaggeration. In state after state, dynamic new programs are still in the blueprint stage because of the wall between private psychiatry and the state mental hospital systems. Many of the very psychiatrists who are the most caustic and condescending in their public discussions of the deficiencies of public psychiatry are the ones who cannot spare even one hour of their busy week for teaching in a state mental hospital.

This reluctance has sown a tragic harvest. Because so few psychiatrists are available for public work, bidding for them is all out of proportion to their worth. One state bids $5,000 more a year and pirates a psychiatrist from another state. Everyone is quite surprised, because they know the psychiatrist in question didn't exactly set the world on fire in his native state. But he fulfills the prime requisites —he breathes fairly regularly, he is available, and the Governor has grown weary of interviewing psychiatrists who, unlike Jenny, can't say "yes."

I am weary of attending psychiatric conventions which have become recruiting depots for mental health officials offering fantastic prices for proven mediocrities. The whole procedure is unhealthy, and it is building up powerful additional resentments against psychiatry. Another Governor expressed it to me this way:

"My state mental health commissioner makes far more than I do, and far more than any other cabinet officer. In addition, he is paid for some teaching he does, and I understand he handles a couple of patients. He is not a very popular person in the cabinet. In fact, my state health officer, a competent physician with years of experience, is champing at the bit. I am afraid I am going to lose him."

In many of these situations, the day of reckoning is close at hand. The Governors and the people can't wait forever. Some of the leaders of the American Psychiatric Association are quite alarmed because several of the Governors are now leaning toward lay administrators for their state mental hospital systems. In the minds of the Governors, there is one powerful argument in favor of a lay administrator: he is available, and he doesn't want $25,000 a year to serve the people.

On several occasions, I have been guilty of helping to dissuade a Governor from taking this step. It flies in the face of all we have tried to accomplish in the past decade in taking the state mental hospitals out of patronage politics. But I have been hurt, and hurt badly, by the very thing that now upsets many Governors. From 1945 to 1948, I watched thousands of people in Oklahoma work endless hours, in the face of heartbreaking setbacks, to revolutionize the care and treatment of more than ten thousand people of that state. Then, for the next five years, I watched a high-priced commissioner "stolen" from another state break the hearts of those people because he wouldn't stand up and fight.

After all, the psychiatrists themselves say we all have a breaking point.

11. BOTTLENECKS

AND SOLUTIONS

IN APPROACHING a fundamental solution
to the staggering shortages of psychiatrists
in public mental health agencies, there is a
tendency on the part of many medical leaders to skirt the basic
difficulty—the general shortage of doctors in this country. Of course,
this reluctance to speak out on a controversial issue is somewhat
understandable. The high priests of Organized Medicine have
tried, for years, to remove the existing doctor shortage by a series
of encyclicals and incantations. They have also forbidden their disciples to even discuss the naughty subject.

However, those of us who are dedicated to the proposition that
we must train more psychiatrists in this country cannot fall back on
voodoo or fouled-up IBM punch cards. We know that the supply
of potential psychiatrists is absolutely limited by the number of
students graduated by the medical schools each year. Since a psychiatrist must have an M.D. degree, our total recruitment pool is
limited to the actual output of the medical schools.

In 1955, the nation's medical schools graduated approximately
6,800 students. Twenty-nine medical specialities were in active competition in the recruitment of these fledgling M.D.'s. The speciality
of psychiatry picked off 450 of them, or a little better than 7 per cent.
Contrary to the popular impression, this was only a small increase
over the 6 per cent of medical students who chose psychiatry as their
speciality thirty years ago. While this may seem somewhat incredible
in view of the vastly heightened interest in psychiatry over the past
generation, it is not surprising to those of us who know that psy-

chiatry is still a stepchild in most medical schools, relegated to the bottom of the financial ladder and patronized by the older departments of organic medicine.

There is a further hitch to be considered. Of the approximately 450 doctors who complete the three-year psychiatric residency, an average of 250 each year immediately go into private practice. This leaves public psychiatry with about 200 recruits, little more than enough to replace the older psychiatrists who die off or retire.

In attacking the problem of more psychiatric personnel, we must then, of necessity, do something about increasing the number of doctors in the nation. In late February, 1955, the Health Resources Advisory Committee, part of the executive branch of the Eisenhower Administration, reported to the Office of Defense Mobilization on a year-long study of health manpower. The Committee, headed by Dr. Howard A. Rusk, associate editor of the New York *Times,* includes some of the top names in American medicine.

"The past few years have seen a significant increase in the number of physicians," the Rusk committee reported. "This increase is being offset, however, by the rapid increases which are taking place in our population. . . .

"The gross ratio of physicians to population is now 1.32 per 1,000, and the net ratio (active physicians only) is now 1.18, both slightly lower than just before World War II. The net ratio of active physicians has dropped somewhat further than the total, since an increasing proportion of physicians is in the age group over 65. . . .

"It is estimated that the total population will reach 177,000,000 by 1960. The net effect of this rapid increase is that our over-all physician-population ratio in 1960, despite the increase in the output of physicians, will be almost what it was before Korea. The over-all 1960 gross ratio can be expected to be about 133 physicians per 100,-000 population, as compared to 137 in 1950."

In the body of the report, the Rusk committee paints a graphic picture of the glaring financial and personnel weaknesses of our medical school plant, weaknesses which are at the core of our failure to train more psychiatrists.

"A basic problem in the increase or even the maintenance of medical school enrollment is the maintenance of teaching staff in those schools," the report notes. "Medical schools find it difficult to maintain adequate staffs. The problem is an intricate one, with

financing and the shortage of qualified health manpower both playing an important part. . . . Most medical schools rely heavily upon
part-time personnel, especially for instruction in clinical subjects. In
the 1951 survey, medical faculties included 3,933 members with
full-time and 11,630 members with part-time appointments. Eighty
per cent of the physician faculty members were serving on a part-
time basis. . . .

"The Joint Committee on Medical Education in Time of National Emergency has proposed a national emergency staffing standard of one equivalent full-time faculty member for every four pre-
clinical students and one equivalent full-time faculty member for
every three clinical students—29 equivalent full-time faculty members per 100 students. Only 21 of the 72 four-year medical schools
reported staffing which met this standard. . . . Even allowing for
differences in objectives and programs, it is apparent that many
schools are operating with a serious shortage of faculty members. . . .
The most recent specific report on this subject is found in the 1953
Education number of *The Journal of the American Medical Association* which states that for the school year 1953, the number of
unfilled full-time positions in the instructional staffs of medical
schools was 283."

Another section of the Rusk report points out the manner in
which general and psychiatric hospitals are hamstrung in the care
and treatment of patients because of crippling shortages of interns
and residents. These interns and residents are the backbone of the
permanent hospital staffs, as the Rusk report notes:

"Hospitals and practicing physicians have come increasingly to
rely on these 'house staffs,' and physicians in advanced training have
become an important factor in the provision of medical care which
goes with the increased use of hospital facilities and services. . . .
In 1952–53, 28 per cent of internships and 24 per cent of the residencies in hospitals were unfilled."

There would be twice as many vacancies in intern and resident
training were it not for alien doctors, most of them European
refugees. Of a little more than twenty-five thousand filled internships
and residencies in our nation's hospitals, close to six thousand were
occupied by aliens. Most of them were there, not by choice, but
because of various restrictions placed upon their entrance into
private practice.

The Rusk report points out that these aliens comprise close to 25 per cent of the staffs of our mental hospitals. In some of the Northeastern states, they comprise more than 50 per cent of mental hospital staffs. Those of us who have visited state mental hospitals over the past decade know that, in hospital after hospital, these refugee doctors have held the dike gallantly against the overwhelming flood of patients. Frequently ostracized by the communities surrounding mental hospitals, invariably excluded from all official activities of Organized Medicine, they have fought language barriers and professional condescension to bring succor to the sick. A number of them, unable to obtain medical staff positions, have worked as ward orderlies. And, in the face of all this, the minions of Organized Medicine have trumpeted about an adequate supply of doctors!

In the field of public health, in which psychiatry is playing an increasing community role, the Rusk report emits some well-documented cries of alarm:

"Although there has been a rapid growth of public health services in this country, at least thirty million people live in areas without organized health departments. A survey made jointly in 1951 by the Public Health Service and the Health Resources Advisory Committee showed that budgeted vacancies in the existing State and local public health departments amounted to 20 per cent for physicians, 21 per cent for dentists, 14 per cent for sanitary engineers, 6 per cent for sanitarians, 10 per cent for veterinarians and 9 per cent for nurses. If optimum staffing standards were applied, the shortage is more than double. Even without the threat of atomic attack, or biological warfare, a shortage of this size is serious; with these threats existing, the shortage might threaten preventable disaster."

A little over a year ago, the American Psychiatric Association issued a superb bulletin on psychological first aid in civil defense. It made nice academic reading, for the simple reason that today we don't have even the minimal amount of psychiatrists to fill existing vacancies in our public mental health clinics, schools, courts, detention homes, etc.

The over-all doctor shortage gets us caught up in a treadmill of related deficiencies. Because the average doctor works sixty hours a week, he has little time for teaching. Result: The medical schools are understaffed and therefore unable to accelerate the training which would produce more doctors.

There are two big obstacles which must be overcome before we can begin to train the thousands of additional doctors we need. The first is the serious financial plight of our medical schools. In the academic year 1954–55, the basic operating budgets of the nation's eighty medical schools totaled $93,408,312. Of this sum, only $18,-182,000, or approximately 20 per cent, was provided by students' tuition. Most of the remainder came from dwindling private endowments, charges upon general university budgets, and the running-up of deficits.

The capital plant of the medical schools is cracking at the seams. In 1948, the medical schools estimated a need for approximately $330,000,000 for construction of facilities, over and above operating fund needs and research fund needs. The need is still pressing; the September 11, 1954, issue of *The Journal of the American Medical Association* stated: "Medical schools indicate that large sums are still needed for construction of new buildings, remodeling and modernization of existing facilities, and the purchase and installment of new permanent equipment."

The second big obstacle is the recruitment of medical students. For a number of years, the number of applicants wanting to enter medical school has far exceeded the number admitted. While some of these may not have been qualified for a medical career, there is general agreement that, over the past decade, thousands of students who would have made good doctors have been rejected. In the past two years, the number of applications has dropped to the point where about one student is admitted for every student rejected. While this drop in the number of applications makes a few smug deans of medical schools happy—they say this margin of rejection is the desirable minimum with which they need to operate—it makes competent economists point the finger of alarm.

Why? In the first place, many students are being priced out of the medical market. Average tuition fees have gone up from $391 in 1940 to approximately $800 in 1955–56. One New York medical school recently raised its tuition to $1,000 a year. And this is not all. The 1954 Education number of *The Journal of the American Medical*

Association pointed out that it now costs the average student $9,520 in tuition, books, laboratory fees, and minimal living costs to get through the four years of medical school. We are heading toward restriction of medical education to the sons and daughters of the wealthy.

There are a great many additional restrictions. A number of state medical schools permit the matriculation of only a minuscule number of out-of-state residents. This is particularly hard on students from states where there are no medical schools. Furthermore, the big schools in the East and Midwest are so swamped with applications that a candidate has to produce an almost straight "A" college average even to be interviewed. Over and above these and other obstacles, there is a growing feeling among college graduates that medicine isn't really interested in recruiting them; if it were, why would it put so many roadblocks in the way?

To trained economists, this artificial restriction of supply in the face of enormous public demand makes as much sense as sacred-cow taboos in India. Testifying before the President's Commission on the Health Needs of the Nation, Harold M. Groves, Professor of Economics at the University of Wisconsin, expressed his own bewilderment, and that of many of his colleagues, in these words:

"A fundamental of free enterprise, or at least of competitive free enterprise, is freedom of entry into all fields of endeavor. . . . The question, 'How many doctors are enough?' is one that may be approached from many angles. The simplest and most direct is the free-enterprise approach which says that we have enough doctors when a freely recruited supply is equated with a freely manifest demand."

This economic paradox is beginning to stir up the Governors. At the National Governors' Conference on Mental Health in 1954, they exhibited a bitter awareness of the American Medical Association's heavily financed campaign which has bottled up all Federal aid to medical education bills since 1949.

The fireworks went off the very first day of the conference during a luncheon speech by Judge Luther Youngdahl, former three-time Governor of Minnesota. Describing the sweeping reforms which had brought new hope to the mentally ill of Minnesota, Youngdahl charged that many of them had not been fully implemented because of inability to obtain the needed personnel. His voice rising in anger, he warned the leaders of Organized Medicine to open their profession to thousands of duly qualified applicants or face the alternative of government measures to insure this desired end.

The controversy boiled through the remainder of the conference and hit a new peak when the chairman of the final general session, Ohio's five-time Governor Frank J. Lausche, lit into the medical profession for what he described as "actions contrary to the national interest." Lausche, an eloquent orator of the old school, pounded the lectern and shook the rafters with an appeal for the doubling of our national output of doctors.

Yet all this was as the calm before the storm which erupted at the Midwestern Governors' Conference on Mental Health in Chicago in November, 1954. The delegates were quietly pursuing the prepared agenda when Governor George Craig of Indiana was called upon for a few remarks. Flanked by distinguished members of the medical profession, including a number high in the councils of medical education, Governor Craig displayed a masterful surgical technique as he probed for the sore spot.

"I have always thought it the duty of governmental leaders to follow the advice of the professions in those technical matters in which they are competent," Governor Craig told the conference. "I have regarded our job as giving them the necessary tools, and then letting them do the job without any interference.

"However, government cannot stand by idly when the leaders of the medical profession fail to face up to their responsibilities. In Indiana, we have begun a sweeping reform of our mental hospital system. We have been handicapped in these efforts by the national shortage of doctors. I am losing patience, and I know a number of my fellow Governors are, with the current tactics of the medical profession. The people of this great nation have demanded, in no uncertain terms, a new day for the mentally ill. Ours is a wealthy country, possessed of the brains and the means to accomplish any goal we pursue. We will not be hindered in the pursuit of this goal by any professional obstacles."

Governor Craig's remarks stirred up a tempest of debate. When representatives of the medical profession began the usual filibuster about increased enrollment jeopardizing the quality of medical education, Craig jumped up.

"I am the first to agree that you must maintain your professional standards," he remarked impatiently. "But you must admit that the present quality of medical education, which you esteem so highly, is jeopardized by inadequate financing. In Indiana, we have at the same time raised our medical school enrollment and increased the quality of instruction through larger legislative appropriations. Other states must follow this pattern, and the medical profession must stop throwing dead cats in the path of progress."

The Governors are not alone in this fight for more, and better-trained, medical personnel. To an increasing degree, the leaders of American psychiatry are speaking out for a new emphasis upon personnel.

This was dramatically illustrated on February 16, 1955, when Dr. Will Menninger addressed a historic joint session of the Ohio legislature. Pulling no punches, Dr. Menninger advised the Ohio legislators to "give the first priority to buying brains—professional staff—to provide treatment, and the second priority to buying bricks. Discard the erroneous impression about the incurability of mental illness and recognize that it has a higher probability of recovery than almost any other type of illness."

He urged the Ohio legislature to appropriate increased moneys to the medical schools for the training of psychiatrists and to raise present salary levels for psychiatric personnel. The Cleveland *Plain Dealer* of February 17 listed these specific prescriptions which the good doctor gave to the legislature:

"Establish training programs for every type of personnel needed. Accept the fact this must be a long-term program, with even three years before it could more than get a good start.

"Enlist the help of the departments of psychiatry of the medical schools; tie to them as closely as possible and provide financial support to make this possible."

For the past several years, Dr. Daniel Blain, the dynamic Medical Director of the American Psychiatric Association, has put all the strength of his office behind a new emphasis upon trained personnel. In a thoughtful article in the March, 1954, issue of *The American Journal of Psychiatry*, Dr. Blain and Robert L. Robinson, APA public information officer, contrasted the success in gaining public support for new mental hospital buildings with the lack of success "in obtaining really adequate staffs to operate psychiatric facilities."

"A recent survey by the A.P.A. Mental Hospital Architectural Study has brought to light a most impressive amount of new construction in the past decade—complete new hospitals, intensive treatment buildings, special units for tuberculosis and the aged, modern laundries, central heating plants, kitchens, medical and surgical departments, and so forth," the authors wrote. ". . . But no progress, in comparison with capital expenditures, has been made in securing the personnel essential for effective use of the new facilities, let alone development of the essential non-hospital elements of a dynamic long-range program."

Pointing out the danger that even leaders of psychiatry have "unconsciously given in to building programs as the easy way out," the authors asked for a new understanding of the prime importance of trained personnel:

"It is not a new idea that the key to success in dealing with mental illness lies in people. No one will disagree that personnel is the common denominator of all treatment programs. What demands our immediate attention is that we are in danger of losing the battle against mental illness by default if we do not marshal the facts, formulate and back up hypotheses that will support a primary stand for adequate personnel. To the extent that we settle for more physical facilities without personnel to operate them, we work under a presumption of pessimism. . . . Cries of despair to the contrary, we contend that psychiatry, like other medical specialties, has matured to the point where it is imperative to say boldly to the people: Give us the tools and we will carry out a program that will lessen the burden of mental illness to the nation.

"There are reasons enough to make such a presumption of optimism: we know that discharges from mental hospitals are directly proportional to the size of their staffs. We know that there is an enormous lag between our present scientific knowledge of therapies and their application in the hospitals. We know that hospitalization can be shortened by early intensive treatment. We know that thousands of hospitalizations can be avoided, postponed, or shortened by establishing lines of defense in the communities— i.e., clinics, half-way houses, sheltered workshops, rehabilitation agencies, community health centers, and the like. We know, as scientists, that research has and will continue to pay off. We know that psychiatry is rapidly maturing to the point of general acceptance as a basic medical science."

The authors concluded with a plea for an accelerated personnel program involving these essential points:

An over-all plan to bring all categories of personnel in the mental hospitals up to American Psychiatric Association standards within six years, with emphasis on doing as much as possible in that direction in the first two years.

A plan for an all-out educational program reaching into secondary schools, colleges, medical schools, and other basic training centers to draw people into medicine and related professions and eventually into the mental health field.

A recruitment effort backed by solid inducements of salary, professional opportunities, and the essentials for good family living that will attract and hold efficient staffs.

Subsidies for universities and medical schools to enable them to carry out a vastly expanded training program in all categories.

The financing of literally thousands of training fellowships covering all professional categories, a significant number in the first year while training facilities are being prepared, and advancing to the maximum needed within three years.

Dr. Blain doesn't confine his convictions about increased production of psychiatric personnel to the pages of technical journals. During the past three years, he and staff members of the American Psychiatric Association have completed broad-scale surveys of mental health resources in Louisiana, Indiana, Arkansas, and Kentucky. Working through local committees composed of prominent doctors and laymen interested in mental health, Dr. Blain has spread the doctrine of more research and training and less building.

The pioneer study, the one in Louisiana, was completed in April, 1954, and received the enthusiastic endorsement of Governor Robert Kennon. It proposed a new and revolutionary philosophy in tackling the problem of mental illness on a state-wide basis, and its challenging recommendations have influenced programs in a number of other states.

"Louisiana must launch a total program of training, research, treatment and prevention," the report recommends. "Otherwise there is no hope of reducing the enormous and ever-increasing economic burden of providing custodial care for the hospitalized mentally ill, and of lessening the socially disastrous effects of mental illness, in the community. . . . Estimated capital construction expenditures for new custodial beds to eliminate overcrowding and take care of the patient pile-up would cost by 1975 the staggering sum of $130,000,000. Louisiana must either invest now in a program that gives promise of solving this problem, or embark on a vastly expanded program of custodial care for the next two decades—and thereafter. . . . The Survey Committee is convinced that mental illness can be reduced if all possible existing skills and knowledge are utilized and new treatments are developed through research. There is ample evidence to justify this conviction. There is also ample evidence to support the statement that this is the *only* rational course for any state to take. No state has yet tried it. The Survey Committee hopes that Louisiana will be the first."

In the body of the two-hundred-forty-page report, the committee charts a series of detailed proposals to enable Louisiana to begin the basic job of training its own native sons in the psychiatric disciplines. The core of these proposals is the linking of the state mental hospitals and the medical schools in a joint training program. Dr. Blain knows the importance of this; as the first Director of Neuropsychiatric Services in the revamped Veterans' Administration following World War II, he broke down the wall of isolation between the VA mental hospitals and the medical schools. In breaking down a comparable wall between the Louisiana mental hospital system and the medical schools, his committee suggested the following steps:

Louisiana State University and Tulane University should be assigned responsibility for training professional personnel and for maintenance of treatment standards in all the operational units of the mental health program.

In carrying out these added responsibilities, the medical schools and their parent universities should be aided by state appropriations for additional faculty, physical facilities, etc.

Each university department of psychiatry should undertake to have, ultimately, fifty psychiatrists in residency training, with fifteen to seventeen graduating each year. It will probably require at least four years to build up to this ceiling, beginning with eight to ten residents in the first year and increasing the number of entrants to sixteen to seventeen for each university by the third year.

In a few other states, solid programs of training which tie the state mental hospitals in with the medical schools, general hospitals, clinics, and private mental institutions are being developed. Usually referred to as Associated Psychiatric Faculties, they pool the training resources of an entire area to give the psychiatric resident the broad indoctrination he needs.

One of the most outstanding is the Psychiatric Training Faculty of Massachusetts, established in 1949. Co-operating organizations include three state mental hospitals—Boston Psychopathic, Boston State, and Worcester State; three medical schools—Harvard, Tufts, and Boston; and a number of additional medical installations—Massachusetts General Hospital, Massachusetts Memorial Hospital, Beth Israel Hospital, the Judge Baker Guidance Center, and the James Jackson Putnam Children's Center. Psychiatric residents rotate through all of these institutions, and there is a real sharing of faculties and facilities.

Kansas has also developed a remarkable degree of pooling between its various psychiatric installations. The Menninger Foundation School of Psychiatry, which trains about 10 per cent of all the psychiatric residents in the country, has affiliate relationships with the Topeka State Hospital, Winter Veterans' Administration Hospital, and a number of local mental health agencies.

In 1949, Topeka State was designated by the Kansas legislature as the pilot psychiatric teaching hospital for all of the Kansas mental hospitals. Since then, a five-year curriculum for the training of residents has been developed. Under this program, the resident spends eighteen months of training at Topeka State, follows with two years at another state mental hospital, and then returns to Topeka for his final eighteen months. In the Topeka phase of his training, he spends a great deal of his time receiving academic and clinical training at the Menninger Foundation and the Winter VA Hospital. This program is already showing evidences of success. Because the residents are exposed to both intensive work in state hospitals and the finest in academic training, most of them come out of the five-year program with a desire to remain in the Kansas public psychiatric system.

The affiliate training idea is spreading. The Nebraska Psychiatric Unit has developed excellent rotation among the state hospitals, the state medical school, the Omaha VA hospital, and a number of clinics. Norristown State Hospital in Pennsylvania uses the teaching resources of the University of Pennsylvania and Jefferson medical schools. The State of Illinois is developing a new research and training institute under the joint supervision of five Chicago medical schools. In the next decade, these and related efforts should do much to bring the state mental hospitals into the main stream of American medicine.

12. STATE GOVERNORS TAKE UP THE TORCH

IN 1768, Governor Francis Fauquier of Virginia made an appeal to the House of Burgesses on behalf of a "poor, unhappy set of People who are deprived of their Senses." Responding to his plea, the good Burgesses passed an act in that year providing for the support and maintenance of "Ideots, Lunatics and other persons of unsound Minds." Five years later, the first institution in the Colonies devoted exclusively to mental patients opened its doors at Williamsburg. From that time on, it was assumed that the care of the mentally ill was primarily a tax responsibility of the individual states.

During the nineteenth century, state after state built one or more institutions for the care of the mentally ill within their confines. However, in most cases these mental hospitals, or "lunatic asylums" as they were most frequently designated, were forbidding dungeons where chains, wristlets, and iron chairs were the prevalent form of "therapy." These institutions were built in isolated rural areas, cut off by design from the main stream of daily life and activity.

For more than a hundred and fifty years following the erection of the Williamsburg structure, there were heroic individual attempts to bring the plight of the mentally ill to the conscience of America.

Dorothea Lynde Dix, one of the most courageous of the nineteenth-century reformers, brought about the construction of many state institutions and singlehandedly succeeded in convincing Congress to establish a Federal hospital, the famous St. Elizabeths. In the early part of the twentieth century, Clifford Beers, a former mental patient who wrote *A Mind That Found Itself,* established the National Committee for Mental Hygiene to foster citizen interest in better care for the mentally ill.

But there was a discouraging rise-and-fall cycle in these attempts at reform. There was temporary public arousement, a crescendo of righteous citizen indignation, and then a falling back into the slough of despond.

Following the advent of World War II, with its dramatic demonstration of the crippling effects of mental illness upon our armed forces, there came a powerful demand for a new approach. Many returning veterans were in need of hospitalization for serious emotional illnesses, yet the Veterans' Administration mental hospitals were, for the most part, custodial snake pits. In a brilliant series of articles in the newspaper *PM,* Albert Deutsch laid bare the deficiencies of these hospitals. His exposés, and those of Albert Q. Maisel in *Life,* led to a basic shake-up in the whole concept of the public mental hospital. Under General Omar Bradley, Drs. Paul Hawley, Paul Magnuson, and Dan Blain pulled the VA hospitals into the community of American medicine, tying their programs into the medical schools. They insisted, despite club-hammer pressure from some congressmen, that the new VA hospitals be built in or near the major medical centers of the nation.

Just as Johns Hopkins Medical School became, before World War I, the model for a major revolution in medical education, so now the Veterans' Administration program, entirely tax-supported, became the model for public psychiatry generally.

In a number of states, newspapers began all-out campaigns to inform their readers of the rotten conditions prevalent in the mental institutions. In most cases, the campaigns were of the hit-and-run variety; starry-eyed reformers, unaware of the perseverance needed to remold public thinking, thought a six-article series and a newspaper editorial would change the world overnight. In a small number of cases, newspapers kept at it for several years, and major changes were made.

Although I had kept at our crusade in Oklahoma for four years, I had the constant feeling that something more was needed than periodic assaults upon the emotions of the citizens. That feeling had taken me to Topeka where, in many long evenings of conversation with Drs. Karl and Will Menninger and members of their staff, I voiced the dilemma facing all of us.

A crusading side-trip to Florida gave me part of the answer. Having heard of my work in Oklahoma and adjoining states, the publisher of the Miami *Daily News* called my publisher and asked him if I could be spared for a few weeks. I went to Florida in the spring of 1949, my visit timed with the biennial session of the Florida legislature. In a three-week period, I raced up and down the entire state. I wrote a number of articles, addressed every major civic organization in Dade County, and climaxed my visit with an address to an informal joint session of the legislature in Tallahassee. On the surface, the crusade was a big success. The legislature added several millions to the budget for the mental hospitals, Dade County (Miami) closed a private institution which was bilking the taxpayers of the county at the rate of eight dollars per day for every mental patient, and the mental health association got hundreds of new members.

But on the plane back to Oklahoma City, I couldn't get out of my mind something that Fuller Warren, then Governor of Florida, had said to me. I was telling the Governor of some of my experiences while visiting Chattahoochee, the big Florida mental hospital hidden off in the northwestern part of the state. Each time I criticized some deficiency, I would have to go into a long explanation of what some other states were doing, and why this was better.

"Mr. Gorman," the handsome Governor drawled, "I am finding it very hard to follow you. Let me put it this way. If we were discussing highways, we could both refer to basic standards and studies, both state and Federal, on what makes a good highway system. However, in mental health, there seem to be no basic blueprints to which we Governors can turn for information and guidance."

Soon after returning from Florida, I had several speaking engagements in Minnesota. For the past several years I had been working closely with Minnesota Governor Luther Youngdahl, an evangelical crusader who was coming into national prominence as a result of his magnificent fight for a new state program for the mentally ill. After one of my speeches, I visited the Executive Mansion and, over seemingly endless cups of powerful black coffee, I told the Governor of my worry that the current rash of mental hospital exposés had run the gamut and we were about to go down into the valley of despond again. The Governor said he had been thinking hard about the same thing, and he had decided to do something about it.

"I am going to the National Governors' Conference at Colorado Springs this summer and propose that the Governors of the forty-eight states sponsor a comprehensive study of our entire state mental hospital system," he told me. "I know I'm in for a tough fight on this. One negative vote can veto this kind of study, and I am afraid some of my fellow Governors would just as soon not bring this problem out into the open."

The Governor of Minnesota trekked off to Colorado Springs that summer and, between massive doses of black coffee, put his oratorical gifts to their supreme test. He won out, and the forty-eight state governors unanimously endorsed a year-long study of the state mental hospital system.

At the 1950 Governors' Conference, the three-hundred-seventy-seven-page study, *The Mental Health Programs of the Forty-Eight States,* received the governmental and technical acclaim it so richly warranted. It proved to be the desperately needed primer every state official wanted, filled with statistics and charts on the size and nature of the hospitals, patient costs, types of administrative organization used by the several states, personnel shortages, legal provisions governing commitment, staff salaries, raw food costs, and so on.

The Mental Health Programs of the Forty-Eight States also included a list of forty recommendations, most of them of a legal and administrative nature. Buried deep in the long list, however, were two which were to foreshadow future state action in the field. Recommendation No. 26 had this to say:

"Few if any state hospitals for the mentally ill meet the standards recommended by the American Psychiatric Association with respect to the required numbers of physicians, psychiatrists, clinical psychologists, graduate nurses, psychiatric social workers, and various other types of therapists. Proper care and effective treatment of patients cannot be provided unless competent personnel in sufficient numbers are made available. All states should carefully appraise the personnel situation existing in state hospitals and should make every effort to provide the necessary professional and other therapy staff."

And the very last on the list, Recommendation No. 40, which was to prove in time that the last shall truly become the first:

"Research in the field of mental disorders is conducted to an extremely limited extent, particularly when compared with research in many fields of physical sickness, such as cancer, heart disease, and poliomyelitis, despite the fact that mental disease is one of the most extensive, serious and costly illnesses to which we are subject. More resources and facilities should be provided for comprehensive and intensive research in the field of mental illness; more attention should be given this subject in state hospitals and medical schools; every effort should be made to co-ordinate research programs and activities that now exist; and the states should encourage and support professional associations, institutions and agencies in giving careful consideration to the development and expansion of major research programs in this field."

The 1950 study had considerable influence upon state programs. Many of its technical recommendations were used as yardsticks in the blueprinting of new state plans. It had a particularly strong impact in the area of administration; before the issuance of the report, only a few states had their mental health programs centralized in a separate department. In the past five years, a number of states have overhauled their entire administrative machinery to bring all mental health functions under one central structure.

In the year subsequent to the release of the report, I traveled to a number of states to talk to the Governors about ways of whipping the problem. During that very fruitful year, the National Mental Health Committee decided to create a closer tie between its activities and those of the Governors. We agreed to ask a few of them to become honorary chairmen of our Committee; we hoped we might wind up with three or four. Luther Youngdahl was the first to accept. Earl Warren, then Governor of California, was the second; G. Mennen Williams of Michigan the third, and before we knew it we had forty Governors on our Committee.

In the many conversations I had with the Governors, I found most of them still groping for a way to reverse the continuing annual rise in total number of mental patients hospitalized. The need for additional thousands of beds had forced a number of Governors to support construction bond issues aggregating several hundred million dollars a year. They were on a treadmill, and they wanted off. I told them the only way out lay in increased appropriations for research and training, but they replied that this was a tough thing to sell the legislatures and the people. They cited several instances where state legislatures had voted money for research projects, then later had cut off the funds because of public impatience with the results obtained. The California legislature had recently done this, and I had journeyed out to Sacramento to talk to Dr. Frank Tallman, then the State Mental Health Director.

"Mike, you have got to undertake a campaign to sell psychiatric research as a hardheaded business investment which will pay the states incalculable dividends," Dr. Tallman, who had headed programs in Ohio and Michigan before coming to California, told me. "You can't expect a legislature to get too far in front of the people."

With Dr. Tallman's advice in mind, I journeyed to Lansing to talk to Michigan's Governor Williams. Williams, then in his second term, had begun to tackle the mental health problem with a painstaking, driving force which I had found rather rare among the states' chief executives. He had appointed a superb professional committee to survey the state's psychiatric facilities, and their report set him to thinking hard. Although the citizens of Michigan had approved a bond issue of $60,000,000 for mental hospital construction in 1950, the mounting rate of admissions and the over-all annual increase of the patient population forced him to the reluctant conclusion that another construction bond issue would probably be needed in the next couple of years unless some way could be found to reverse the trend.

I asked the Governor if he would be willing to sponsor a resolution at the 1951 National Governors' Conference calling for a specific study of ways in which the states could reverse the rising patient population trend through increased emphasis upon psychiatric research and the training of psychiatric personnel. He said he would take a stab at it, and I agreed to go to the conference and work on the individual Governors.

The 1951 National Governors' Conference was held in the small resort town of Gatlinburg in Tennessee's Great Smokies. It was unbearably hot during those four days, and the heat seemed to multiply in force as it poured down in the valley between the mountains. The accommodations were the smallest I had ever seen at a Governors' Conference; each Governor was assigned only one room for his personal use. Furthermore, the political lines were being drawn for the 1952 Presidential campaign—the Eisenhower draft was picking up a head of steam and political tempers were on edge.

I was parked out in a tourist cabin about half a mile from the center of town. I was pretty discouraged as I hiked toward town the first day but soon found reason for some optimism. There was only one main street running through the town, and political conferences were going on every ten or fifteen yards. Furthermore, it was too blazing hot for the Governors to hide off in their one-room accommodations; they did their relaxing on the hotel front porches. This was a real break; you could bag them before they had a chance to run for cover. Actually, we had the nearest thing to a captive audience you could achieve at this kind of conference. The only escape was up to the mountains, and most of the Governors were too weary to conduct such a safari.

During the first three days of the conference, I followed a fairly set schedule. I would emerge from my log cabin over the creek early in the morning and head up toward the one street in town. I had a list of the forty-five Governors at the conference, and I checked off the names as I got their agreement to the Williams resolution. I buttonholed them at any vantage point and felt I had hit the jackpot whenever I found a group of them clustered on one of the hotel porches. When I ran into a Governor who was somewhat lukewarm, I would invariably appeal to the chief executives of his neighboring states to work on him. I had a tremendous ally in Governor Johnston Murray of Oklahoma, whom I knew well from my newspapering days in Oklahoma. When I ran up against a really tough one, I would ask Governor Murray to have words with him.

Governor Williams and his bright young aides kept a score card of their own, and late each evening we would get together on the porch of the New Gatlinburg Hotel and compare notes.

On the night before the vote, we sat up until 1:00 A.M. reworking the resolution and planning final strategy.

On Saturday afternoon, we tasted sweet victory when the forty-five Governors voted unanimously for a two-year study of "ways in which the states might work toward prevention and cure of mental illness." The Governors specifically directed that it include:

1. A survey of methods of training personnel and conducting research into the causes, prevention, and cure of mental disease;

2. An investigation of the possibility of setting up in less populous areas regional mental health bodies which could pool the training resources and research of a number of states in a common fight against mental illness; and

3. An inquiry into the possibility of some over-all mechanism whereby the states could plan and co-ordinate their research and training programs toward a mutual goal of preventing mental illness and reducing the population of mental institutions.

The resulting report, *Training and Research in State Mental Health Programs,* proved to be a classic of its kind, the culmination of almost endless digging, of scores of questionnaires, and of the imaginative search for specific solutions to the massive problem of mental illness. It received the unanimous acclaim of the psychiatric profession for both the solidity of its documentation and the farsightedness of its recommendations.

The heart and core of the 1953 report is contained in these words:

"Care and treatment for mental patients are continuing, major functions of the state governments. . . . But care and treatment alone, along present lines, cannot cope with the present and emerging situations. Hope for the future lies primarily in widening and deepening the knowledge of mental disorder—in the discovery and application of better means of treatment and prevention. These can be attained only through more research, and through training of mental health personnel. Research and training thus are the essential bases for reducing admissions to mental hospitals and, ultimately, for reducing hospital populations."

The report was officially presented to the 1953 National Governors' Conference in Seattle. My journey out to Seattle was not for the purpose of witnessing what I guessed would be a routine adoption of the major recommendations of the report. Rather, it seemed to me the time was ripe for pushing an idea we of the National Mental Health Committee had dreamed of since 1949— a National Governors' Conference called to deal exclusively with the problem of mental illness.

On the Sunday preceding the opening of the Seattle conference, I went into a huddle with Governor Williams' very bright aides: Robert Steadman, then Michigan State Comptroller; Lawrence Farrell, Governor Williams' executive secretary, and Paul Weber, his press secretary. We all agreed on the idea of a national conference on mental health, and we spent several hours hammering out a resolution to cover all points. We knew we had our work cut out for us. All of the big resolutions were already in print and in the hands of the Resolutions Committee. Besides, we were breaking new ground—special Governors' Conferences on specific problems were as rare as the impromptu resolution we were trying to push through.

At lunch on Monday, we all got together with Governor Williams in a private room far removed from the main festivities. Governor Williams was enthusiastic about the conference idea and expressed a strong desire to have it in Detroit.

The next couple of days were somewhat of a repetition of the Battle of Gatlinburg, with notable geographical exceptions. There was more than one main street in Seattle, and the Governors were pretty widely scattered. I spent most of Monday afternoon and night trying to track down the elusive Governors.

Our big break came on Tuesday, when the Governors and their parties were shepherded onto four yachts for a trip to Treasure Island in Puget Sound. On the way up to the Island, I was on the yacht with Governor Theodore Roosevelt McKeldin of Maryland, a stanch Republican, and Governor Frank Clement of Tennessee, a stanch Democrat. Both deeply interested in mental health, they worked both sides of the yacht in bipartisan fashion between competitive renditions of "Maryland, My Maryland" and "The Tennessee Waltz."

The Island itself proved even more wonderfully captive than Gatlinburg—here the only escape was a dive into the Sound. We made our biggest hay that day, and the next day the resolution whipped through.

On February 8, 1954, a day that always will be celebrated and venerated by all of us in the field, Governor G. Mennen Williams called the historic National Governors' Conference on Mental Health to order. Ten state Governors were present, and there were state legislators, mental health officials, and leading psychiatrists from forty-six states and the Commonwealth of Puerto Rico.

"This can well turn out to be one of the historic turning-points in the ancient struggle of mankind against disease," Governor Williams told the conference in his magnificent opening address. "We are meeting here to launch the most determined attack ever made against ailments of the human mind. . . .

"We are gathered here today for the purpose, primarily, of considering ways and means to make progress in preventing mental illness, and in effecting rapid cure of mental illness when it does occur.

"We are doing this for two main reasons:

"First, because humanity requires a determined effort to stop the terrible toll of human suffering which is caused by mental illness.

"Secondly, we are doing this because the cost of dealing with mental illness on the present basis is becoming too great to be borne. We simply cannot go on building more and more mental hospitals to house more and more patients. The burden upon taxpayers is already becoming intolerable, and there is no relief in sight."

During the ensuing two days, leaders of American psychiatry— Drs. Kenneth Appel, Jack Ewalt, William Malamud, Winfred Overholser, Robert H. Felix, Harvey J. Tompkins, Mesrop Tarumianz, Henry Brill, Karl Menninger, and others—participated in exciting panels with the Governors and state legislators.

Speaking for American psychiatry in the closing address of the conference, Dr. Menninger caught the spirit of the meeting.

"Don't underestimate the idealism of the average American," Dr. Menninger warned. "Give him the facts. Tell him what it costs to end this misery. He will tell you to go ahead and he will willingly pay the bill. . . . If all legislatures now catch the vision of our Governors and give their people a chance, human welfare and American civilization will have been vastly promoted."

As their closing action of the historic conference, the assembled

Governors formally adopted a ten-point set of recommendations which the Detroit *Free Press* aptly characterized as a "Bill of Rights for the Mentally Ill." Here is the text of the Bill of Rights:

1. By far the major share of a state's mental health resources must be used for the care and treatment of patients in state hospitals for the mentally ill. Psychiatric treatment with the fullest of existing knowledge can return many more people to productive and useful lives. Increased appropriations for additional qualified mental health personnel (including psychiatrists, psychologists, social workers, nurses and related personnel) and intensive treatment programs should be provided by the states at their next legislative sessions to increase the number of patients discharged from state mental hospitals.

2. Training and research in the field of mental health are essential elements of effective mental health programs. The serious accumulation of patients and costs can only be reduced by discovering new knowledge and new methods of treatment and by more adequate training and development of mental health personnel. State legislatures are urged to appropriate specific sums for training and research in addition to the regular appropriations for care and treatment.

3. Ultimate reduction of the population in state mental hospitals can only be achieved by efforts to prevent mental illness. This requires facilities for early identification, for early treatment and for aftercare and supervision of those on leave from state hospitals. State governments should take the initiative with both financial and professional assistance in stimulating local public and private agencies to participate actively in preventive programs.

4. At present it is estimated that less than one per cent of total state mental health budgets is expended for research—$4,000,000 out of a total expenditure of about $560,000,000. Based on a comprehensive survey of state mental health officials, it is recommended that the states should devote a much larger percentage of their total mental health budgets to basic and applied research in the biological and behavioral sciences and to the training of personnel in research methods.

5. Effective training and research programs cannot be

achieved without effective organization. A position of director of training and research should be established within the mental health agency in each state to assume responsibility for the co-ordination of mental health training and research within the state's jurisdiction. A technical advisory committee, composed of scientists and educators in the field of mental health, co-operating with scientists in universities and industry, should be established in each state to advise and assist the mental health agency and other state departments concerned with the co-ordination of training and research activities.

6. State institutions which are not accredited for residency or as affiliate training centers for psychiatrists, clinical psychologists, social workers, nurses and other professional groups should receive support from Governors and legislatures in their endeavors to raise the level of teaching and supervision in their institutions to secure accreditation.

7. The states should provide stipends for graduate training in the psychiatric field, should adjust salary scales and should provide educational leaves of absence so that state mental hospitals may compete effectively for the limited personnel available to fill treatment, teaching and research positions.

8. One of the important obstacles to adequate evaluation of procedures and therapies is a lack of uniformity in statistical methods in mental hospitals and clinics throughout the country. All states should co-operate with the United States Public Health Service and the American Psychiatric Association in the adoption of uniform terminology for statistical reporting procedures in the field of mental health.

partially achieved by periodic regional mental health con-

9. Joint action by groups of states may provide one of the most fruitful means of attacking mental illness. This can be ferences, regional programs such as that now sponsored by the Southern Regional Education Board, and by active participation in the Interstate Clearinghouse now established through the Council of State Governments by request of the Governors' Conference. The clearinghouse, in co-operation with existing public and private agencies, will provide a medium for exchange of pertinent information among the states, will assist the states in organizing more effective mental health programs,

and will help in developing interstate agreements so that groups of states can utilize to the fullest extent existing training and research facilities.

10. State and community mental health organizations should play important roles in educating the public to the problems of mental health and the methods of improving psychiatric services. The states should encourage and support mental health education in the schools, good relationships between hospitals and their surrounding communities, and the provision of adequate community psychiatric services. These may, in the long run, be most important in determining the mental health of the nation.

13. KEEPING
THE FIRES
BURNING

THE National Governors' Conference was an inspiration to all of us in the field, but those of us who had generated it harbored no illusions that we had saved the world by proclaiming a ten-point Bill of Rights for the Mentally Ill. Resolution Nine emphasized the need for regional efforts to implement the many far-reaching recommendations contained in the 1953 report of the Council of State Governments.

For a long time, I had been watching with great interest a remarkable regional co-operative effort which had gotten under way in the South in 1948. In the period 1948–53, fourteen Southern states had built regional co-operation in higher education to the point where millions of dollars were crossing state lines to support the training of several thousand students, most of them in the health professions. The program had proven most beneficial in medical education, where it had given states lacking medical schools the opportunity to send their native sons to the larger medical schools in the South which agreed to train them for a contracted fee.

In order to establish a sound mechanism for this unique effort in co-operative education and planning, the Southern Governors brought into being the Southern Regional Education Board. Headed by Dr. John E. Ivey, a brilliant young sociologist who came off the campus of the University of North Carolina, the Board staff included a top-notch group of enthusiastic young educators and administrators. After the first couple of years of existence, they had moved from relatively simple arrangements for mutual training of students to complex, far-reaching surveys of ways in which the educational institutions of the South could combine their programs to avoid uneconomic duplication and provide a higher quality of graduate training. In the period prior to 1953, bold experiments in regional planning were launched in the fields of forestry, marine and petroleum science, and nursing.

The Board's work was financed by individual contributions from each of the states participating in the regional compact. Moving at breakneck speed, the Board staff soon found itself a good bit out in front of the thinking of the average Southern legislator. In 1952, therefore, it initiated an annual legislative work conference to pull the legislative leaders of the South into the detailed planning of both existing and future compact arrangements. This type of conference was without nation-wide precedent, for it brought legislators from fourteen states together to make decisions in terms of an entire region rather than in the narrower patterns of state sovereignty.

So a superb organizational mechanism existed in the Southland for a regional survey of mental health resources. I therefore packed my carpet-bag and hied off to the Southern Governors' Conference at Hot Springs, Virginia, in November, 1953. Prior to the conference I had sent Governor Lawrence Wetherby of Kentucky, the Chairman of the Southern Regional Education Board, a draft of a proposed resolution authorizing the Board to make a year-long study of the potentials for psychiatric research and training in the South.

Since the resolution was not on the formal agenda of the conference, back-alley and second-story proselytizing was again the order of the day. However, the physical arrangements for skulduggery were perfect—we were all domiciled at the beautiful old Homestead Hotel, and the weather was perfect for outdoor buttonholing. Things were moving fairly smoothly the first day of the conference until I ran into Governor Wetherby late in the afternoon. He apologized for not being able to bring up the resolution, but he had to be back in Kentucky on Tuesday to vote. I went into a nice, solid depression for about fifteen minutes, then started the hunt for a new resolution-introducer. I set my sights for Governor Frank Clement of Tennessee, the youngest of the nation's chief executives. He had created a sensation at the

National Governors' Conference in Seattle the previous August with his brilliant defense of TVA in the presence of President Eisenhower.

Governor Clement latched on to the idea with his characteristic energy and bounce. He made a ringingly eloquent speech to the Resolutions Committee, and the next day the assembled governors unanimously adopted the following resolution:

1. That the Southern Regional Education Board begin an immediate survey of facilities for the training of psychiatric personnel in the South, and that it report to this Conference those institutions best qualified to take additional students in the psychiatric disciplines from states which have no such facilities.

2. That the Board also initiate a survey of institutions doing mental health research in the South, and that it recommend to the Conference those institutions capable of being enlarged to do additional research.

3. That upon completion of the above surveys by the Board, but in any case not later than July 30, 1954, a Southern Regional mental conference be held to discuss the surveys and draw up interstate compacts in mental health research and training.

4. That, in the interim, the individual states make official surveys of their training and research facilities—with particular emphasis upon raising mental institutions in each state to the level of residency or affiliate accreditation—and that the results of these surveys be presented to the 1954 regional mental health conference.

5. That the Southern Regional Education Board be requested to report the results of its study and any action taken to the 1954 Southern Governors' Conference.

Delighted by the specificity of the directives handed to them by the Governors, but plenty worried about the shortness of time available for their accomplishment, the SREB staff moved into action quickly. By January, 1954, they had set up a project staff in Nashville under the capable direction of Dr. Nicholas Hobbs of Peabody College. A supervisory Commission on Mental Health Training and Research, with Governor Clement as Chairman, was also appointed, and it met twice in January to outline the scope of the survey project. The young "pros" of the SREB staff then began the shrewd enterprise of chopping the big job up into digestible bites. They formed technical panels which met a number of times on the most thorny problems: how to develop a regional research program, how to draw more professionals into mental hospital work, the basic assumptions underlying a successful preventive program in psychiatry, tying the entire resources of a community into the objectives of modern psychiatry, and so on. These panels were composed of leading health professionals, educators, sociologists, lawyers, ministers, and citizens from the South and from many other parts of the country. Their discussions and recommendations, published as a separate volume by the Board, are loaded with enterprising ideas.

While the panels were grinding away at regional meetings, individual state committees appointed by the Governors began the enormous job of collecting the data which had to precede recommendations to the individual state legislatures. These state committees ranged in size all the way up to sixty-seven members, and they worked at a feverish pace. They sent out questionnaires to every facility and agency touching, in any conceivable way, the problem of mental illness. In addition to a number of meetings within state confines, these committees held four joint regional meetings, two of them in conjunction with the Commission on Mental Health Research and Training and the Southern Legislative Work Conference.

The importance of these individual state surveys cannot be overestimated. In addition to the invaluable detail they contain on psychiatric personnel and location of research, their far-reaching recommendations in many instances created revolutionary blueprints for a fresh attack upon the whole problem of mental illness.

Space does not permit a detailed analysis of the sixteen state reports. However, in a newsletter I sent out to the membership of the National Mental Health Committee subsequent to the publication of the reports, I highlighted some of the outstanding recommendations as follows:

Alabama.—An annual legislative appropriation of $622,000 for research and training programs.

Delaware.—An appropriation of $214,000 for the 1955-56 biennium solely for research and training programs.

Florida.—A proposal for a Florida Research Council with funds furnished by the legislature to encourage and co-ordinate research, and a proposal for a state mental health conference to push the recommendations of the Florida Research and Training Committee.

North Carolina.—A proposal that the North Carolina Research and Training Committee develop a ten-year plan covering the total mental health needs of the state and that a paid Executive Secretary be assigned to this permanent Committee.

Oklahoma.—A proposal that a State Council for Mental Health Research be set up composed of Oklahoma's leading scientists. That the state legislature appropriate at least $150,000 per year for research against mental illness and that the State Council for Mental Health Research seek additional funds from private foundations and the general citizenry.

Tennessee.—A proposal that the state legislature appropriate $1,065,000 to carry out the many training programs recommended by the state survey committee.

Texas.—A five-year plan for the building up of research and training programs in Texas, with a specific recommendation for establishment of an Institute of Psychiatry dedicated exclusively to mental health research and training.

Virginia.—A specific appropriation by the legislature of $593,000 for 1955 training and research programs.

In the publication *An Atlas on Mental Health Training and Research in the Southern States,* the Southern Board compressed into seventy-three pages of maps, charts, and statistics a superb picture of the region's resources and deficiencies in these areas.

Now there came the problem of pulling all the diverse recommendations into a document for submission to the legislative conference in September and the Governors' Conference in November. At a work conference in Atlanta during four torrid days in July, 1954, 170 of us literally took off our coats and sweated it through. After three days and nights of plowing through the mounds of assembled data, we got together on Saturday and agreed on the following key proposals for transmission to the Southern Governors:

1. The Southern states should increase appropriations to their universities and agencies which prepare mental health personnel and are able to undertake mental health research. These funds should be in addition to funds appropriated for the operation of mental

hospitals and clinics. Amounts needed to expand training and research should be defined by each state.

2. States which need trained people but lack training facilities should first consider establishing regional arrangements with states or universities which can provide opportunities for training. These arrangements may be regional contracts, grants, fellowships, or other types.

3. The states should jointly encourage the growth of regional mental health research centers, based upon present concentration of facilities and professional people in such locations as Baltimore, New Orleans, Nashville, Durham-Chapel Hill, and others. Such centers, if properly organized, encouraged, and supported, could contribute greatly to improving treatment and reducing occurrence of mental illness.

4. The states should establish a Regional Council on Mental Health Training and Research with a highly qualified staff to assist states to strengthen their training and research in mental health by consultation and advice, by working out regional arrangements as appropriate, and by searching for various ways to promote training and research activities in mental health. The Council would be composed of one person appointed by the Governor of each participating state, with half as many persons appointed by the Southern Regional Education Board with concurrence of the Council. It would be organized as an integral part of the Southern Regional Education Board. It would be supported by an annual contribution of $8,000 from each participating state. The central function of the proposed Council would be to give continuing attention to the expansion and improvement of mental health training and research in the region.

Before presenting these recommendations to the Governors, the young "pros" of the SREB staff wisely decided to run them through a tough political mill. They took them to the third annual Southern Legislative Work Conference meeting in Houston in September. The assembled legislators from sixteen states were so impressed with the whole business that, in their resolution endorsing the Atlanta proposals, they asked that representatives of the Legislative Work Conference be an integral part of the proposed Southern Regional Council on Research and Training.

A year of fantastically dedicated and detailed work culminated in the presentation of the mental health project recommendations to the Twentieth Annual Southern Governors' Conference in Boca Raton, Florida, November 11-13. In his keynote speech at the round table on mental health, Governor Clement brushed aside the chaff and went to the deep core of the problem in a moving challenge to his fellow governors.

"It is not merely that any humane view, any just view of our ailing fellow man, gives him an unalienable right and claim upon our resources to restore him," Governor Clement told the conference. "It is not merely that the Bill of Rights of mental health imposes that obligation upon us all, in behalf of the mentally ill. It is not merely that this therapy may restore the mental patient to his or her family and community, and that such a restoration ends an expense to the public (usually your state government) and generally benefits society.

"Our ultimate and inescapable social self-interest—that is, the wholesomeness, the very existence of our society itself, dictates that we attack the causes of this deadly mental cancer, rather than merely trying to follow a policy of containment through custodial care. Obviously, custodial care will not improve our mental health. Obviously, custodial care will not increase our resources for treatment and cure. Obviously, custodial care on the part of government is not enough. Insofar as I know, it has never been the attitude of any Governor of any Southern state to defend custodial care in his state on the ground that it is the full extent of the public interest in the mentally ill. Indeed, we know here that every member of this conference of states provides some therapy for its mental charges. I speak advisedly when I say *some* therapy.

"I believe, also, that no one here will dispute the point with me, when I assert that no Southern state as yet has appropriated *enough money* to provide adequate therapeutic treatment in its mental institutions. I believe that most of us have become more appreciative of the importance of increased financial support for these institutions."

And then, in these words, the big problem facing the conference:

"Yet, here in the South today, even if we appropriated ample funds for complete and comprehensive therapy in our mental institutions, we would still be unable to realize it because there are not a sufficient number of properly trained personnel available to do the job, and because we need new knowledge to do the job more effectively."

The resounding thunder of applause at the conclusion of Clement's address told all of us there what we wanted to know: the Southern governors were unanimously behind a greatly expanded research and training program in the South.

The key proposal for a permanent regional research and training council made great progress during 1955. Initial contributions from a number of states, plus a temporary grant from the National Institute of Mental Health, started the ball rolling. At a meeting in Atlanta in May, representatives appointed by the governors of all sixteen states came together to plan for the organization, staffing, and program of the new council. The council came into being formally on July 12, 1955, and since then has begun the recruitment of staff. Its organization holds tremendous promise for a complete revolution in the care and treatment of the mentally ill in the South.

The National Governors' Conference on Mental Health, held early in 1954, had one whoppingly wonderful side-effect in addition to all its major accomplishments. In a quiet hotel room far removed from the pulsating throng, Governor G. Mennen Williams of Michigan, host to the conference, one evening privately hosted Governor George Craig of Indiana, the most powerful Republican Governor at the conference. Governors Williams and Craig both deplored the demise of the Inland Governors' Conference, which left the chief executives of the Midwestern states without a mechanism for regional co-operation. Governor Williams then suggested that a few of the states in the Great Lakes area have a go at a regional project in mental health. Governor Craig allowed as how he was more than willing and suggested Indianapolis for the organizational meeting.

Since the Midwestern states lacked a staff comparable to that in the South, the burden of most of the detail fell upon the Council of State Governments. The Council, located in Chicago, had done a magnificent job in the field of mental health since 1949; it had not only prepared two definitive reports for the Governors' Conference, but had worked closely with state officials and legislators in the drafting of much mental health legislation.

Sidney Spector, Director of the Council's recently formed Interstate Clearinghouse on Mental Health, was given the big job of handling the Midwestern project. He started out by getting the Mid-

western Regional Conference of Commissions on Interstate Coop-
eration, composed mostly of legislators, to endorse the idea of research and training surveys in the Midwest. He then set up the first
organizational meeting for June 7-8 in Indianapolis.

Dr. Margaret Morgan, Indiana's dynamic Mental Health Commissioner, presided at the conference. Governor Craig spoke at both
a morning and a late evening session. After two sixteen-hour days
of hauling and pulling, we came up with a timetable leading to a
Midwestern Governors' Conference on Mental Health late in November. This meant that the ten states in the project—there were
seven at the start and three more asked to be included—would have
to complete research and training surveys by October. Dr. Dan
Blain of the American Psychiatric Association agreed to work up a
questionnaire for use in the surveys.

In response to the recommendations of the Indianapolis meeting,
the Governors of the following states appointed committees to undertake the surveys: Illinois, Indiana, Iowa, Kansas, Michigan, Minnesota, Nebraska, Ohio, South Dakota, and Wisconsin. These survey
committees put in a brutal four months of strenuous work before
making their preliminary reports at a two-day meeting in Minneapolis late in October.

The Minneapolis report hit hardest at the deficiencies in psychiatric research:

"Where effective treatment or preventive methods have been
found, the problems of buildings, of facilities, of personnel shortages
disappear. For example, once the diet deficiency basis for pellagra
was discovered, there were enough persons to treat the pellagrins.
The same is true for paresis when its infectious origin was found.
Once the effective drugs for the control of epilepsy were revealed
there was enough personnel in epileptic hospitals to prescribe the
drugs. Today, tuberculosis hospitals are being closed because of the
sharp decline in the number of patients. The ten Midwest states
in this survey are running a $127,000,000 a year business in mental
health, but they expend relatively small amounts for research. The
staggering sums which they now devote to the care and treatment of
the mentally ill, and which increase from year to year, constitute
in large degree a measure of our lack of basic knowledge. . . .

"The Midwest, of course, is one of the most fertile centers of research in the field of mental health of any region in the nation. Its

universities, research hospitals, and other institutions have made major contributions to the nation's store of scientific knowledge of mental disorders. However, with few exceptions state governments themselves have not undertaken to invest heavily enough in the research efforts of the region. As yet they have not emphasized sufficiently the importance of imaginative research programs in state hospitals, their effect on attracting outstanding personnel and on revitalizing present treatment methods."

However, the Minneapolis sessions took note of some hopeful signs in framing recommendations for the Governors.

"To provide a stimulus for research efforts in the field of mental health, the Governors attending the National Governors' Conference on Mental Health adopted a Ten Point program which included a recommendation that special appropriations for research and training should be made in addition to the regular appropriations for care and treatment," the report emphasized. "Since then there has been a movement in a number of states to provide for an additional 5 per cent of the mental health budget to be appropriated for research and 5 per cent for training. In some states this is already an accomplished fact. In Ohio, 5 per cent of the budget is devoted to research; in Illinois, the legislature in 1953 appropriated more than five million dollars from the mental health fund for research; in Wisconsin, special appropriations are made for training, as is true in other states. . . .

"It is suggested, therefore, that an additional 5 per cent of the mental health appropriations in each state be appropriated for research, and a second 5 per cent for training. Wherever possible and feasible, each state should appoint a director of psychiatric research and training who, with the assistance of a professional advisory council, would advise the commissioner or director on the allocation of research and training funds. Enactment of this proposal would add approximately $12,000,000 for research and training over the amounts expended in 1953."

Governor William Stratton of Illinois was host to the first Midwestern Governors' Conference on Mental Health in Chicago on November 30, 1954. After adopting a series of progressive recommendations in the areas of research and training, the governors voted to set up a permanent committee on mental health composed of twenty members, the ten mental health commissioners and one additional representative from each state chosen by the Governor. The committee was instructed to meet several times a year to further co-operative regional action. The staff of the Council of State Governments, which had carried the burden of the work in making the conference a success, agreed to provide secretariat services for the committee.

The regional conference mechanism has caught on in other parts of the country. In the Far West, a Western Interstate Commission for Higher Education had been formed a few years back along the lines of the Southern Regional Education Board. In late March, 1955, the Western Governors and their state mental health officials met for several days in San Francisco. The Governors agreed to appoint survey committees in each of the eleven states, and the Western Interstate Commission agreed to serve as the co-ordinating staff. The surveys were well under way by the fall of 1955 and received the enthusiastic go-ahead of both a legislative conference and the Western Governors' Conference.

Even in staid New England things are moving, although more along traditional lines. In the fall of 1954, there was a cautious meeting of the Northeastern Mental Health Authorities in Hartford to discuss possible areas of regional co-operation. Those of us who had been in the midst of the sound and fury of the Southern and Midwestern movements were impressed with the antiseptic manner in which New England inspects a new idea. Six months later, at a Northeast State Governments Conference on Mental Health in Wilmington, New England and its neighbors got a little closer to the water without quite going in for a swim. However, a New England Compact for Higher Education is coming into being, and this mechanism will undoubtedly further co-operative efforts in regional mental health work.

The results of all these efforts, both nationally and regionally, have far exceeded the expectations of even the most euphoric of us. In testifying before a Senate committee in the waning weeks of the 1955 session. I pointed out that, in many states, more progress had been made in 1955 than in the previous decade. Although additional appropriations were exceedingly important, they were overshadowed by the widespread endorsement of the cardinal principle that research and training were major items of governmental concern requiring separate budget allocations. They could now be fought for in each legislative session on their own merits and not buried in the general housekeeping budgets of the various hospitals.

In an interim report on state legislative action through May, 1955, Sidney Spector wrote:

"What have been the results of all these meetings and interest? Partially, as a direct consequence, training of personnel and research into the causes and prevention of mental illness have been emphasized in state legislatures this year more than ever before. For example, Governor Williams in Michigan recommended that $4,500,000, or about 9 per cent of the total mental health budget, be devoted to training and research. This amount becomes really significant when you consider that it almost equals the total amount that all states were spending for research just two years ago. In Indiana, $200,000 was appropriated as a basis for a $1,000,000 psychiatric research foundation to be supported by private as well as public funds. In Illinois, the Mental Health Fund, comprised of patient fees, has accumulated around $9,000,000 for research and training, $5,000,000 of which has been appropriated for a psychiatric institute to conduct research and to train a greatly expanded number of psychiatric residents. Other states, such as Minnesota, Wisconsin, Nebraska, California and many others I could cite, have expanded their research budgets in amounts ranging from $100,000 to $500,000. Some states have made special provisions for research this year for the first time."

And as to appropriations for the operations of mental hospitals and clinics, Spector summarized:

". . . Budget recommendations in nearly every state call for increased mental health appropriations over the previous fiscal period, mainly for personnel reasons. According to a very rough survey of proposed budgets in twenty-two states, the average increase recommended was around 10 per cent, going up to almost 30 per cent—and practically all for increased numbers of personnel. . . .

"These figures mean, for example, that in Indiana operating expenditures for mental hospitals rose from $34,500,000 to $46,000,000. Funds for clinics went up from approximately $70,000 to $290,000. A new family care program was instituted with an appropriation of $100,000, and the daily per capita expenditure in six psychiatric institutions will be $3.35 in fiscal 1956, and $3.87 in fiscal 1957. Compare this with $1.97 in Indiana institutions in 1953.

"Similarly, in the State of Washington operating funds for mental hospitals have risen from $13,357,000 for the biennium 1953–55 to $17,477,000 for the next biennium. In Tennessee, appropriations went up from $7,290,000 in 1953–55 to $9,350,000 for the next biennium, plus capital outlays of $10,000,000.

"In Kansas, $750,000 was reappropriated for the mental hospital training fund for fiscal 1956. It will be used to pay extra staff necessary to maintain training programs in five mental institutions and to pay the salaries and wages of employees while in training. In addition, $500,000 was appropriated as a 'salaries and wages contingent fund' which is a new approach, at least in Kansas, to budgeting for personnel. This $500,000 will be available to pay for staff which cannot be secured at present but may become available later. . . . . In 1954, per capita cost in Kansas was $4.30 a day; their estimates for fiscal 1955 are $4.57 and for 1956, $4.66. This compares with an average for the nation in 1953 of $2.70.

"In Nebraska, both the outgoing and incoming Governors recommended approximately a 20 per cent increase for the state hospital and an earmarked fund of $150,000 for the Psychiatric Institute, as well as $125,000 for community services. . . .

"In Texas, the legislative budget called for expenditures of $53,-400,000. This is contrasted to the approximately $40,000,000 appropriated for the present biennium and does not include a $5,000,000 appropriation for capital outlay, to come out of a special cigarette tax. There also is a recommendation for a $600,000 appropriation for a mental health research institute to be established in the Texas Medical Center in Houston. . . ."

And so it goes—in almost every state across the land. There are some who say, with considerable documentation from the unhappy past, that this is just another "boom" phase in the up-and-down cycle of mental health reform in this country. I say to them that they haven't examined the present movement very carefully. This current push is no one-time play upon the emotions. It is calculatedly directed toward committing Governors, budget directors, and legislators to the principle of line-item budget support for specific research and training activities. And it has paid off in deep-seated changes in the whole state governmental handling of the problem.

RESEARCH PROGRESS AGAINST THE MAJOR MENTAL ILLNESSES

14. SCHIZOPHRENIA

IN TERMS of human suffering, economic wastage, duration of the illness, downright complexity, and all-around bafflement, schizophrenia is the greatest scourge ever visited upon the mind of man.

Statistics only begin to tell the story of its frightful impact. Of the more than 600,000 hospital beds in this country occupied by the mentally ill, over 300,000 are devoted to one terrible disease: schizophrenia. The average stay of a schizophrenic in a state mental hospital is estimated at about fifteen years. Most telling of all is the vicious ability of schizophrenia to cut down the young in the prime of life. First known as "dementia praecox"—a disease of adolescence or youth—it unleashes its greatest ravages in the 15-to-54-year age group. Compare it with cancer, long regarded the deadliest of diseases. Approximately 27 per cent of male new cancer cases are in the 15-54 year group, but more than 75 per cent of schizophrenics fall in this age group.

Dr. Benjamin Malzberg of the New York State Department of Mental Hygiene has done some studies on the economic toll exacted by schizophrenia. Presenting statistics which show an average loss of sixteen working years for schizophrenics admitted to New York State mental hospitals, Malzberg estimates that the 2,427 schizophrenics admitted to these hospitals in the fiscal year ending March, 1948, lost more than $50,000,000 in net future earnings.

"Schizophrenia is undoubtedly the major clinical and theoretical problem confronting psychiatry today," writes Dr. Robert P. Knight of the Austen Riggs Foundation. "Its incidence is the highest—approximately one-half—of all psychiatric disorders among hospital-

ized patients. . . . The problem of numbers does not end with the
hospitals but spills over into many aspects of non-hospital life. Many
undoubtedly schizophrenic individuals are unhospitalized, or
ambulatory, and pursue their bizarre ways without the dubious
benefit of psychiatric diagnosis. Many others become identified as
schizophrenic only after they have exhibited explosive, destructive
behavior which has gotten them into the toils of the law. Still others,
in unknown numbers, are being carried as outpatients by psychiatrists in clinic and office practice."

What Is Schizophrenia?

Amid the welter of disagreements as to what schizophrenia is, and
what its causes are, there is a generalized consensus that it involves
a breakdown of personality integration and a resultant loosening of
acquired thought and behavior ties with reality. Certain psychological
tests—Rorschach, Word Association, Thematic Apperception—re-
veal this loosening of associations with the external environment.

In recent years, many psychiatrists have tended to follow Eugen
Bleuler's lead in differentiating two types of schizophrenia—primary and secondary. According to this schemata, those aberrations
we identify most readily as schizophrenic—hallucinations, delusions,
generally regressive behavior—are a secondary overlay of a much
more basic and earlier disintegration of the ego function. The
organicists, who also describe the primary type of schizophrenia as
"nuclear," contend that the disorder must be traced back to fundamental physiological failures at birth and in very early childhood.

There are theoretical concepts galore, but no definitive data to
buttress these imaginative speculations. We don't have even the most
rudimentary knowledge of the origin and development of schizophrenia in the human mind and body. As Dr. Frederick C. Redlich
puts it in *Psychotherapy with Schizophrenics:*

"We do not know whether schizophrenia is an organic illness of
unknown etiology or a behavioral maladjustment brought on by ad-
verse events in the life history of the individual, as we assume it in
the psychoneuroses. Possibly both assumptions and any combinations
of such assumptions may prove to be correct. We do not even know
whether we are justified in assuming one disorder, as the diagnostic
term implies, or whether there are many different reaction types

and processes conveniently grouped under the term schizophrenia or dementia praecox."

The Treatment of Schizophrenia

Despite our lack of fundamental knowledge, we must treat illness empirically. In organic medicine, we treat diabetes, cancer, high blood pressure empirically; without precise knowledge of the cause of the disease, we can still reduce its ravages and keep the patient functioning.

"The many enthusiastic, frequently uncritical, attempts at treating schizophrenia represent in part a response to the challenge of the unknown," writes Dr. Eugene B. Brody. "They are probably also to a significant degree a function of the tremendous social and economic pressures under which we labor. . . . In spite of this urgency, the fact remains that there is still no generally effective, definite single therapy of schizophrenia."

Psychotherapy with Schizophrenics

Psychotherapy uses psychological methods—suggestion, persuasion, psychoanalysis, re-education—in an attempt to bring the schizophrenic back to reality.

Many of the ardent disciples of Sigmund Freud have ignored the warnings of the Master as to the inadequacy of psychoanalysis in treating schizophrenia. On a number of occasions, Freud took pains to state his belief that analysis did not generate sufficient quantities of energy to produce profound behavioral changes. In a conversation with the Minister of Culture of Prussia in 1927, Freud expressed the hope that future advances in endocrinology would supply the powerful energies needed, and that then psychotherapy might serve as an auxiliary handmaiden to this newly developed science.

The psychiatric journals are loaded down each year with scores of papers by analysts telling of their success in treating schizophrenia. That they are not "scientific" papers puts the criticism rather gently. Adequate controls have not been set up, physiological data is sparse, and the "proof" of the author's hypothesis is frequently one case told in laborious, jargon-ridden English. At the annual conventions of the American Psychoanalytical Association, papers running up to forty pages in length describe a "new" theory of schizophrenia and then prove it with one case. While this revolutionary approach is being described, there is usually a great hubbub in the hall—all the other analysts are either grunting and groaning their disapproval or verbalizing their own "revolutionary" theories of schizophrenia.

It is impossible to summarize the vast analytic literature on schizophrenia in such a limited space. I have been trying valiantly to follow the bends, twists, and turns of the various schools for the past ten years, and I confess an inability to bring coherence out of the semantic and doctrinaire chaos. There are elaborate theories of the analytic personality required to treat schizophrenia successfully: it should be passive, not attempting to threaten the defenses of the schizophrenic, or it should be active and direct (Dr. John Rosen), setting up a close, empathetic identification with the schizophrenic. In furthering identification one should use the dream language of the patient, or one should exchange grunts with the patient (Tidd).

Dr. Gregory Zilboorg warns of the dangers of rational interpretations to schizophrenic patients, while some of his colleagues persist in arguing that the adult aspects of the schizophrenic must be appealed to.

Despite all the frenzied theorizing and all the hostile froth whipped up every time two schools of psychoanalytic love congregate in the same room, few would be prepared to dispute Redlich's conclusion that "actually only a very small fraction of schizophrenic patients are treated adequately by psychoanalytic therapy at present."

However, one must pay tribute to a small band of dedicated souls who have devoted years of heart-rending effort in an attempt to penetrate the schizophrenic's defenses and bring him back to an adjustment with reality.

Dr. Frieda Fromm-Reichmann and her co-workers at the Chestnut Lodge Sanitarium in Rockville, Maryland, have done intensive work with hospitalized schizophrenics. Dr. Fromm-Reichmann's theories of the basic make-up of the schizophrenic have undergone major alterations over a period of several decades. In a beautifully reasoned paper given at the 1954 convention of the American Psychiatric Association, she stressed the meaningfulness of schizophrenic symptoms as a point of departure for active therapeutic collaboration between the patient and the psychiatrist. This is in contrast to her earlier views that caution and permissiveness on the part of the therapist were paramount in the handling of the schizophrenic.

Gertrud Schwing, a Swiss analyst who worked for years as a psychiatric nurse, is widely known for her dedicated work with schizophrenics. No one can read her *A Way to the Soul of the Mentally Ill* and not develop a great respect for her devotion. She emphasizes the approach of motherliness—the unselfish giving of oneself to the patient. She stresses the importance of bridging the schizophrenic's unbearable loneliness through a meeting of the therapist's unconscious and the patient's unconscious.

However, these and other attempts to lower the barrier between the schizophrenic and reality are highly personalized efforts; they cannot be duplicated on a wide scale. Mrs. Schwing admits that her patients relapsed after her departure from the hospital. Dedication is a magnificent thing, but it cannot substitute for scientific knowledge in treating a malady as universal as schizophrenia.

Physical Treatment of Schizophrenia

In the last fifteen years, several kinds of shock treatment have been given to schizophrenics. These treatments induce varying lengths of coma (with or without convulsions) by the introduction of certain drugs (insulin, metrazol) or by electrical stimulation applied to the brain through plates attached to the forehead.

Insulin shock, the first of the shock treatments to be widely used, had all sorts of extravagant claims made for it during the late thirties and early forties. However, increasing evidence has borne out the contention that it fails to sustain recoveries in a great majority of cases. The initial improvement is frequently considerable; after a series of insulin treatments, the patient will frequently abandon regressive patterns of behavior and move dramatically back toward reality. However, over a period of time, the improvement does not hold up in most cases.

Again we are plagued with a lack of scientific effort in evaluating therapy. Claims and counterclaims flood the literature, but they are not of much more value than testimonials for a favorite breakfast cereal. High recovery rates are claimed for standard, full-coma insulin shock or for subcoma shock; arguments rage as to the number of shock treatments to be given, and whether they are to be given daily, or weekly, or what.

In reviewing some of these puffed-up claims in *The American Journal of Psychiatry* Drs. D. M. Palmer and T. Riepenhoff wrote: "Insulin shock treatment is certainly not sufficient as a sole form of treatment in schizophrenia. It may have more value when used as a preliminary approach to psychotherapy or milieu therapy. On the other hand, the low social recovery rate after 40 months (average) of evaluation is discouraging."

The picture with regard to electroshock is pretty much the same. There is general agreement that electroshock reduces tension in some patients, making them more amenable and co-operative. The Committee on Therapy of the Group for the Advancement of Psychiatry, in a special report on electroshock, concluded that it was effective only in cases where the initial prognosis for recovery was good.

A not very well documented debate has raged over the past few years as to whether insulin or electroshock is the more effective in treating schizophrenia. While the general belief is that insulin shock is more effective, J. K. Morrow and J. P. King, in a limited follow-up study of shock-treated patients, found very little difference between the two. Not one whit daunted, partisans of the various treatments flood the technical journals with graph-laden papers "proving" their particular technique to be the best. Dr. Eugene Brody sums up the futility of the debate in these words:

"In spite of the fact that it is becoming increasingly evident that the schizophrenic patients who respond to electroshock (as well as to insulin) are predominantly those exhibiting favorable prognostic indications, controversy continues regarding technique, frequency, number of shocks, and the actual character of the electrical impulse that is used."

Parenthetically, the evaluations of the new drugs are geared to avoid these pitfalls. As Dr. Henry Brill of New York State noted in his testimony before the U.S. Senate, rigid controls and wide sampling were continually neglected in evaluating the shock treatments. As pointed out in previous sections of this book, drug evaluation projects have already covered thousands of patients and, in many of the major studies, have used the latest experimental control designs. Furthermore, the drugs have been used on the toughest, most regressed patients in an honest effort to put them to the acid test. Finally, the top Canadian and American researchers have been exceedingly careful in making no claims about the permanence of the effects produced by the drugs. On the contrary, they have constantly emphasized the point that they are only at the beginning of the chemotherapeutic era and that much more research and experimentation are desperately needed.

Psychosurgery

Psychosurgery is brain surgery performed for the relief of severe mental symptoms. Prefrontal lobotomy, the first and most drastic of the surgical procedures, cut the white nerve fibers connecting the frontal lobe of the brain with the thalamus. It was a rather crude operation. A hole was drilled in the skull and a leucotome (tube) through which a wire was passed cut the nerve fibers. Since the operator was forced to manipulate the tube blindly, frequently much more cortical tissue was cut out than necessary.

Starting in 1947, prefrontal lobotomy has been increasingly supplanted by topectomy, an operation developed by the Columbia-Greystone group. In this much more precise operation, the approach is from above the cortex—the brain surface is exposed and certain prefrontal areas are removed.

These psychosurgical procedures have a common rationale. In mental illness, it is thought the balance between the prefrontal cerebral cortex, controlling ideas, and the thalamus, controlling emotions, is upset. If the fibers connecting the thalamus with the prefrontal cortex are cut, the thalamus can no longer charge a patient's ideas with symptom-producing emotions.

Since the inception of these operations, the invective has flown high, wide, and handsome among the pro and the anti groups. In an effort to clear the air, the National Mental Health Institute sponsored three annual research conferences on psychosurgery. A careful reading of the proceedings of these conferences is *not* conducive to improving one's mental health. True, the experts assembled at the three enormously long gabfests do make feeble attempts to conceal the full force of the invective, but there are a surprising number of minor Civil Wars throughout the proceedings.

The consensus seems to be that psychosurgery makes patients more socially acceptable; it reduces anxiety and painful discomfort from past emotions and associations. It does not seem to reduce the intellectual ability of the patients. However, its critics argue that it brings about a general depersonalization—a loss of the capacity to feel.

New Research Leads Against Schizophrenia

When one turns to the more recent research projects upon schizophrenia, most of them concentrated within the past five years, the picture brightens considerably. There is a determination on the part of most of the investigators to renounce the inflated claims of the past and to set up scientifically controlled experiments to test their hypotheses. A sizable portion of the projects are attempts to trace the organic changes produced by schizophrenia. Despite the difficulty of these endeavors, there is an air of optimism about this new crop of investigators—a refreshing contrast to the pessimism prevalent a few years back whenever anyone suggested the possibility of developing a rational treatment for schizophrenia based upon known cause and predicted effect.

In 1953, for example, the National Institute of Mental Health awarded thirty-five separate research grants for projects on schizophrenia. Causes, diagnosis, and treatment are being investigated by psychiatrists, psychologists, pharmacologists, biochemists, neurophysiologists, and others. The studies are being done at the Institute's Clinical Center in Bethesda, Maryland, and at state hospitals, clinics, universities, and other research centers throughout the country.

One of the most interesting lines of research endeavor is the experimental reproduction of a schizophrenic-like state in normal persons through the use of various drugs. The very fact that drugs can produce such a state in mentally healthy personalities is a strong argument for some chemical causative factor in schizophrenia.

Earlier experiments on the induction of psychosis used the drug mescaline, a derivative of a Mexican cactus commonly known as peyote. Normal persons given mescaline reported depersonalization experiences similar to those reported by schizophrenics—feelings that the intellect was functioning separately from the emotions, hallucinations, incoherence, speech disorders, etc. Given to schizophrenics, mescaline heightened and exaggerated their symptoms. However, mescaline had to be given in huge doses to alter the conscious mind, and it was unsatisfactory for many experimental purposes.

Within the past few years, a new drug, lysergic acid, diethylamide-25 (LSD), has proved much more satisfactory. It is effective in as small dosages as one half-millionth of a gram per kilogram of body weight. It is tasteless and, mixed with water, is easily taken by mouth.

Several research projects involving the use of LSD are in operation at the present time. At the National Institute of Mental Health, Drs. Charles Savage and Edward Evarts are studying, under controlled conditions, the chemical changes produced in the healthy body by the administration of LSD. Also at Bethesda, Dr. Louis Cholden is experimenting with administration of LSD to chronic deteriorated schizophrenics.

The most intensive work on lysergic acid is being done at the Boston Psychopathic Hospital. Since 1949, staff workers have taken the drug themselves and have administered it to more than one hundred normal volunteers. Psychiatrists have made careful observations of their own experiences and feelings after taking the drug. The data they have gathered is invaluable in enabling them to see the schizophrenic patient as he sees himself, particularly since the patient is rarely able to communicate his inner experiences and feelings.

In a summary report to the 1954 convention of the American Psychiatric Association, Dr. Max Rinkel of the Boston group had this to say about the group's theory of schizophrenia:

"Our intensive studies of the LSD effect, which comprised clinical and sociological psychiatric observations, psychological tests, physiological examinations of the nervous system, and biochemical investigations, have resulted in reflections on a new chemical theory of mental illness. According to this theory, one of the important factors in the causation of mental illness seems to be a chemical which originates in the human body itself. This chemical may be 'adrenoxine,' an intermediary product in the decomposition of adrenalin. We do not know why this chemical is not metabolized in the natural course of the adrenalin cycle. One could speculate that inborn factors are operative, as in diabetes (in which sugar is not completely metabolized), or that stress situations have an influence.

"Our studies have placed mental illness again in the realm of the diseases of disturbed chemical metabolism," Dr. Rinkel concluded. "More studies will help further to pinpoint the noxious agent, until its final discovery will lead to the development of the successful pharmacological prevention and treatment of mankind's greatest plague, insanity."

Before this final discovery, however, much more basic research work must be done. At the Milbank Conference on the Biology of Mental Health and Disease, Dr. Paul Hoch of the New York Psychiatric Institute, who has done considerable work in the experimental induction of psychoses, pointed out that "comparative drug studies in untreated and treated patients will have to be extensively undertaken in order to assess the different treatment methods used in psychiatry today in relationship to the alterations they produce." Dr. Harry C. Solomon, Medical Director of Boston Psychopathic, called for "the collaboration of our chemical associates in order to show whether certain syndromes which result from the use of a drug are characteristic of changes in the enzyme (organic compound) systems that are produced by that particular drug." In a subsequent chapter, studies of changes in the enzyme system will be discussed.

A number of additional research projects are being conducted along biochemical lines. Drs. Norman P. Goldstein and Marian Kies have reported on experiments at the National Institute of Mental Health which indicate an increase in the antidiuretic (urine-checking) substance of the blood in response to harmful stimuli. This is being tested with normal and schizophrenic individuals. The investigators feel that the antidiuretic hormone may be an important link in the organism's response to stress.

At the Einstein Medical Center in Philadelphia, Drs. William Sacks and Henry A. Shenkin are investigating one of the most important enzyme systems in the brain, the tricarboxylic acid cycle, in an effort to determine whether disturbances in brain metabolism are related to schizophrenia.

Several studies are concentrating on the adrenal glands (situated near the kidneys). At the University of Utah, Drs. C. H. Hardin Branch and Leo T. Samuels are studying the effects of stress and electroconvulsive therapy on the activity of the adrenal cortex (outer wall of the gland). At the Worcester Foundation for Experimental Biology, Dr. Hudson Hoagland and his associates have developed new chemical procedures to isolate and separate nearly fifty hormones produced by the adrenal gland and to analyze for quantities as small as one microgram (1/30,000,000 of an ounce).

Dr. Carl Pfeiffer of the University of Illinois College of Medicine is studying the possible occurrence of convulsive metabolic products which are of causative significance in epilepsy. If identified, their convulsive properties might also prove useful in the treatment of schizophrenic patients.

Along psychological lines, there are a number of significant experiments being carried out. At Duke University, Dr. Eliot Rodnick and his associates are studying the relation between motivation and the withdrawal behavior characteristic of schizophrenia in an effort to find out how schizophrenic disturbances in thought behavior develop.

Dr. Joseph Zubin of the New York Psychiatric Institute is testing the relation between perception and the ability to think abstractly. He is attempting to relate this knowledge to the development of a technique for determining whether a schizophrenic patient is likely to improve under psychiatric therapy.

At the National Institute of Mental Health, Drs. Juliana Day and Irving M. Ryckoff are studying both acutely ill schizophrenic adolescents and their mothers, gathering pertinent data regarding onset of the illness and the nature of the significant relationships within which specific symptoms appeared. The adolescents are hospitalized and the mothers are seen as outpatients.

The role of psychologically traumatic events in the causation of childhood schizophrenia is being investigated through careful studies of child-parent and family relationships at the James Jackson Putnam Children's Center in Boston.

Dr. Theodore Lidz of the Yale University School of Medicine is studying the family environment of adult schizophrenics in an attempt to correlate patterns of development, personality, and pathological reactions.

A Multidisciplinary Attack upon Schizophrenia

Down at Tulane University in New Orleans, Dr. Robert G. Heath has launched a massive research project built around a new theory of schizophrenia. His six-hundred-page book, *Studies in Schizophrenia,* is a painstaking report on one of the most courageous and promising endeavors in the annals of modern psychiatry.

At the root of all Heath's work is a clear-cut operational concept of schizophrenia. Along with Eugen Bleuler, Heath argues that the attack must be made on *basic* schizophrenia, which underlies all the later secondary symptoms which Kraepelin first described as "dementia praecox."

"As a result of experience in psychoanalysis and in intensive psychiatric observation and treatment, more persons are tending to accept Bleuler's concept that a primary disease process is present long before the Kraepelinian symptoms of dementia praecox appear," Heath writes. "Several investigators are attempting to learn more about the nature of this basic disease process. Clinical observations, as well as increasing experience with unhospitalized patients, have made it quite apparent that disordered behavior begins very early—in fact, as far back as observations are valid. It is assumed by many that the disease process is either present at birth or results from early environmental trauma."

This disease process is manifested in basic deficiencies in the ability to feel (emotions) from early infancy. This results in maladaptation—in the inability of the organism to handle stressful experiences. Heath agrees with Cannon and Selye in relating this maladaptation, in part, to failure of the key glands to perform adequately under situations of severe stress.

But Heath goes a step further. His experiments have led him to the belief that there are certain nerve pathways to and from the brain which play a key role in the individual's adaptation to stress.

Behavior is basically motor activity, he contends, and the motor responses reflect profound alterations in mental activity. In tests of simple motor acts, the schizophrenic group was found to be markedly slow in performance.

"The points to be stressed here are that the greatest inhibition on motor performance was found among retarded schizophrenic patients," Heath writes in the brilliant introductory chapter of his *Studies in Schizophrenia*. "This is the group which showed chemical evidence of underactivity of the stress mechanism and which, when examined psychiatrically by introspective techniques, also showed a marked disturbance in basic affect [emotion]."

Heath then goes on to conjecture that certain of these nerve pathways facilitate mental and bodily processes (facilitatory circuits) while other pathways suppress activity (inhibitory circuits).

To test his theory, Heath assembled a remarkable interdisciplinary team of psychiatrists, psychologists, neurologists, biochemists, neurosurgeons, electronic engineers, photographers, etc. A number of the team, including Heath, were veterans of the Columbia-Greystone psychosurgery projects. The assembling of such a magnificent group is a rarity in modern psychiatric research—most of it is done with spit, polish, and glue.

The first experiments were conducted on animals. Into the brains of these animals were inserted fine electrodes that made possible the recording of electrical impulses from selected areas of the brain. The findings bore out the theory of facilitatory and inhibitory circuits. When stimulation was applied to the region associated with facilitatory nerve pathways, the animals became very alert and active. When applied to the region associated with inhibitory circuits, the animals became sleepy. Important biochemical patterns were also observed with changes in stimulation.

The experiments were then extended to hospital patients. The group consisted of twenty deteriorated schizophrenics, all but one of whom had received extensive shock and other treatments during their long periods of hospitalization. Electrodes, which could be removed at any time, were implanted in deep areas of the brain. The patients were then given a mild electrical stimulation (producing no convulsions as in the cruder electroshock). In experiments preliminary to administration of the mild stimulation, investigators noted in the schizophrenic patients a physiological abnormality which manifested itself in unusual intensity and duration (spiking) of the brain waves from a key region in the facilitatory circuit.

Under stimulation, many of the patients who had been stuporous and mute showed dramatic changes in emotional responsiveness. A number exhibited anger and rage, verbalizing hostilities which had been bottled up within them for long periods of time. Dr. Heath has recorded a number of these remarkable changes on films made before and after electrical stimulation of patients. No one who has seen these films can fail to be impressed with this evidence of the importance of basic nerve pathways in influencing emotional responsivity.

Of the nineteen patients remaining in the group after one death —in no way related to the experimental procedures—ten were able to leave the hospital. While this is a remarkable showing, especially in view of the fact that the prognosis for all of them was exceedingly poor, Dr. Heath cautions that there must be many more tests and follow-ups before any major therapeutic claims can be made.

At a symposium on the experimental work of Heath and the Tulane group held at New Orleans in June, 1952, many of the country's leading psychiatrists, neurologists, and anatomists gathered together to evaluate the early findings. Dr. Heath discussed with them the need for improved techniques of implanting electrodes accurately and described his recent use of a mechanical means (stereotaxic apparatus) to increase the possibility of precise implantation.

There was general agreement among the scientists attending the New Orleans Symposium that Heath's experiments were enormously significant in forwarding knowledge of the basic organic maladaptations present in schizophrenia. Dr. Herbert S. Gaskill, Professor of Psychiatry at the Indiana University School of Medicine, summed up the feeling in these words:

"Dr. Heath and his associates have presented a new therapeutic approach to the treatment of schizophrenia. . . . The clinical aspects of this therapeutic approach are impressive. After having heard a discussion of the clinical results, seen a number of patients in sound film, pre- and post-operatively, and subsequently interviewed a number of these patients themselves, and finally to have participated in an actual operative and stimulation procedure, leaves little doubt in our minds that something fundamental happens to the patient. The withdrawn, affectless individual whose thinking is so autistic and irrational when samples can be obtained, during the process of stimulation shows an immediate and perceptible change in his psychic and somatic responsiveness. This change is so dramatic and real that one is reminded of the fairy story of 'The Sleeping Beauty.' "

And Dr. George C. Ham, Professor of Psychiatry at the University of North Carolina Medical School, pointed up the real importance of the team concept in modern psychiatric research in commenting on the rare qualities of the Tulane study.

"The fact that the concept grew out of the collaboration of many different disciplines and approaches, was developed through animal experimentation and shown to occur in man, was in itself an example of a beautifully conducted piece of scientific reasoning and study," said Dr. Ham.

But we need fifty—nay, a hundred—more team attacks of the Tulane type if we are to pinpoint the cause-and-effect relationships in schizophrenia. If the money is provided, the men will come. All of Heath's work since 1950 has cost only a few hundred thousand dollars, most of it supplied by the Commonwealth Fund. Yet with this small amount of money he has built up a superb investigative team. Right in the Louisiana state hospitals where Heath has done some of his work, the budget for the care of schizophrenics runs to several millions a year, an ever-increasing drain upon the resources of the state.

15. SENILE

DEMENTIA

THE term "senile dementia" is somewhat of a misnomer, since it blankets the mental ills of the elderly into a diagnostic category which supposedly covers behavior ranging all the way from mild deterioration and confusion to severe regressions to infantile behavior. The harshness and finality of such a classification had real meaning several decades ago, when the elderly were consigned to the back wards of our mental hospitals with the fervent hope they would die off quickly and open up additional beds for waiting patients. The picture has changed considerably since then therapeutically, but in size the problem of the elderly mentally ill has assumed alarming proportions.

Today our mental hospitals have more first admissions for senile dementia than for any other single mental illness, including schizophrenia. Twenty-seven per cent of all first admissions to mental hospitals are in this senile group, an increase of more than 25 per cent over the 1940 figure. In the same span of time, the proportion of persons in the age group 65 and over in the general population has increased 17 per cent.

More significant is the increasing length of stay of these patients in our mental hospitals. With the advent of the antibiotics and other drugs, the majority of the elderly ill no longer die off in the first year of hospitalization. With the decrease in mortality, the average stay of the senile is now about two and a half years, and it will continue to rise as new medical advances are made.

As the problem grows, an increasing number of investigators are working their way to the back wards of our mental hospitals to try new treatments designed to get these old people on their feet and, in many cases, out of the hospital.

New Research Projects Against Senile Dementia

At the 1954 convention of the American Psychiatric Association, Dr. Donald F. Moore, Chief of the Neuropsychiatric Service at the Veterans' Administration Hospital in Louisville, reported on a new treatment combining two drugs which were given intravenously for thirty days to elderly patients with cerebral arteriosclerosis. Dr. Moore used both histamine, which expands the capillary vessels and increases gastric secretion, and nicotinic acid, which forms a part of the vitamin B complex and has been used successfully in treating psychosis resulting from malnutrition.

The majority of the eighty patients showed marked improvement after administration of the combination of drugs. They became more alert, showed more interest in their surroundings, and developed a greater degree of self-confidence. One year or more after the last injection, sixty-five of the eighty patients left the hospital and returned to their homes. Of these sixty-five, twenty-four are back at full-time work and another eighteen are working part-time.

In his paper, Dr. Moore pointed out that group occupational and recreational therapy, individual and group psychotherapy, electro-shock treatment and intensive case work with families were used in the program whenever needed.

In commenting on the work at the Louisville Hospital, Dr. Moore gave voice to the new optimism which now motivates research upon senile dementia.

"In general, the investigators (at Louisville) believe that the usual pessimistic attitude towards this illness is unjustified," Dr. Moore told his fellow American Psychiatric Association members. "The main block to effective treatment is still the passive 'do-nothing' attitude of patients, family and physicians. This is augmented by the lack of sharp diagnostic methods for this group and the difficulty in finding physicians adequately trained in multiple skills and having the patience to work with this time-consuming and non-dramatic phase of medicine."

At the Gerontologic Study Center of the Norristown State Hospital in Pennsylvania, Dr. Maurice E. Linden and his colleagues administered metrazol, a powerful stimulant to the brain and the central nervous system, to fifteen patients over a period of a year and a half. The average age of these patients was seventy-six years. A closely matched group of fifteen patients received placebos.

To test the effectiveness of the drug, the research group used a number of observers from various disciplines who were not told which patients were getting the metrazol. The outside group included a psychiatrist, clinical psychologist, research psychologist, statistical analyst, medical internist, laboratory pathologist, electroencephalographer, and psychiatric nurse.

All observers attested to the remarkable improvement brought about by metrazol. Of the fifteen who received it, nine were able to leave the hospital as against only three in the matched group which did not receive it. The drug also produced unexpected improvement in anemic conditions, in the electrical activity of the brain, and in sleep habits.

Dr. Sol Levy, formerly Clinical Director of the Eastern State Hospital at Medical Lake, Washington, has reported great success in treating senile dementia with an elixir combining metrazol and nicotinic acid. In the December 5, 1953, issue of *The Journal of the American Medical Association*, he wrote:

"This combination has proved safe and simple as well as practical and inexpensive, and thus can be used without hesitation on an ambulatory basis. With its use it should be possible to ease the burden of caring for the mildly confused and mildly deteriorated aged patients in public and private psychiatric institutions. Thus a smaller proportion of hospital personnel and budget would be needed for what previously amounted only to custodial care of this group of patients. This saving would eventually enable the mental hospital to return to its primary function, namely, the treatment and rehabilitation of younger mentally ill patients, instead of becoming a purely custodial organization for the aged. . . . Many of these patients, with the aid of this elixir, or possibly similar acting drugs, would therefore not inevitably have to be committed to psychiatric institutions and could be permitted to live in the community with safety and without harm to others."

Dr. Levy has also used coramine, a circulatory stimulant, to bolster elderly patients to the point where they can receive a series of electroshock treatments. In a recent experiment, he used coramine combined with electroshock on fifty aged patients, twenty-five of whom could not have received the shock treatment without coramine to strengthen them. The average hospital stay of these elderly patients was reduced to three weeks, as against eight months for untreated aged patients. The saving to the hospital in this one small experiment is calculated at about $50,000.

An even more extensive use of electroshock on seniles was reported on in the September, 1954, issue of *Mental Hospitals* by Dr. Gunther E. Wolff of Camarillo State Hospital, California. Between August, 1952, and June, 1953, electroshock was given to 154 women aged fifty to ninety.

"These women were among 600 housed in a brand-new wing," Dr. Wolff wrote. "Their behavior was in great contrast to the peaceful, pleasant surroundings of the new facility. They banged doors, screamed, tore up their mattresses and clothing, were untidy and combative. . . . We selected the most disturbed and pitiful cases and requested staff approval for EST."

The results were quite remarkable. Only sixteen cases remained unchanged. Of the remainder, seventeen were released from the hospital; sixty-five, who were rated as "much improved," were able to help with work on the ward or leave the hospital on convalescent status, and the fifty-six who were rated as "improved" were easier to manage and free of combativeness, although in need of further treatment from time to time. Of a total of 3,300 separate shock treatments given these patients, only one resulted in a minor accident.

In summing up the new, optimistic attitude toward the administration of physical treatments to the elderly, Drs. Lothar Kalinowsky and Paul Hoch write in the latest edition of their *Shock Treatments*:

"Our previous impression that EST [electroshock] has no indication where senile changes are the cause of the depressive manifestations must be replaced by the statement that wherever a depressive element is present, EST should be applied. . . . Increasing experience has shown that senile depressions respond especially well to EST."

However, Dr. Levy and many of his colleagues take the position that drug treatments are more effective in milder cases of senile dementia. In those where there is severe organic and intellectual impairment, they stress the need for much additional research.

Much future knowledge of senility will depend upon advances in our understanding of hardening of the arteries. Hardening of the arteries of the brain (cerebral arteriosclerosis) is responsible for thousands of cases of senile dementia.

Dr. Irving Wright of the Cornell University Medical College has experimented with the early use of anticoagulants in patients with cerebral thromboses. Further exploration in the field of anticoagulants is needed to treat and prevent the thromboses which lead to senile dementia.

Dr. T. Duckett Jones, the late Medical Director of the Helen Hay Whitney Foundation, told the 1954 conference of the National Health Council that science is on the threshold of important biological developments that ultimately will reverse the process of hardening of the arteries. Recent discoveries, he pointed out, have made possible reversal of the process that leads to hardening of arteries in animals. When these discoveries are extended to humans, the incidence of senile dementia will be reduced tremendously.

Several investigators have recently pointed out that the process of senescence is accompanied by a progressive decrease in the blood and oxygen supplied and used by the brain. At the National Institute of Mental Health, Dr. Seymour Kety is studying this decline intensively with a view to finding means of preventing it.

Also at the National Institute of Mental Health, Dr. James Birren is working on the decrease in speed of reactions found in the senile. Studies of the peripheral nerves of rats at different ages show little change in conduction velocity in the latter part of the life span, leading Dr. Birren to the belief that the decrease in reactivity in old age must be in the brain itself rather than in the nerves which carry the messages.

These and other physiological investigations offer great promise. All of the newer drugs—Reserpine, Chlorpromazine, Meratran, and Frenquel—have been selectively effective in treating either the agitated or the depressed senile. Apart from their immediate therapeutic effects, they have contributed enormously to the fostering of the principle that these old people are treatable, and that many of them can be returned to useful lives in the community. Dr.

Walter Bruetsch anticipated the potential of the new chemotherapy and the allied sciences in the battle against senile dementia when he uttered these prophetic words in 1950 at the Milbank Conference on the Biology of Mental Health and Disease:

"The problem of the rapidly mounting admission rate of patients with cerebral arteriosclerosis will ultimately be solved by the physician with sound knowledge in the biologic sciences. The 'modern psychiatrist' with his predominant training in dynamic psychology will contribute little if anything to the fundamental issue of this mental disorder."

On the psychological side, a few pioneer studies are producing evidence that many cases of senile dementia are actually depressive reactions on the part of elderly people who suddenly find themselves isolated and without status. Autopsies on individuals who were well adjusted and productive in their old age have revealed brain deterioration comparable to that found in patients suffering from senile dementia. This indicates that many cases of senile dementia have precipitating social and psychological causes. At a number of mental hospitals, planned programs are being organized to reawaken an interest in life among the senile.

At an excellent symposium, "Constructive Medicine in Aging," held in December, 1954, in Cincinnati, several of the participants pointed up the importance of psychological factors in predisposing the individual to premature aging and senile behavior.

"Longevity is with us, but not with full health and continued accomplishment," famed gerontologist Dr. Edward J. Stieglitz noted. "Sacrifice of depth and breadth for length is not profitable. Mere duration is not enough. What is most significant is the character of living. Our task in applying constructive medicine to adults is to build greater health, both mental and physical, adding to depth and breadth as well as length to life and thus to the accomplishments of humanity. We no longer have the choice of dying young or living into ripe old age. In the past only the toughest and most fit survived, but today the young often survive into old age full of disabilities, handicapped and a liability to the community. With constructive medicine, we can hope to help many grow into old age with continued usefulness. The potential rewards are immense."

In discussing the psychological stresses of middle life and old age, Dr. Lloyd J. Thompson of Bowman Gray School of Medicine pleaded for a new medical attitude oriented toward preparing older people for effective handling of manageable physical and emotional problems.

"Going beyond the individual man or woman, we find that society in general fosters a rather dismal outlook for the middle-aged person and thereby increases his stress," Dr. Thompson told his colleagues. "Studies have been made by Landis, Tuckerman and Feifel that bear out this statement. Feifel says there is little doubt concerning the need for an educational program to train people for adjustment to old age. This program should have the broad aim of anticipating and preventing the anxieties and maladjustments attendant on growing old."

16. MENTAL

DEFICIENCY

THERE are 113,000 patients in our tax-supported institutions for the mentally defective, most of them doomed to a lifetime walled off from society. Of these 113,000 unfortunates, 65 per cent are twenty years of age or older. In a recent survey of the patient population of one large state institution, it was disclosed that one in every four of the patients had been in the institution for forty years or more!

Custody of these mental deficients costs the state governments scores of millions of dollars each year. Yet research to find the organic causes and develop preventive measures for the various kinds of mental deficiency is disgracefully inadequate. There are only a handful of scientific investigators devoting themselves to research upon this entity of disease which brings untold suffering to the parents and families of those afflicted.

A careful reading of the scientific literature on mental deficiency is an irritating, disillusioning experience. Although many kinds of mental deficiency were described a century and more ago, there is still only the most rudimentary knowledge of the growth of the disease processes.

For example, Mongolism is a mental deficiency which is familiar to a large segment of the public. Its features are distinguishable and unmistakable: flattened skull, oblique eye-slit, shortness of the thumbs and little fingers, and a tendency toward obesity. It was described as a clinical syndrome in 1865 by Langdon Downe, and science has come a long way since the early supposition that this disease was racial evidence of the Mongol in our family tree.

Yet what do we know about Mongolism today beyond the fact that several thousand Mongoloids are born each year to normal, average families which expect a normal child?

In a discussion at the 1953 convention of the American Psychiatric Association, Drs. Clemens E. Benda and Malcolm J. Farrell of the Walter E. Fernald State School, Waverley, Massachusetts. had this comment to make on our present knowledge of Mongolism:

"Anyone familiar with the condition of Mongolism can only wonder that it is so difficult to establish more definite physiological data in a condition that is so strikingly different from the normal, and which can be so easily diagnosed even by physicians and laymen who have little experience otherwise. A child who is not only mentally defective but is so obviously dwarfed in its physical development, with nutritional difficulties in infancy, inclination to obesity, and anomalies in practically every system, should offer more striking biochemical anomalies and yet all research has not yet been able to discover one single persistent metabolic anomaly which could be found in every case."

In the past few years, a few investigators have taken the first steps toward bringing Mongolism out of the Dark Ages. In his excellent monograph, "Mongolism and Cretinism," Benda pointed out there was little evidence indicating a hereditary origin for Mongolism; in one of his studies, he found that only two out of 255 families with one Mongoloid child had a second. At the 1950 Milbank symposium, Benda stated his belief that Mongolism is a nutritional deficiency of the embryo acquired during the sixth to twelfth weeks of fetal development. Among abnormal factors present in mothers of Mongoloid children, he cited frequent bleeding in the first three months of pregnancy, continuation of menstruation, increased occurrence of abortion in other pregnancies, inability to carry a child through pregnancy, and abnormal hormonal regulation of the fetal environment.

Dr. Theodore H. Ingalls of the Harvard School of Public Health, in essential agreement with Benda on the basis of a number of his own studies, describes the causation of Mongolism in these terms:

"The fetus has been blighted by what might be called intrauterine drought. The term has the desired connotation that the process is temporary. However, drought has to do with dryness or water lack, while the analogy sought is a metabolic drought, a biochemical upset, transient vitamin or enzyme deficiency, or oxygen lack. This broad concept is suggested by the demonstrable association between Mongolism and intercurrent infections and vaginal hemorrhage of the mother during the first trimester of pregnancy."

More recently, Dr. J. W. Gofman and his colleagues from the University of California have reported on experiments which show a greater number of large-molecule lipoproteins (combinations of lipids and proteins) in Mongoloids as contrasted with both other mental defectives and normals. Dr. Gofman's findings take on added significance in view of the fact that he and his co-workers have shown previously that a similar elevation of lipoprotein molecules is found in arteriosclerotic patients.

Dr. George A. Jervis of Letchworth Village, New York, has commented in a number of his studies on abnormal biochemical functionings associated with various types of mental deficiency. He has broken these down into three large groupings: (1) types associated with disorders of the lipid metabolism; (2) types associated with abnormal metabolism of amino acids (essential in human nutrition); and (3) types associated with aberrant metabolism of carbohydrates. Dr. Jervis' classification portrays the need for literally hundreds of studies to isolate the metabolic changes occurring in the various mental deficiencies.

Some progress has been made in tracking down the prime causes of a few kinds of mental deficiency. Through the work of the Australian physician Dr. N. M. Gregg, it has been demonstrated that some cases of mental deficiency develop in the fetal stage if the mother contracts German measles during the first three months of pregnancy. Gregg's initial findings were corroborated by epidemiological observations during a 1940 epidemic of German measles in Australia.

It has also been discovered that some mental deficiencies are caused by incompatible Rh factors in the blood of the mother and infant. These can be prevented by total blood transfusions of the newborn.

Dr. Asbjörn Fölling, a Norwegian physiologist, discovered phenylpyruvic oligophrenia, a form of mental deficiency caused by a defect in the metabolism of phenylalanine, an essential amino acid. The disease is characterized by inborn mental defect, sometimes complicated by epileptic attacks and psychotic episodes. Several American investigators are working on synthetic diets in an attempt to counteract the failure of the amino acid to be properly absorbed by the organism.

In a lead editorial, "Amino Acid Metabolism and Mental Deficiency," in the May 14, 1955, issue of *The Journal of the American Medical Association,* a discussion of the work of British investigators experimenting with special diets to correct faulty amino acid metabolism in mental deficients concludes with a plea for prompt diagnosis leading to possible amelioration:

" . . . If the mental status of these persons can be improved by biochemical means, it is highly desirable to diagnose the conditions early before irreversible deterioration has set in. Fortunately, a simple urine test for phenylpyruvic acid is available, and it has been suggested that this test be applied to every baby in whom there is any suspicion of mental retardation or, alternately, that it be used routinely on all newborn infants."

Key investigators in the field of mental deficiency have shed the pessimistic attitudes of the past in hunting for the major causes of the various kinds of mental deficiency. They now believe it is just a matter of time before most of them will be traced back to organic failures. They admit to discouragement only when agreeing that these diseases are needlessly cutting down thousands of children each year while we devote a pittance to a research attack upon them. Dr. Robert H. Felix, Director of the National Institute of Mental Health, expressed this feeling to the House Interstate Commerce Committee during its 1953 investigation of the medical research needs of the nation.

"The advances in our ability to deal with mental deficiency have been relatively recent," Dr. Felix told the congressmen, "for it has only been recently that much research attention has been devoted to this problem. Too little research, however, has as yet been concentrated on this area, and more work needs to be encouraged if the few hopeful leads are to be followed up and further developed."

In the nonorganic field, Dr. Felix told the Congressional Committee of recent studies which have demonstrated that if adequate educational, social, and vocational services are available, a great number of those whose mental deficiency or retardation is mild are able to find work and keep their jobs successfully, without the necessity of prolonged residential institutional care.

Rehabilitation of the mentally retarded is being explored in two special studies. At the University of Illinois, Dr. Samuel Kirk is attempting to determine whether a special preschool educational program will prove effective in speeding up the mental and social adjustment of young mentally retarded children. At Vanderbilt University, Dr. George Coppel is attempting to find out whether the IQ's of mentally retarded children can be raised by means of special therapy and instruction programs. This study is also investigating what factors of intellect and personality determine whether children can profit from such special programs.

In one of the most significant steps taken at the state level, the 1954 New York legislature appropriated $50,000 to set up twelve experimental classes for the education and training of severely retarded children. Half of the appropriation is being used to finance a research team which will evaluate the results for the State Mental Health Commission.

However, general dissatisfaction with the amount of research upon mental deficiency reached the explosive point during the 1955 session of Congress. The fur began to fly in February when Representative John E. Fogarty of Rhode Island, powerful Chairman of the House Appropriations Subcommittee which handles health matters, put Dr. Felix on the grill in the following colloquy during an official hearing.

MR. FOGARTY: Now, Doctor, what are you doing in the field of retarded children, or exceptional children?

DR. FELIX: I wish I could say we are doing more than we are, Mr. Chairman. At the present time we are working in this field to the extent of about $155,000 a year. We have about $120,000 or $121,000 a year in research grants in this field on various aspects of it—learning procedures, chemical causes, organic studies and so forth.

MR. FOGARTY: (*Obviously not very impressed*) Will you supply for the record a breakdown of all these grants and show whether they are directly connected with the problem of mentally retarded children or indirectly connected, how much they are and what schools they have been given to?

Dr. Felix listed a magnificent total of seven grants. Only two of the grants exceeded $25,000 and both were in nonphysiological areas.

Chairman Fogarty then continued his sharp line of questioning.

MR. FOGARTY: What else are you doing at the Institute that is directly connected with this problem?

DR. FELIX: We have $24,500 a year for a pilot study at Peabody College, to develop better trained people to work in institutions for mentally retarded individuals, to attempt to rehabilitate these children. As you may or may not be aware, just because a child is retarded doesn't mean he must always be a complete drag on society. Many of them can be rehabilitated to a surprising degree when really skilled people get to work on them, but there are so very few of these. In addition to this, we have one of our scientists who is working full time at present in our own National Institute of Health setup on the retarded child, and I would calculate his salary, plus other expenses, at about $8,500.

MR. FOGARTY: (*Incredulous*) One scientist?

DR. FELIX: One scientist; yes, sir.

Chairman Fogarty did some tall thinking after that testimony. When he brought the health appropriations to the floor of the House of Representatives on March 21, he singled mental deficiency out for major attention in a brilliant speech.

"I became interested in the program," he told his House colleagues, "because of being asked to address the parents of retarded children in my state of Rhode Island last December. It was not until I had accepted that invitation to speak to the parents of these retarded children that I really knew of the tremendous problem that exists all over the country in this particular field. As the result of that talk, when we started the hearings in January, I asked many questions of the people in our Department of Health, Education and Welfare, from the Secretary on down. What are we doing for these children? All down the line I found that we were not doing much of anything for these particular children. . . . As the result of the answers that we received and the problem that exists in this area, the committee approved an amount, over and above the budget request, of $750,000 to start a program of research for these children."

Mr. Fogarty then informed his fellow congressmen of what the new money would mean to the program.

"A limited program of research and training related to the prevention and treatment of the mentally retarded is presently being undertaken separately and together by the National Institute of Mental Health and the National Institute of Neurological Diseases and Blindness. It would be a mistake to consider that their efforts represent a full-scale attack on the problem. Yet it is just such an attack which is needed—just such an attack which, considering the facts, has been too long postponed. . . .

"Much more new knowledge is within reach. Mental retardation at birth has been definitely linked in many cases with the fate of the mother and child. Pregnancy and birth records, however, because they are incompletely kept, do not permit analysis of all the factors which might lead to brain damage and mental retardation. The time has certainly come when a study should determine what data is needed concerning the pregnant mother and newborn child, with a view to isolating those as yet unknown factors or characteristics which can lead to mental retardation.

"There are many other studies which should be directed to prevention of mental retardation. What happens to the embryo during pregnancy? How does the brain develop? What causes brain abnormalities? How is the brain nourished? And when it is adversely affected during embryonic growth, can the destructive process be reversed by administration of drugs or other substances? . . .

"It is my hope that the Congress will now make it possible to begin such a program in earnest by increasing appropriations to both these Institutes in the coming fiscal year, emphasizing research for prevention and training for rehabilitation."

The House of Representatives could resist neither the logic nor the eloquence of the gentleman from Rhode Island; it appropriated the full amount of $750,000 requested for special research on mental deficiency. The Senate concurred later in the session, and the money is being expended during the current year.

In addition to the special Congressional allocation, Reserpine and

Chlorpromazine are being tried on mental deficients in a number of state schools. Preliminary reports by investigators in New York, California, and a number of other states indicate that the drugs are of enormous help in making the more regressed mentally retarded patients amenable to rehabilitation. Many of these patients who drained the energies of ward personnel because of their refusal to dress and feed themselves and perform other bodily functions are now co-operating fully and are far more responsive to their environment.

17. ALCOHOLISM

AND DRUG

ADDICTION

Down through the centuries, millions upon millions of alcoholics have staggered their sodden way, tearing up their own lives and those of their families and ripping great holes in the ordered fabric of society.

The problem is still with us, increased in its severity by the tensions of modern life. There are more than one million chronic alcoholics in the United States today, and another three million who are considered problem drinkers, fighting a battle to keep from tippling over.

The general public seldom connects alcoholism and the state mental hospital system, preferring to believe that the troublesome alcoholic is sent off to some nice, quiet rest home where he sleeps off his jag. In actuality, alcoholism with and without accompanying psychosis accounts for more than 12 per cent of first admissions to our mental hospitals—more than fifteen thousand admissions for alcoholism each and every year!

For centuries, too, the alcoholic has rejected the ministrations of his loved ones and shunned the brimstone and hell-fire warnings of the moralists. With the advent of modern psychotherapy, we began to gain insights into the emotional sickness of the alcoholic— his need for alcohol as a means of temporarily stilling his anxieties and fears. However, psychotherapy had little real success with the hardened alcoholic; he was admitted to the hospital, he was "dried out," he had a number of hours of individual therapy, and he went out into the world freshly laundered and shaved. Frequently, a few months later, he was wheeled back into the ward—a sodden, unkempt mass of jangled nerves.

When I first started touring mental hospitals in 1945, I shared the not uncommon illusion that it was a pretty simple matter to "cure" an alcoholic. Several years later, after I had finished inspecting the mental hospitals of a large Western state, the director of one of the finest receiving hospitals west of the Mississippi invited me to his home and, over a couple of glasses of a well-known Scottish beverage, unburdened himself of the essence of more than twenty years' work with alcoholics.

"When I first started out in the practice of psychiatry, I thought alcoholism would be relatively easy to treat," he said a little sadly. "I know better now. The alcoholic is as tough, or tougher than, the schizophrenic. Our hospital has had less success with alcoholism than with any other type of mental illness. We get them out, we think we have them on their feet, and then they bounce back in again and almost break our hearts."

"Why is this so?" I asked him.

"We just don't know enough about the basic metabolic failures that bring on alcoholism," he replied. "Of course we know the alcoholic is unbalanced emotionally, unable to handle his anxieties. But you take Jones and Smith, both of whom have pretty much the same dependent personalities and roughly the same problems, fears, and anxieties. Both resort to alcohol, a depressant which stills the harsh voices of their inner selves. Both take about the same number of drinks. Jones keeps functioning, but Smith becomes an alcoholic. When we get Smith, our job is to strengthen him, make him able to stand up to the same stresses Jones is handling, however imperfectly. But frequently we are unable to—psychotherapy is not enough. We need additional knowledge, physical means of building Smith up so that a couple of light punches won't tip him over."

In the past few years, research investigators have been acquiring, at a really remarkable rate, this knowledge my medical friend needed so badly. So marked and dramatic has been this progress that the November 7, 1953, issue of *The Journal of the American Medical Association* devoted its lead article to "Present-Day Medical Management of Alcoholism," a discussion of the many organic treatments now at the disposal of the general physician in treating the three most common alcoholic states—acute, chronic, and post-alcoholic.

The acute alcoholic state is the end result of a period of uncontrolled drinking—a binge of considerable proportions. Up until fairly recently, it was considered disastrous to attempt treatment on a patient in the acute phase of alcoholism. The newer attitude is expounded by Drs. Daniel J. Feldman and Howard D. Zucker in the AMA *Journal* article:

"If the therapy administered can successfully break the circle and ease the difficult immediate post-alcoholic period, as many of the newer methods can, then much unnecessary suffering is eliminated and the possibility of a serious tragedy may be avoided."

In controlling the overexcitability, restlessness, and nausea of the acute alcoholic, the adrenal hormones are powerful agents. Both ACE (adrenocortical extract) and ACTH (the pituitary hormone which influences the action of the adrenal cortex and causes release of cortisone therefrom) are used in separate intravenous injections. In most cases, the use of these substances results in rapid relief of the intoxication.

Other organic treatments are used as indicated to get the patient on his feet again. Acute alcoholics frequently suffer a severe salt depletion, which is counteracted by the administration of salt tablets or by salting ingested fluids heavily. In most cases, there is a shortage of vitamin supply due to the substitution of alcohol for food over a period of days. The use of vitamins, particularly the B group and vitamin C, is effective in restoring bodily strength. In addition, it is believed the effect of the vitamin B group on the state of the liver, and of C on the adrenal gland, is beneficial.

The post-alcoholic state, when the patient has been taken off alcohol, is characterized by tremors and intense nervousness which frequently drive him to a resumption of drinking. The most severe complication of the post-alcoholic state is delirium tremens, distinguished by excessive nervous agitation, visual and auditory hallucinations, and a high pulse rate. No amount of psychotherapy, Couéism, or moralizing can reach a patient in this stage, but the adrenal hormones can and do get to him. Commenting on the effectiveness of these hormones, Drs. Feldman and Zucker write:

"The use of the adrenal steroids in delirium tremens has resulted in a really significant advance in the management of this condition, and not infrequently, has been lifesaving. . . . It is interesting to speculate as to how often the development of delirium tremens may have been avoided by the early use of adrenal steroid therapy in acute alcoholism."

Several other investigators have confirmed these findings over a long period of experimentation. Both Drs. James Smith of French Hospital and Hugh Lovell of New York Hospital have reported particular success with ACTH in bringing alcoholics out of delirium tremens promptly.

The big problem, of course, is keeping the chronic alcoholic from drinking. Throughout history, remedies ad infinitum and ad nauseam have been tried in an effort to keep him from taking that first drink. None was really effective until the advent of disulfiram (Antabuse). Given one small Antabuse tablet daily during the therapy, the alcoholic cannot take a drink without becoming violently nauseated. Drs. Feldman and Zucker quote a woman patient who had been unable to stop drinking during several years of psychotherapy.

"My psychotherapy has helped me in every way except with the drinking," she said. "Antabuse has been a godsend. I still get in rages against my husband and against my psychiatrist, and always before, when I was angry like that, I would get drunk. Now I can't, and by the time I can, if I stop the pills, I'm not angry any more and so I start the pills again."

Two independent and extensive investigations, one reported by Dr. N. M. Mann and his associates in the May 3, 1952, issue of the AMA *Journal* and the other by Dr. R. C. Larimer in the September 13, 1952, issue, agree that close to 80 per cent of chronic alcoholics treated with Antabuse have been rehabilitated to a considerable degree.

In maintaining the ability of the patient to go without alcohol, a number of significant leads are being worked on. In his *Nutrition and Alcoholism,* published in 1951, the distinguished biochemist Dr. Roger J. Williams proposed a massive vitamin therapy for those unable to stay off alcohol. He has had considerable success with this therapy, and other investigators have reported good results, particularly with the vitamin B group.

Drs. Smith and Lovell have reported success in getting patients to stop drinking for long periods of time through daily and, later, weekly injections of adrenal cortical extract. There is considerable evidence of adrenal depletion in chronic alcoholics, and further studies are going on to detect additional hormonal irregularities.

In long-range research on alcoholism, a group of investigators is on the track of a chemical test that would identify potential alcoholics and forewarn them. According to a description in the January, 1954, issue of *The American Journal of Psychiatry,* the investigators have noted that glandular imbalance and disturbances in body-building processes are important contributing factors in the genesis of alcoholism.

On the psychological side, much more investigation is needed on the peculiar emotional components of the alcoholic. In many cases, the organic treatments calm the patient down to the point where he is amenable to psychological re-education. There are still many leads to be explored, but there is ample justification for the optimistic manner in which Drs. Feldman and Zucker summarize present-day knowledge about alcoholism:

"Alcoholism is a medical problem with somatic and psychological aspects, both of which may be modified by modern treatment. There is no longer any reason for the hopeless attitude that formerly surrounded this affliction."

The greatest rays of hope are coming from the biochemical area. Since May, 1954, when Drs. Cummins and Friend of Peter Bent Brigham reported on the effectiveness of Chlorpromazine in easing the agonizing withdrawal of alcohol, there have been scores of clinical reports on the use of both Reserpine and Chlorpromazine in treating alcoholics suffering from either delirium tremens or severe psychomotor agitation. These drugs are now the treatment of choice in most of the state and municipal hospitals and clinics handling severe cases of acute alcoholism. The Blue Hills Clinic in Hartford, a pioneer state agency, last year reported remarkable results in over 90 per cent of three hundred acutely intoxicated admissions treated with Chlorpromazine. Similar reports have come from the District of Columbia General Hospital, Baylor University Hospital in Houston, and a number of public and private hospitals in New York City.

The states are attacking the problem in an increasingly vigorous fashion. Since the first state commission on alcoholism was set up in 1945 in Connecticut, twelve additional states have established commissions responsible for an over-all treatment, training, and research attack upon alcoholism.

However, the problem is far from licked. In the December, 1954, issue of *State Government,* Raymond M. McCarthy, Director of Alcoholism Research for the New York State Mental Health Commission, documented the need for much greater expenditures.

"A Committee of the National States' Conference on Alcoholism surveyed activities in twenty-eight states for the twelve-month period ending June 30, 1954," McCarthy wrote. "They reported that 6,500 cases had been treated in state-supported specialized clinics and hospitals. If to this number are added patients treated by private physicians and in private institutions and those active in Alcoholics Anonymous, the total number receiving service during the year would be approximately 5 per cent of the four million people reported to be suffering from uncontrolled drinking. The same report indicated that state appropriations for alcoholism services during the twelve-month period amounted to approximately $2,500,-000. Since completion of the survey, additional state services have been inaugurated, and it is probable that approximately $3,500,000 is now allocated annually in the country. If consideration is given to the seriousness of the problem of alcoholism as it affects the individual, his family, welfare agencies, industry and the emotional climate of the community in general, the total financial investment in treatment is disproportionately small."

One can hardly argue with Mr. McCarthy on this point, nor with his plea for more systematic research upon alcoholism.

"Establishment of a series of clinical research centers devoted exclusively to study of the problem as a whole would constitute an extremely valuable contribution" according to McCarthy. "Such centers should be primarily concerned with research. They should not be expected to provide service to the community beyond that necessary for a selection of patients for study. The staff of such a center would include not only a psychiatric team but also competent research specialists from the fields of pharmacology, physiology, sociology, anthropology and biostatistics. An adequate budget should be provided to ensure a program of at least five years. It would be desirable for the center to be established in conjunction with a medical teaching staff."

Research Progress Against Drug Addiction

Like addiction to alcohol, addiction to drugs has long resisted curative treatment. The withdrawal period is a particularly painful one, and psychological and educational retraining of addicts has had little success in preventing relapses.

At the Addiction Research Center of the National Institute of Mental Health in Lexington, Kentucky, a number of physiological studies are under way to find means of relieving the grip of the addiction upon the patient.

Acetylmethadol, a new drug synthesized at the National Institute of Arthritis and Metabolic Diseases, has been tested at Lexington and found to be useful in the management of morphine addiction, greatly reducing the severity of the reactions. The new drug can be given by mouth, thus doing away with the need for sterile hypodermic equipment.

In further experiments to determine the specific action of morphine and related drugs, investigators discovered these drugs relieve pain by reducing anxiety rather than by "doping" the patient's capacity to feel pain. This has led to further experimentation in evaluating the pain-relieving properties of addictive drugs. Along similar lines, work with barbiturates (sedatives) has led to the belief that they may be addicting drugs. When they are abruptly withdrawn from a patient who is clinically intoxicated, characteristic withdrawal symptoms ensue.

In the field of prevention, studies at Lexington have demonstrated the value of N-allylnormorphine in determining quickly whether a person is physiologically addicted to opiates. This drug has also been found useful in treatment of acute opiate poisoning.

As in alcoholism, Chlorpromazine and Reserpine have proved the most potent new weapons against both anxiety and withdrawal symptoms in victims of drug addiction. Furthermore, both drugs perform a valuable function in increasing the pain-killing powers of narcotics by 50 per cent or more, thus lessening the risk of addiction among patients suffering from intractable pain.

Dr. Charles E. Friedgood of Maimonides Hospital in Brooklyn

reported last year on a small series of patients who had become addicted to morphine to ease unbearable pain. Given Chlorpromazine
for a week in the hospital and another four weeks on an out-patient
basis, the patients began to sleep regularly, their agitation, nausea,
and diarrhea were brought under control, and they lost their craving for addictive drugs.

At the 1955 New York Academy of Sciences Conference on the
new drugs, Dr. Eugene F. Carey, surgeon of the Chicago Police
Department, gave a remarkable paper on the use of Reserpine in
relieving the agonizing withdrawal symptoms common to drug addicts. Pointing out that doctors sometimes tend to underestimate
the severity of the symptoms, Dr. Carey described the condition of
the typical addict picked up by the police in these graphic terms:

"He is detained in a concrete-floored, steel-barred cage or cell after
he has been catalogued and screened. Then he is left to his own
resources to think and to meditate. Also, there may be other addicts in the same cell with him. None knows what is next on the
agenda, what is to happen to him, or where he will go. In time,
the drug within each addict's system begins to wear off. One yawns;
then they all yawn. Next follows lacrimation, retching, vomiting,
running bowels, twitching, jerking. Their vertebral canal seems to
fill with ice water, they say, and soon this chilly ache becomes an
agonizing, unbearable, freezing pain, not alone in the back, but all
over the body. The pain causes them to cry piteously, scream, and
convulse. This condition is withdrawal sickness."

For a number of years, Dr. Carey had been trying to ease the
agonies of these addicts. Under the Harrison Act, he was prohibited
from giving them drug substitutes such as Demerol or Dolophin,
since the addicts were confined to the jail for only a few hours. He
had used heavy doses of both bromides and barbiturates, but they
had severe side-effects and introduced new problems of addiction.

Reserpine proved the answer to the doctor's long search. Used
on more than three hundred addicts, it not only tranquilized them
but had a further benefit in reducing the craving for addictive drugs
among those suffering severe physical or psychic pain. For an addict suffering from ulcers or rheumatism, the quieting effect produced by Reserpine removed the burning need for a pain-killer.

18. PSYCHOSOMATIC MEDICINE

Psychosomatic medicine involves the study of the interaction of the mind (psyche) and the body (soma) in the production of disease. It is particularly directed toward ferreting out the emotional disturbances underlying specific mental disorders.

The influence of the mind and the emotions in the creation of bodily ailments has been suspected for centuries. Dr. Ian Stevenson, pointing out that Greek, Roman, and medieval Arabian physicians incorporated this knowledge in their treatments, used the following quotation from John Wesley's *Journal* to illustrate the depth of this perception several centuries ago:

"Reflecting today on the case of a poor woman who had continual pain in her stomach, I could not but remark the inexcusable negligence of most physicians in cases of this nature. They prescribe drug upon drug, without knowing a jot of the matter concerning the root of the disorder. Whence came this woman's pain? (which she would never have told, had she never been questioned about it)—from fretting for the death of her son. And what availed medicine, while that fretting continued?"

The great contribution of psychiatry and allied medical disciplines in recent years has been the exhaustive documentation of the ways in which physical changes in the human body, associated with emotional disturbance, lead to impaired physiological functioning and, eventually, structural damage of tissues.

When the first studies were published describing the emotional stresses underlying hypertension, peptic ulcer, asthma, hay fever, colitis, and other rather common ailments of the human frame, the conservative elements in organic medicine raised their distinguished eyebrows in pained skepticism. Today, several decades and hundreds of investigations later, the eyebrows are back in position, and there is general agreement in the medical fraternity that the treatment of these and other illnesses must give primary attention to the emotional disturbances which bring them into being. The general practitioner who observes an excess of acid pouring into the stomach and eating away the lining, or the knotting-up of the intestines leading to inflammation of the colon, knows the ebb and flow of these malfunctionings and their relation to specific emotional crises in the life of the individual.

For more than twenty years, the Chicago Institute for Psychoanalysis has done significant team studies on a number of organic disorders and their emotional components. Their first published study, on emotional stress and gastrointestinal disturbances, was one of the great pioneer projects in psychosomatic medicine. Many of the studies completed since then—on disturbances of the respiratory system, hypertension, skin diseases, migraine headaches, glaucoma, and others—are reported in their *Studies in Psychosomatic Medicine*. The Chicago Institute also founded the journal *Psychosomatic Medicine,* which publishes the newest experiments in this fast-growing field of medicine.

Currently, Drs. Franz Alexander and Thomas M. French and their associates at the Institute are engaged in a large research project to validate the physiopsychological correlations found in their previous studies of bronchial asthma, hypertension, mucous and ulcerative colitis, rheumatoid arthritis, and other syndromes.

The breadth of the Institute's approach is revealed in a statement by Dr. Alexander in the introduction to *Studies in Psychosomatic Medicine.*

"The attempt to single out certain diseases as psychosomatic is erroneous and futile," he writes. "Every disease is psychosomatic because both psychological and somatic factors have a part in its cause and influence its course. This assumption is valid even for such specific infectious diseases as tuberculosis. Apart from exposure to the bacillus of Koch, the resistance of the organism is an equally important factor in this disease."

There are many psychiatrists who regard most types of tuberculosis as primarily emotional in origin, a willing collapse of the organism in an effort to escape from the pressures of reality and the threat of severe mental disorder. In substantiation of their thesis, they point to the significant number of patients who, when the defense-from-reality of tuberculosis is removed by curative drugs, lapse into a severe psychosis. The high rate of tuberculosis among the hospitalized mentally ill is explained along somewhat similar lines; those who can no longer endure the frightful pressures of confinement in a mental hospital succumb to a disease which removes them from some of the more severe demands of the hospital.

Impressive evidence of the psychogenic origins of tuberculosis has been recently documented by Dr. Thomas H. Holmes of the University of Washington Medical School. Dr. Holmes told the 1955 convention of the American Trudeau Society of a research project he had completed which linked personality disturbances to the onset of tuberculosis.

Dr. Holmes and his associates set up a control study at the Firland Sanatorium in Seattle. They investigated the case histories of twenty employees who had contracted active tuberculosis after they had started to work at the institution, and contrasted these with twenty employees who had not contracted the disease. Both the experimental and control groups were carefully matched as to age, marital status, financial condition, type of employment, and other factors. An elaborate inventory was taken of each person in the study, including a complete battery of psychological tests, medical histories, investigations of home and community life, and minute analyses of personality disturbances before and during the onset of the disease.

Dr. Holmes told the Trudeau Society that the lives of the twenty tuberculosis victims, before the onset of the disease, were characterized "by increasing personality distortion and maladaptation." In nearly all of the cases, a severe emotional crisis brought about by these personality failures occurred approximately two years before the onset of tuberculosis. The twenty employees who did not contract the disease also suffered varying emotional disturbances, but they did not develop into paralyzing crises. In explaining this, Dr. Holmes noted that the tuberculosis victims exhibited a distinctive personality pattern. They had a marked tendency to mask their personality difficulties, and exhibited "a consistent and overwhelming tendency to elaborate, procrastinate and make diffuse rather than specific responses."

Dr. Therese Benedek of the Chicago Institute group has carried out a fascinating series of studies over a period of more than fifteen years on the relation between the physiology of the female sexual cycle and resultant behavior patterns indicative of the major phases of the cycle. From an analysis of the psychological material in the case records of a number of women of childbearing age, Dr. Benedek was able to predict the precise phase of the sexual cycle, which was validated by an estimation of the ovarian hormone production through vaginal smears and basal body temperature measurements. She established the importance of two ovarian hormones in the emotional life of women: estrogen in the preovulation phase and progesterone in the postovulative phase. It is interesting to note that Dr. Benedek's studies show specific psychic responses to physiological changes, whereas most psychosomatic studies show physiological responses to psychic stresses. Her book *Psychosexual Functions in Women* is a superb revelation of the painstaking techniques involved in this kind of investigation.

Dr. Roy R. Grinker, Director of the Institute for Psychosomatic and Psychiatric Research and Training of the Michael Reese Hospital in Chicago, has pioneered in the analysis and publication of scores of case histories of psychosomatic ailments. His *Psychosomatic Case Book*, published in 1954, is an invaluable collection of seventy-nine patient histories gathered over many years by himself and his associates at the Michael Reese Hospital. Grinker's researches lay particular stress upon the role of depression as a cause of emotionally induced ailments.

"In our many case reports which included a wide variety of clinical syndromes," Grinker writes in the summary chapter of his *Case Book*, "the affect of depression lurked somewhere in the history. Sometimes it appeared in the premorbid personality; often it immediately preceded the recognition of physical symptoms, or was experienced during the height of suffering. Depression seems to be a universal phenomenon associated with psychosomatic disturbances."

An increasing trend in psychosomatic medicine has emphasized the development of elaborate measuring techniques to trace the precise physical changes occurring during emotional disturbances. Dr.

Harold G. Wolff and his associates at Cornell University Medical College have published scores of papers measuring the extent of metabolic disturbances under stress.

At the 1954 convention of the American Psychiatric Association, Dr. Holmes and Dr. Herbert S. Ripley, also of the University of Washington Medical School, exhibited a graphic series of films depicting dramatic changes in body function produced during psychiatric interviews in which anxiety and conflict were aroused in the patients. Drs. Holmes and Ripley found that feelings of anxiety produced metabolic changes identical with those produced by toxic agents or the pollen of hay fever: inflammation of the nasal mucous membranes with swelling increased secretions, and acute discomfort. When the interview moved away from the situation causing the anxiety, the membrane swellings went down and the secretions dried up.

At the National Institute of Mental Health, Drs. Phillipe V. Cardon and Norman Goldstein have embarked on a challenging research project relating hormonal output to emotional crises. Through chemical methods, they are measuring the quantities secreted during stress of the naturally occurring hormones epinephrine and norepinephrine. Since these adrenal hormones have a powerful effect in increasing blood pressure and accelerating the heart rate, the Institute findings will be of great importance.

Recent investigations are also moving in the direction of the long-term illnesses. Up until a few years ago, most of the studies were concentrated upon diseases with an episodic course: peptic ulcer, hay fever, colitis, etc. In these ailments, it was easier to determine the root emotional disturbances because the disease pattern fluctuated with the extent of the emotional involvement. However, there is an increasing realization that the real work ahead lies in uncovering the emotional imbalances contributing to the major chronic illnesses.

"Recent work has demonstrated the great significance of emotional factors in heart failure and in diabetes," writes Dr. Ian Stevenson. "Indeed, there now remains no organ of the body in which physical changes related to emotions have not been proved of major importance."

Several teams of investigators are on the track of specific personality constellations which characterize certain diseases. An investigative team composed of scientists from both the National Institutes of Mental Health and Arthritis and Metabolic Diseases is making intensive personality studies of all patients suffering from rheumatoid arthritis admitted to the Public Health Service Clinical Center at Bethesda, in an effort to check the hypothesis that this disease occurs in certain constitutional types.

There have been some exciting studies in the past couple of years on the connection between the emotions and cancer. Research teams in New York, Chicago, and Los Angeles have come up with some remarkably analogous data on the personality pattern of the cancer victim: an inability to express basic drives such as anger or aggressiveness, an inhibited sex life, and a façade of pleasantness covering over severe inner turmoil. A recent report in *Psychosomatic Medicine* by a group of researchers from the University of California at Los Angeles Medical School states the experimental thesis in these terms:

"Our impression is that the very development of cancer in man might conceivably result from the physiological effects of inner stress, which has remained unresolved by either outward action or successful adaptation."

However, much more experimental work must be done before we achieve a sound, therapeutic understanding of the role of behavior disturbances in the genesis of physical illness. Dr. Franz Alexander, in *Modern Attitudes in Psychiatry,* summed up both the problem and the research challenge.

"The interrelation of biochemical changes and emotions is today which, however, can be studied psychologically because these brain processes are perceived subjectively as emotions and can be communicated to others by the use of language. The combined biochemical and psychological approach is now only in its beginnings Body chemistry and emotions do not represent two different sets of facts, one physical, the other mental. When we speak of emotions, we refer always to definite physical processes in the brain, beyond question," he wrote. "Emotional tensions through the autonomic nervous system do influence the body chemistry, and the changed body chemistry in turn reacts upon the emotional life. With the clear recognition of such mutual influences the cleavage between emotional and organic factors can be relegated to the past.

but will undoubtedly become the main trend of future research and therapy."

In the whole area of physiological research upon mental disorders, there has been no more exciting development in the past decade than the development of new tools and new methods for studying the nervous system and for assessing chemical changes in metabolism.

Infrared, ultraviolet, X-ray, and electron microscopy have been effectively applied to a minute study of nervous tissue. At the University of Minnesota, Dr. H. Francis Hartmann and associates are utilizing the electron microscope to study the structure of nerve cells within the central nervous system. At Harvard University, Dr. LeRoy Conel is mapping the basic microscopic structure at various stages in the growth of the infant. His massive studies will illuminate the effects of disease or injury on the cortex.

Even more exciting advances are taking place in the delicate process of measuring nervous impulses. At the National Institute of Mental Health, measurements have been made of the changes in electrical resistance of the gray matter of the living brain occurring within thousands of a second during the passage of a nerve impulse. In a companion effort, Dr. John Lilly of the Institute staff has devised a method of recording spatial patterns of electrical activity in the cerebral cortex and relating them to behavioral changes in the organism. In a third Institute effort, Dr. Karl Frank has devised a microelectrode so tiny that it may be inserted in a single nerve cell to record electrical activity. Through such intensive studies of the electrical activity of individual pulses, a better understanding of the electroencephalogram or brain-wave pattern is obtained. These data, recorded from millions of cells, are indispensable in the accurate diagnosis of many nervous system diseases.

Another tremendous technical advance has been the development of techniques for the measurement of the circulation and metabolism of the living human brain. These techniques have already been helpful in probing the metabolic changes which occur in senile psychosis and organic cerebral diseases. They have also been used to assess the effectiveness of a number of drugs and surgical procedures designed to improve the nutrition of the brain.

The practical importance of these new tools is dramatically illustrated in a new technique developed by Dr. Seymour Kety for the measurement of blood flow to every part of the human brain. Through these studies, Dr. Kety has established the important fact that there is a perceptible reduction of blood flow to the brain in senile dementia.

Of comparable importance is an elaborate technical study of the nucleic acids which make up the genetic apparatus of the cell. At the National Institute of Mental Health, these nucleic acids were first measured accurately several years ago. There are indications that they behave in an unusual manner in the brain tissues of psychotic patients.

19. PSYCHOLOGICAL
FACTORS

Psychotherapy, which is the treatment of mental disorders through psychological means, has spawned scores of schools and cults which proclaim the particular virtues of highly individualized techniques. Since few of these claims are subjected to scientific controls—most of the "scientific" papers cite one or two treated cases as "proof" of the superiority of whatever psychotherapeutic technique is being advocated—it is almost impossible to winnow the small kernels of wheat from the jargon-ridden chaff.

Advocates of psychotherapy and its most widely recognized subdivision, psychoanalysis, are in pretty substantial agreement that the psychological techniques are most successful in the treatment of the neuroses, emotional disorders in which the personality remains relatively intact and the individual is able to function to some degree despite psychological impairment. Since this book is primarily concerned with the more serious mental illnesses requiring hospitalization, this section will merely attempt to discuss a few of the research projects designed to make psychotherapy more effective and widespread in its application.

One of the most common criticisms leveled against psychoanalysis is that it is too time-consuming for wide clinical application. The average analysis extends over two to three years, with from three to five interview hours a week. Back in 1938, the Chicago Institute for Psychoanalysis launched a lengthy study to discover shorter and more efficient means of psychotherapy. In the introduction to *Psychoanalytic Therapy,* a summary of the Chicago proj-

ect published in 1946, Dr. Franz Alexander criticized ritualistic
psychoanalysis in these forthright terms:

"It is argued by some psychoanalysts that quick therapeutic results cannot indicate deep, thoroughgoing changes in the dynamic
structure of the personality, that years are required to bring about
such fundamental changes. Others excuse the lack of therapeutic
results in prolonged analyses by the patient's 'resistance.' They have
comforted themselves by saying that the patient is not yet 'fully
analyzed' and they are convinced that further treatment will eventually bring the desired results. Then, when results still do not
come, they often take refuge in deciding that the patient is a 'latent
schizophrenic.' "

The Chicago study points out that there is only a narrow line
separating traditional psychoanalysis from other forms of psychotherapy, and that all employ the "same psychodynamic principles"
for the purpose of therapy—"inducing emotional discharge in order
to facilitate insight, and exposing the ego to those unresolved emotional constellations which it has to learn to master."

The Alexander study therefore recommends "the principle of
flexibility in treatment: the application of the technique best suited
to the nature of the case." Warning against an "interminable trans-
ference neurosis in which the patient replaces his old disturbance
with a neurotic relationship to his doctor," the project advocates a
less rigid number of interviews per week, more space between segments of the analysis, more effort on the part of the therapist to
guide the situation, and many other modifications of the standard
Viennese cloak-and-dagger analysis. It concludes on an optimistic
note unusual in psychoanalytic writing:

"The new development will come to expression in the creation
of well-staffed out-patient clinics where the large number of in-
cipient cases—all those whose emotional balance has been impaired
through the complex human relationships in our fluid, ever-chang-
ing and highly differentiated society—will receive rational, dynamic
psychotherapy."

In recent years, a number of research studies have attempted to
evaluate the successes and failures of psychotherapy, relating the results to the techniques used and the types of illnesses treated. A
few projects are also attacking specific problems in the therapeutic
procedure. For example, at the National Institute of Mental Health,

Drs. Morris B. Parloff and Virgil R. Carlson are investigating the communication of anxiety between the therapist and the patient. Because the psychotherapeutic process centers about control of the patient's anxiety, an understanding of how anxiety is communicated is of great importance in the improvement of treatment techniques.

The most dramatic extension of the benefits of psychotherapy has been the development of group psychotherapy, in which a group of patients under the leadership of a trained therapist discuss their problems and try to help each other work them out. In a technical paper, "Twenty Years of Group Psychotherapy," presented at the 1953 convention of the American Psychiatric Association, Dr. Rudolf Dreikurs and Raymond Corsini emphasized that group psychotherapy could not reach its potential in a Europe where authoritarianism prevailed.

"It is not surprising, therefore, that the development of psychotherapy shifted to the United States and advanced rapidly, far ahead of any other country," they told their colleagues. "Group psychotherapy is essentially a democratic procedure, and its use reflects the political climate of a nation. It cannot flourish except in a free atmosphere. It needs a unique social climate, and, in turn, creates one."

Group psychotherapy is in an exciting stage of experimental development at the present time. Many different approaches are being used to help groups of patients release their pent-up anxieties and hostilities—through mutual analysis and verbalization of problems; through directive treatment in which a therapist aids the group in making new adjustments; through skillfully planned group play and drama sessions, and through other techniques too numerous to mention here.

Group psychotherapy has already achieved some noteworthy results. The basic strength of Alcoholics Anonymous lies in mutual help through mutual expression of problems. A great many mental hospitals now use group psychotherapy as standard treatment in alcoholism and related addictions.

One of the most impressive recent experiments in group psychotherapy with hospitalized mental patients was conducted by the Veterans' Administration under the direction of Drs. Jerome Frank and Florence Powdermaker. Their remarkable success with this therapy is detailed in their book, *Group Psychotherapy*, published in 1953.

Since childhood disturbances play such an important role in the causation of mental disorders, much recent psychological research has concentrated on the processes of child development. Several groups of researchers are studying child development from birth on in an attempt to isolate patterns of emotional maladjustment which result in mental illness. A small number of clinical studies of preschool children with severe mental illnesses have isolated pathological relationships which appear to be significant in the origin of these disorders. For example, the father's role in the development of the child's personality is crucial in most families. To test the extent of this influence, Dr. Lois Meek Stolz and a group of her colleagues from Stanford University studied the harmful effects resulting from the war-service absence of a father during the initial year of his first child's life.

Out at the Clinical Center of the National Institutes of Health in Bethesda, Dr. Fritz Redl is making an intensive study of a group of disturbed children whose hostilities have prevented them from adjusting to home and school life. Since the patients live in the hospital, Dr. Redl has been able to create a milieu in which the children may work out their aggressions. Dr. Redl's large staff—there are three times as many professional members as children—is constantly observing those situations which contain an excess of stress for these hyperaggressive children. Child psychiatrists throughout the country are eagerly awaiting the publication of Dr. Redl's findings during the next few years of experimentation.

There are also efforts to trace and measure childhood maladjustment over a period of time. Dr. Jean Walker McFarlane of the University of California has pioneered in the development of methods of measuring mental, emotional, and physiological maturity. These tests are used to measure adjustment problems resulting from discrepancies between rates of physiological development and mental or emotional growth. In Prince Georges County, Maryland, the Mental Health Studies Center of the U. S. Public Health Service worked several years ago with county school personnel in the use of a simple technique for diagnosing maladjustment among more than eight hundred ninth-graders. A follow-up of the students is now being completed to determine the accuracy of the diagnostic methods used.

Efforts to trace adult mental illnesses back to specific childhood maladjustments are somewhat skimpy in their findings, although their proponents make some rather extravagant claims for them. One recent study, for example, purported to show that certain types of mental illness can be attributed to abnormal adjustment during childhood, but that other types, such as manic-depressive psychosis, develop in patients who had apparently normal childhoods. The large number of variables in these studies, the inexactitude of much of the data, the lack of precise diagnostic criteria—all these must be refined before we can give credence to their conclusions.

The same strictures hold for the pronouncements of most psychiatric "experts" about what is normal and what is abnormal in childhood behavior. Women's luncheons and study groups are the usual forums for a lot of unscientific bilge about the evils of thumbsucking, or the traumatic effects of Junior's unrequited love for the cleaning maid.

At the International Institute for Child Psychiatry held in Toronto in 1954, several of the saner minds in the field cried out for a halt to the current nonsense. Dr. Hilde Bruch of the Department of Psychiatry and Pediatrics of Columbia University's College of Physicians and Surgeons denounced the "intimidating techniques" of experts which resulted in "increased disturbance in children, as illustrated by the increasing need for psychiatric treatment of children in families who have followed the psychological advice."

"In the United States, where the teaching of child psychology is propagated most vigorously, there seems to be no decline in the incidence of mental disorders," Dr. Bruch emphasized. "On the contrary, emotional problems and juvenile delinquency are said to be on the increase, involving more and more children from middle-class homes."

Dr. Bruch wound up with a parting shot at the dispensers of advice to harried mothers:

"The outstanding common factor of the many different approaches is the recklessness with which they are recommended as the 'best' for the future development of a child, without an effort having been made to verify these predictions. Yet they are presented to parents as scientific facts, often with the implied or open threat that any neglect might injure the child and result in neurosis in the dim and distant future."

Dr. Benjamin Spock, the famed pediatrician, echoed agreement with Dr. Bruch's plaint, pointing out that numerous programs in the field of parent education "have missed the target and some of them have, in a subtle way, done more harm than good." Professor Kenneth E. Priestly of the University of Hong Kong ended the Toronto symposium with the admonition that "parents might be better employed playing with their children in the back yard than attending lectures by a psychiatrist."

The psychiatric "experts" also have a field day every time some particularly horrendous juvenile crime is reported in the newspapers. Newsmen dutifully call the "experts" who, at the drop of a headline and without any personal knowledge, proceed to elaborate at great length upon the underlying causes of the particular crime. Needless to say, the experts are seldom in agreement.

There are prescriptions galore for the treatment and "cure" of individual delinquents, up to and including the jailing of the parents. A U. S. Senate Committee holds hearings, the Children's Bureau pours out an endless stream of pamphlets, there are mass meetings of irate parents, and the same ministers of God who bless the cannons during wartime denounce the juvenile delinquents who are at war with their society. In the past ten years, I have waded through scores of documents outlining favorite recipes for the eradication of juvenile delinquency, but the only ones that have made any sense at all have appeared in the writings of Dr. Rudolf Dreikurs, a psychiatrist who has experimented widely with group psychotherapy and is also Director of Chicago's community child-guidance centers.

At the first International Congress on Group Psychotherapy, Dr. Dreikurs noted that juvenile delinquents do not generally respond to individual treatment—that treatment of the problem must involve the community as a whole. Pointing out that a generation of children is at war with a generation of adults and that mass juvenile delinquency is an expression of this conflict, Dr. Dreikurs warned that "our children are becoming our equals and can no longer be pushed down by adults."

Dr. Dreikurs described the social values of juvenile delinquents as merely a distorted image of the values of the community, values which centered on "personal prestige and glory, the seeking of gratification and making easy money."

"We have to make peace between adults and children," he told his colleagues. "We have to give juveniles a place in society. We must change adult attitudes toward children."

In the field of psychotherapy relating to childhood disorders, there is a growing realization that physiological factors at the root of many behavior disturbances are being neglected. At the 1954 International Congress on Mental Health, Dr. Paul Lemkau of Johns Hopkins, a psychiatrist not usually found in the "organic" camp in the past, took the psychodynamic school for quite a rough ride.

" . . . There may well be a factor of brain injury in a goodly proportion of school behavior problems," he pointed out, "and psychiatrists have, in all probability, been prone to overlook this possibility in an orgy of psychodynamic thinking that excludes all other possible etiological [causative] factors."

Buttressing his argument, Dr. Lemkau cited the evidence of prenatal damage to a child as a contributing factor in many cases of epilepsy, mental deficiency, and cerebral palsy. He emphasized the crucial importance of current and future research on organic changes in the infant from conception to birth.

Turning to psychological research upon adult behavior, we find increasing attention being paid to a discovery of the laws governing normal behavior so that deviations from successful patterns of living can be traced. For example, there are a number of research projects studying the processes of perception, thinking, and motivation—processes which are frequently badly distorted in the neurotic and psychotic. At the National Institute of Mental Health, Drs. Virgil R. Carlson and Ralph W. Ryan are concentrating upon acquired distortions in the perception of self, of others, and of key events in an attempt to find out what distortions are acquired and how they are acquired.

Recent experiments have shown that amazing distortions in perception can be brought about experimentally through induced anxiety or reduction of calorie intake. Experiments conducted by the distinguished physiologist Ancel Keys at the University of Minnesota have shown that simple semistarvation can produce personality distortions corresponding to psychoneurosis.

The experimental induction of neuroses in animals through conditioned reflex has thrown great light upon the underlying psychological mechanisms of comparable neuroses in man. Dr. Howard Liddell of Cornell University has worked for more than twenty-five years with sheep, goats, and pigs, inducing neurotic behavior in them through the application of various kinds of psychological stress. The disturbed behavior—refusal to eat, isolation, extreme nervousness—persists in the animals until they are retrained. From the work of Dr. Liddell and others, the conclusion is inescapable that many kinds of neurosis previously regarded as typically human are really rooted in the mammalian family tree. Recent intensive studies of the pronounced metabolic changes produced in animals during periods of fear and stress are also throwing considerable light upon comparable processes in the human body. There is general agreement that animal experimentation, in which situations can be manipulated much more easily than in human experimentation, should be pursued much more vigorously in the coming years in the effort to shed additional light upon the basic physiological and psychological processes connected with anxiety, fear, stress, and other emotions.

20. EPIDEMIOLOGY

EPIDEMIOLOGY, according to Hirsch's widely accepted definition, is "the science which gives (1) a picture of the occurrence, distribution, and types of diseases of mankind in distinct epochs of time and at various points on the earth's surface, and (2) will render an account of the relation of these diseases to the external conditions surrounding the individual and determining his manner of life."

Epidemiology has been enormously useful in the detection and control of the infectious diseases. Its painstaking effort to tabulate incidence of disease and relate the figures gathered to specific causative agents in the environment has paid off handsomely since Snow's epoch-making surveys which showed that cholera was caused by drinking water contaminated by fecal matter.

However, the attempt to move the precise tools of epidemiology into the field of mental illness has met with little success to date. Attempts to tabulate the amount of mental illness in a community have bogged down because of the lack of specific diagnostic criteria for the major mental illnesses. It isn't hard to spot a case of cholera; it is clearly marked by severe diarrhea, vomiting, cramps, suppression of urine, and other distinguishing characteristics. But how about a schizophrenic? Frequently the answer is based on which psychiatrist you read, for one psychiatrist's schizophrenic is frequently another's obsessional neurotic, and so on.

In the literature on the epidemiology of mental illness—and there are a fantastic number of studies; Gruenberg lists 362 in *The Epidemiology of Mental Disorder*—two are often referred to as "classics."

The Baltimore surveys of 1933 and 1936, conducted by Lemkau, Tietze, and Cooper of the Johns Hopkins University School of Hygiene and Public Health, were attempts to measure incidence of the major mental illnesses in a large city. The surveys themselves were limited to the Eastern Health District, an area about one mile square with fifty-five thousand inhabitants, one-quarter of whom were Negro.

The number of cases of ten different categories of mental illness running the gamut from "minor and possible disorder in adults and children" to senile dementia and schizophrenia, were tabulated by studying the written records of forty-three institutions which handled problems of mental illness. No cases were examined by the survey psychiatrists. The 1936 survey showed 3,337 active cases of mental disorder among the fifty-five thousand studied, a prevalence rate of approximately six per hundred.

The Tennessee survey of 1935-38 was an attempt to go a little deeper. Drs. W. F. Roth, Jr., and Frank Luton mapped out a survey area in Williamson County, Tennessee, a typical agricultural community with an area of 586 square miles and a population of twenty-five thousand. In an effort to check the validity of statistics and uncover additional cases, the staff spent considerable time living in the community. More than half of the cases of mental illness reported by agencies were examined by members of the staff, which included a psychiatrist, social workers, and nurses. In addition, an intensive house-to-house survey of mental illness was conducted in three selected areas.

As of September 1, 1938, there were 1,721 cases of mental illness among the twenty-five thousand inhabitants of Williamson County, a prevalence rate of about seven per hundred, as against the six per hundred found in the Baltimore survey. However, Roth and Luton cast doubt upon the validity of this figure by pointing out that in the intensive house-to-house survey, the prevalence rate was twice as high as compared with areas where no staff canvass had been made.

The weaknesses in the Baltimore and Tennessee studies are fairly obvious. The whole question of imprecise definition looms large. For example, the Baltimore survey lists only 171 psychoneurotics in a population of fifty-five thousand. Since there were no personal interviews, how many different criteria for psychoneurosis were used by forty-three different agencies in making the diagnosis? In the

Tennessee survey, "conduct and behavior disorder" is the largest single category of mental illness—more than 16 per cent. But this is a loose diagnostic category, subject to normative interpretation. And how compare this category with the Baltimore findings, which list three kinds of behavior disorder?

Dr. Lemkau, who has devoted several decades to both academic and field work in the epidemiological area, raised some thoughtful questions about his own Baltimore surveys in a brilliant address at the 1954 International Congress on Mental Health.

"In both the 1933 and 1936 surveys it appears that the prevalence rate of neuroses is lower than that of psychoses, a fact clinical experience leads most psychiatrists to doubt," Dr. Lemkau told the international delegates. "It is clear that what was measured included only neurotic cases who were ill enough to seek treatment and were recognized and diagnosed by physicians. . . . A second example of the frustrations of this sort of investigation is found in the rates for psychopathic personality. There were, according to the Eastern Health District surveys, three times as many psychopaths in 1933 as in 1936. We surmise, without too much confidence, that the operational definition of psychopathic personality changed to this extent, probably because in 1933 joblessness and changing jobs was interpreted as indicative of psychopathic personality, while in 1936, when the extent and severity of the world depression were recognized more clearly, there was a tendency to evaluate such data very differently."

From his specific experience in the Baltimore surveys and his familiarity with the looseness of most epidemiological studies, Dr. Lemkau then pleaded for more precise definitions and less grandiose projects in the field.

"Experimentation in this field awaits a great deal more thinking about what the optimal state of man may be, and what the tolerable variations are under certain given conditions, before mental health can be defined well enough for epidemiological methods to be applied in experimentation," he warned. "It may well be that the best way to do research on mental health in our present state of knowledge is to be certain that any investigation on psychiatric diseases includes adequately studied controls drawn from the unaffected population. I am aware that this is a rather unpopular position to take at the present time. It is not my intention at all to dis-

courage effort; it is only to warn that we may not be as well prepared to do the work as some of our propaganda would lead the
public to believe. Our aspirations seem, at times, to have outrun our
methods.

"At the risk of being dubbed old-fashioned and wedded to nineteenth-century mechanistic logic, I think it needs to be pointed out
that it is this logic that has made the epidemiologic method successful in the past and that, in all probability, if we abandon classification and definition as essential in psychiatric research, we also abandon epidemiology. One can do epidemiological research on the
causes, distribution and extent of a fantasy, but one cannot do it
unless the fantasy, the population and the conditions prevailing can
be defined and are not in themselves in the realm of fantasy."

Pioneer epidemiological studies of mental disorder also attempted
to relate the incidence of mental illness to specific socio-economic
factors in society. In the late nineteen-thirties, the sociologists Faris
and Dunham studied records of hospitalized psychotics in Chicago
and related them to the specific areas of the city from which they
came. Their most "arresting" finding was that the slum areas
around Chicago's central business district produced the most mental illness, particularly of the schizophrenic variety, and that rates
of mental illness generally declined as one approached the suburbs.

At the first Milbank conference on the epidemiology of mental
disorder, held in 1949, Dr. Robert P. Knight, Medical Director of
the Austen Riggs Foundation, voiced the skepticism of many of his
psychiatric colleagues with regard to sweeping surveys of the prevalence and socio-economic causes of the major mental illnesses.

"I had always thought of epidemiology as the detective work that
is done to track down a causal agent in order to be able to apply
appropriate measures to prevent the causal agent from acting," Dr.
Knight pointed out. "In that sense, I don't believe there is an epidemiology of the functional [psychologically caused] mental disorder, because there is not now known any single causal agent of
mental illness, and I would feel fairly safe in predicting that no single causal agent ever will be found."

Commenting on some of the more widely known epidemiological surveys on mental illness, Dr. Knight remarked:

"Reading such studies results in the feeling that what has been
produced by the study either confirms something that was obvious

anyway, or that it was an inconclusive report in which one doubts the sources of the figures on which the study was based. As an example of something that is more or less obvious, let us take the study of Clark on the inverse correlation of incidence of alcoholism among men of high income, high prestige professions. Such a study would seem to me to be more or less a waste of time. . . . The same point applies to schizophrenia. . . . To demonstrate by a large-scale study that schizophrenia has a much higher incidence in the slum areas might be regarded as only proving that most people who have in their childhood faced the worst, most intolerable realities would naturally be the ones more likely to be driven to turn away from reality into fantasy. For that is what schizophrenics do."

But the pursuit of the obvious goes on, frequently supported by tax dollars not easily come by when originally obtained from the Congress. Most of the epidemiologists are expert verbalizers, and they can concoct a convincing research project whose end result, after the expenditure of several hundreds of thousands of dollars, is the startling conclusion that most old people are fairly old, and quite a bit older than most young people.

A case in point is an elaborate survey of mental illness as related to social class in New Haven. Two masters of verbalization, psychiatrist Frederick C. Redlich and sociologist August B. Hollingshead, are putting public moneys to use in their grandiose project. The New Haven community was selected because the citizens have been surveyed so many times by eager beavers from Yale that they think it is all part of normal, daily living to be dissected and squeezed into Indices of Social Position.

The community is chopped up into five classes, arrived at by awarding points up to six for residence, and points up to seven for both occupation and education. After more technical business, including *chi*-square tests (?), mental disorders are tabulated as to their frequency in the five classes, which range from tenement families to those listed in the New Haven Social Directory.

And what are the startling conclusions so far, as reported at the 1952 Milbank Conference and in several recent issues of *The American Journal of Psychiatry?* Well, severe mental illnesses are more prevalent in the lower classes, while neuroses are more favored by members of the Social Directory. Obvious? Not on your *chi*-square! Listen to the Messrs. Redlich and Hollingshead:

"Our detailed case records indicate the social distance between psychiatrist and patient may be more potent than economic considerations in determining the character of psychiatric intervention."

In their most recent reports in the APA *Journal,* Redlich and Hollingshead have published some "startling" data on who gets psychiatric treatment in a community. Incredibly, the richer people have more appointments with psychiatrists before winding up in a mental hospital, while for the poorer classes the mental hospital is frequently the first point of contact with therapy.

In New York State, the research unit of the State Mental Health Commission is embarked on an ambitious project to "explore the relationship between the actual occurrence of cerebral arteriosclerotic psychosis and senile psychosis and social-economic conditions of life in order to determine conditions favoring low and high rates of occurrence of these psychoses."

Onondaga County, which includes the city of Syracuse, has been selected as the happy hunting ground for the epidemiological explorers. The county has been cut up into fifty-two relatively homogeneous census tracts, and tabulations have been made of the number of aged admitted to mental hospitals for the period 1935 to 1950 from each of the tracts.

The early returns, as reported at the 1952 Milbank Conference and at the 1954 convention of the American Psychiatric Association, indicate that most of the aged admissions come from census tracts where the average monthly rental is less than $30. However, some of the low socio-economic tracts do not have high rates of senile dementia, while several of the high income tracts do. This set the surveyors back until they could find a new yardstick which would fit the data. This turned out to be multiple dwellings per structure. In census tracts with less than 2.25 dwellings per structure, the senile dementia rate was low, while the reverse was true in those census tracts having more than 2.25 dwellings per structure.

Loose data of this sort beg so many questions that it is futile to attempt to interpret them. Where is cause and where is effect in the data? How many old people gravitate to boardinghouses in low economic areas because they are ill and unable to make a living? Making a direct correlation between an economic area and extent of senile dementia is about as accurate as making a survey of Skid Row in any large city and attributing to it a high causal relation in alcoholism. Furthermore, in the higher income tracts, the families are obviously better able to care for their elderly, and only as a last resort will commit them to a state mental hospital. Introducing the complication of multiple dwellings seems a round-about way of saying that old people who are reduced to renting rooms in homes have to go to a state mental hospital if they get sick and have no one to care for them.

The dangers and inanities of these sweeping surveys, which try to squeeze significant variables into whatever tight epidemiological corset is the fashion of the day, are graphically illustrated in a survey of mental disorder in Austin, Texas. Ivan Belknap and E. Gartly Jaco studied 421 admissions from the capital city of Austin to a state mental hospital from 1946 to 1952.

Their findings, announced in broad daylight, are really startling. First of all, mental disorder is not the same in Austin as in Chicago. Contrary to Faris and Dunham, who pointed out high rates of psychoses in the slum areas around the central business district, our Texas surveyors found a nice scattering of high rates throughout Austin.

Secondly, they found appreciable religious differences in the incidence of mental disorder, obtaining "a highly significant *chi*-square."

"This finding indicates that Baptist, Methodist, Lutheran, Christian, and Church of Christ affiliates have higher incidence rates, Catholic and Episcopalian affiliates lower rates, and Presbyterian and Assembly of God Church affiliates rates neither higher nor lower than their proportion of the sample would lead one to expect," write Belknap and Jaco.

How interpret this strange set of data? Belknap and Jaco find it absurdly simple. They point out that Austin is "a neglected type of city, namely that of a politically functional ecological base, in contrast to the commercial-industrial city-types in which the classical ecological [relation of organisms to their environment] studies have been made." If you won't buy this, they make one final jargon-ridden stab:

"Since variant ecological distribution and incidence rates for several major mental disorders appear in a type of city regarded as functionally different from those previously investigated, it might be concluded tentatively that the ecological approach is probably valid, and that cities with different ecological basis [sic] will have a differential epidemiology of mental disorders. It is clear also that ecological findings in one functional type of city can only very cautiously be extended to other functional types, and finally, that epidemiological research in mental disorders should always take into account the ecological functional base of an area prior to investigation."

In other words, Austin is different from Chicago and, as any good Texan will tell you, Fort Worth is thirty miles from Dallas as the Herefords roam but many light-years removed in its mores and customs.

There is, however, an increasing realization on the part of a number of epidemiologists and psychiatrists that closely knit, intensive surveys relating the origin of mental disorders to specific social attitudes and environmental stresses are of tremendous value in preventive work against mental illness.

At the 1949 Milbank Conference, Dr. Thomas Francis, Jr., Professor of Epidemiology at the University of Michigan's School of Public Health, spelled out the ground rules for narrowed-down, intensive studies.

"The numerous suggestions from epidemiologic information on mental disorders to date must be submitted to test," Dr. Francis warned his colleagues. "The different concepts of the nature of the underlying cause—constitutional, psychological, or otherwise—must be explored on a scientific rather than a wishful basis. Experiment without control is like a compass without a magnetized needle. . . . There must be open-minded tests through continued examination of the effect of stresses and strains of different origins in a screened population of suspects and controls. . . .

"In other words, it seems that one is certainly going to have to ask questions of a more limited nature, and then attempt to approach them in an accurate, clear-cut fashion rather than trying to put them all under one tent and assume because they are in the same tent, that they are similar and that the answers are comparable."

At the 1952 Milbank Conference, after listening to descriptions of some of the loose explorations outlined in the early pages of this chapter, Dr. John A. Clausen, Chief of the Laboratory of

Socio-Environmental Studies of the National Institute of Mental Health, echoed Dr. Francis' plea.

"I have the feeling we need to do an awful lot of small-scale exploration of interrelationships, using social science theory that we have rather than starting out establishing general levels of prevalence," Dr. Clausen remarked.

Matching the deed to the word, Dr. Clausen did a beautifully precise study of the relationship between social isolation and schizophrenia. He concentrated his microscopic sociological lens upon a group of admissions to the Maryland state hospitals over a twelve-year period from the city of Hagerstown. In reporting his study to the 1954 annual meeting of the American Sociological Society, Dr. Clausen tilted a powerful lance against Faris and Dunham and all other practitioners of wide-swinging surveys leading to superficial conclusions.

"Of the several hypotheses relating the frequency of mental disorders to social conditions, none has been more persistently enunciated than that which proposes that schizophrenia is the outgrowth of social isolation," Dr. Clausen noted. "First stated by Faris in 1934, this hypothesis subsequently seemed consistent with, and indeed explanatory of, the findings of Faris and Dunham's classic ecological study of mental disorder. Faris and Dunham ascertained that high rates of first hospital admissions for schizophrenia are found in areas of the city characterized by high residential mobility and low socio-economic status, among ethnic group persons living in non-ethnic areas, and among the foreign-born populations of the slums. All of these indices were regarded as reflecting tendencies toward the social isolation of certain segments of the population."

In the intensive study of the Hagerstown patients, Clausen found that social isolation is a very minor element in the causation of mental illness.

"Our general conclusion must be, then, that the data do not support the hypothesis that social isolation in adolescence is a predisposing factor in either schizophrenia or in manic-depressive psychosis," Dr. Clausen reported. "Only a third of the patients were isolated in adolescent life, and even for them isolation does not seem to have been instrumental in predisposing them to psychosis. Nor does it seem to increase the duration of hospitalization.

"In early statements of the social isolation hypothesis, it was posited that isolation of any person for an extended period of time results in schizophrenia. Later the process was seen as far more complex: a particular type of person, living in a particular social setting, becomes rebuffed and rejected by his peers; after fruitless attempts to gain acceptance, he finally withdraws into a shell of isolation. One wonders why, if this complex series of events is seen as necessary to the schizophrenic process, isolation is seized upon as the crucial element that leads to schizophrenia. Why was the individual rebuffed in the first place? Why did he react so extremely to rebuff as to withdraw from all social interaction? Does not his behavior before he became isolated indicate that his personality development was already quite abnormal?"

Several interesting projects of the Hagerstown type are under way at the present time. The most fascinating is an intensive study of a county in Nova Scotia for the purpose of establishing relations between the distribution of psychiatric illness and the stresses in the social environment which may contribute to these illnesses. It is being done by Dr. Alexander Leighton and a large team from the Cornell University Social Science Research Center.

The importance of the study lies partly in the intensity of the case-finding operation. The mental hospital and other institutional records of admissions for mental illness were merely starting points. In June, 1951, the psychiatric team opened a clinic in the county to examine new patients referred by various community sources and to check and validate the data on previous cases already reported. In a further effort to check findings, the team drew up screening tests for personality traits which were given to both well and ill people.

Independent of the above surveys, a social science team is checking major social stresses in the county: poverty, rapid social change, illness, migration, broken homes, etc. To eliminate biases and preconceptions, the psychiatric case-finding team is working completely separate from the team mapping factors of social stress. When the two sets of exhaustive data are finally compiled, they will be correlated in an attempt to determine specific relationships between certain stresses and mental disorders.

A much more ambitious and difficult exercise in the relating of incidence of mental illness to socio-environmental stresses is under way in an eastern city under a team headed by Dr. Thomas A. C. Rennie. Dr. Rennie is superbly equipped for the task, having published a number of seminal studies on community aspects of mental illness.

Dr. Rennie and his team of psychiatrists, psychologists, sociologists, anthropologists, and statisticians are combing a densely populated area of 188 city blocks, an area tremendously rich in economic, ethnic, and educational diversity. In spelling out the purposes of the project at the 1952 Milbank Conference, Dr. Rennie emphasized the point that the basic epidemiological data will "be turned into a jumping-off point for explorations in the etiological direction of the socio-cultural forces of the more stressful among the life-situation conditions which are significantly associated with and presumptively contribute to personality malfunction. The above statement of our limited etiological objective reflects our acute awareness of the inadequacies of current scientific methods in the face of the enormous complexities involved in tracing personality malfunctions in a large population down to their ultimate tangle of personal and situational causes."

The Rennie team has not only wisely narrowed the focus of its studies but seems quite aware of the chicken-and-the-egg dilemma: Was the mental illness precipitated by the exigencies of a peculiar environment, or did the person with the mental illness gravitate helplessly toward that kind of environment? Dr. Rennie put the problem very nicely at the Milbank conference:

"At first glance there would appear to be the serious analytical problem that we may not be able to assess for these adults whether difficulties they manifest are primarily reflective of (1) intrinsically pathogenic situational conditions precipitated by factors in the urban community setting, or of (2) maladaptive personality dispositions brought to the setting.

"It was precisely this problem that was not recognized by Faris and Dunham in offering their interpretation that urbanization stood in some kind of cause-effect relationship to schizophrenia. It is an oversight that is still current among those students of society who, in addressing themselves to personality disturbances in adults, restrict their etiological questions to factors in the here-and-now social environment, or conversely, among those students of personality who do take account of childhood family setting, but fail to relate the latter to its particular enveloping socio-cultural, neighborhood-community medium. These two points of view obviously overlook the full context of the predisposing etiological factors in childhood, when childhood may have been passed in a very different kind of environment than that in which the adult's personality disorder breaks out."

In digging for personality data in meaningful depth, Dr. Rennie and his associates developed a sixty-five-page questionnaire covering 412 specific queries. The questionnaire takes from one and a half to five hours to administer.

At the 1955 convention of the American Psychiatric Association, Dr. Rennie made a preliminary report on the first three years of the survey. The most interesting and challenging finding so far is the astoundingly high degree of clinically diagnosable illness among the several thousand people surveyed. About 30 per cent suffer from some form of psychiatric illness, and a high percentage of them have concomitant psychosomatic ailments. More than 70 per cent complained of nervousness and admitted to a galaxy of worries running the gamut from health status and loneliness to the current cost of living. About a third of the sample confessed that they drank too much.

In interpreting the preliminary data causatively, Dr. Rennie said the most significant determinant of incidence of mental illness seemed to be educational rather than economic status. As you went down the educational scale—and it pretty much determined the occupational status of people—you found a higher incidence of mental illness.

However, this brings us back to the chicken and the egg. In most cases, did not the existence of early mental illness preclude the achievement of a formal education? This is just one of the many dilemmas facing the Rennie team in its interpretations, but the returns are not all in yet, and it will take another few years to relate the psychiatric illnesses uncovered to the various socio-environmental stresses. The attempt is a valiant one, and it is fortunately in the hands of one of the nation's most sophisticated practitioners of community psychiatry.

In Wellesley, a Boston suburb of eight thousand families, a mental health agency called the Human Relations Service was set up in

1948 by Dr. Erich Lindemann and a team from Harvard University. Among its many objectives, it has been making an almost microscopic study of the origin and transmission of emotional disorders, relating them in particular to certain key critical periods in childhood and adolescence.

Through its clinical services, the psychiatric team has been making a minute study of family patterns as they are affected by the mental illness of a family member.

"The study of the 'normal members' of these families gave us insight concerning a variety of pathological relationships when it could be demonstrated that the well-being of one partner is based on the sickness of the other partner, the first partner succumbing to illness after successful treatment of his sick companion," Dr. Lindemann writes. "We are assembling a typology of pathological forms of family organization with special emphasis on the transmission of emotional disturbances from one member to the other, depending upon certain outside pressures."

In hunting for the point at which social pressures begin to cause breakdowns in vulnerable individuals, the Wellesley group has gradually shifted its sights to a younger and younger age, and is now concentrating on children between five and eight years of age. The group has also worked closely with the public schools in spotting signs of emotional disturbance, particularly during times of critical transition—the move from elementary to high school, from high school to career, etc. It is developing a very valuable cumulative record of behavior observations in such situations for each pupil in the public school system.

The research team has embarked on a number of specific studies: the handling of hostility and aggression in families; the conflicting roles the father plays in the business world and at home; how children handle dependency and fear-of-rejection feelings, and so on. More particularized case studies are focusing on one problem and its handling; for example, how a family handles the return of one of its members from a mental hospital.

Specific epidemiological surveys of people's attitudes can be of tremendous value in planning a mental health program. At the field research station of the National Institute of Mental Health in Phoenix, a survey was made of the community's awareness of the significance of warning signals preceding mental disorder:

exceptional nervousness, feelings of insecurity, habitual stealing in a child, etc. In reporting on the results of the survey, Dr. Robert Felix told a Congressional committee:

"This study conclusively demonstrates that only a small fraction of the population of the United States is now prepared to recognize the signs and symptoms of mental illness unless the patient appears to be violent or threatening."

More studies such as the Nova Scotia, Wellesley, and Phoenix ones are needed, for they pinpoint family and social pressures and attitudes which can be corrected, or at least recognized and dealt with realistically.

21. EVALUATION

AND

FOLLOW-UP

PROBABLY the greatest single weakness of psychiatry today is its inability to present sound, statistical appraisals of the various treatments in common use. In a talk to the 1955 Mental Hospital Institute of the American Psychiatric Association, I pointed out that those of us who have the task of justifying increased expenditures for psychiatric treatment are continually handicapped by the absence of reliable data as to just what these treatments have accomplished in the past. We are utterly fed up with the Lydia E. Pinkham type of testimonials we find in the psychiatric literature. Only rarely does one encounter a treatment evaluation predicated upon a wide sampling and the use of rigid scientific controls.

Research into the Effect of Shock Therapies

While the various shock therapies are of considerable value in the treatment of many major mental illnesses, very little research has been conducted on the effect of shock treatments on the basic human metabolism. Why is electroshock effective, for example, in the severe depressions having their onset during the middle years? What does it do to the body? What metabolic changes occur which can then be related to behavioral improvement?

"We use shock therapies with the hope of altering the underlying pathologic state, whether physiological or morphologic [structural], and by such a fundamental attack on the underlying

259

processes affect directly the course of the disease. It must be admitted that in most instances the etiologic [causative] factors are unknown," writes Dr. Harold E. Himwich, one of the country's outstanding researchers. "We are therefore placed in the baffling position of attacking an unknown enemy in an unknown country. . . . Our methods of treatment are therefore crude at present. One means of refining our attack and giving it better direction is to analyze the effect of these treatments on the brain."

In insulin shock, where the patient goes into a comatose state because the insulin injection sharply lowers the blood sugar level, physiologists are in general agreement that the brain suffers a deprivation of its basic foodstuff—carbohydrate. Other parts of the body obtain their energy from both carbohydrate and fat, but the brain is the only organ completely dependent upon the former. As a result of this sudden loss of its basic foodstuff, the activity of the brain is slowed down considerably. As the blood sugar level falls, the oxygen supply drops and the brain waves slow down. At the termination of insulin shock, when glucose is given to restore the blood sugar, oxygen returns and the rapid brain waves are observed on the electroencephalogram.

In the convulsive therapies—electroshock and metrazol—the disturbances are quite different. The convulsions produced by these treatments, which resemble those common in idiopathic (of spontaneous origin) epilepsy, raise brain activity to such a high pitch that it cannot be sustained by the oxygen and sugar coming to the brain in the blood.

Therapeutically, the slower action of insulin shock, in which a convulsion is rarely produced, seems to have better results on the firmly implanted, hard-to-assault disease of schizophrenia, whereas the quick, convulsive actions of electroshock and metrazol shock are more effective in psychoses involving cyclic emotional disturbances (manic-depression, involutional melancholia).

Further research is desperately needed to find out why a certain shock treatment is more effective in one psychosis than another, and, more fundamentally, to trace the specific effects of shock on the entire bodily mechanism, with particular emphasis upon the endocrines. There are a score of theories which attempt to explain why shock treatments are effective. While there is some general agreement that the shock somehow breaks up the rigid, inflexible defense patterns which have frozen into a severe psychosis, forcing the patient to move out of his shell and back to reality, there is great dispute as to how and why this occurs. Drs. Paul Hoch and Lothar B. Kalinowsky of the Columbia College of Physicians and Surgeons, in their very calm and objective book *Shock Therapies,* made a noble attempt to assess the claims and counterclaims of the various partisans. At the 1950 Milbank Conference, Dr. Kalinowsky tried a summation of the various explanations for the success of shock in these words:

"There are psychologic theories which involve the effect of mechanisms in the patient's fear of death, his wish for punishment, and other psychologic reactions to the treatment. They can be easily disproved by such observations as, for instance, that in electric shock a generalized seizure as response to the electrical stimulus is therapeutically effective in the vast majority of such favorable conditions as depressions, while the same procedure producing only a substantive unconsciousness is therapeutically ineffective, although it involves the same psychologic experience for the patient.

"Everything in our clinical experience points to an organic explanation for the therapeutic effectiveness of these treatments which, undoubtedly, are organic in nature. . . . The approach of the physiologist to our understanding of this mode of action seems to be the only promising one. The work by Dr. Himwich and others in this direction cannot be encouraged enough because only by finding the effective agent will it be possible to replace the crude and empiric methods of today with more rational and less drastic procedures."

Recently, there have been a number of attempts to use and evaluate new treatments not as drastic as the shock therapies. One of the most interesting has been the development of a new type of treatment—photoshock. This consists of giving the patient a small dose of a convulsant drug, Azozol, following which cerebral stimulation is induced by intermittently flickering a light in front of the patient's eyes. The convulsive seizures produced by this new therapy are much milder and have a more gradual onset than those produced by conventional electroshock methods. Because of the mildness of the seizures, it is possible to study the effect of the photoshock on the brain waves through electroencephalographic recordings.

Dr. George A. Ulett and a group of associates from the Washington University Medical School have set up one of the most elaborate experimental research designs in an effort to test the effects of photoshock. Over a twelve-month period, they combed a sixteen-hundred-patient admission group to a mental hospital to get a small number of patients who could be scientifically paired off into four groups: convulsive photoshock, subconvulsive photoshock, regular electroshock, and the control group which received no shock treatment.

In a preliminary report on the first three years of the experiment published in the *Bulletin of the Menninger Clinic,* Dr. Ulett stresses the vital importance of having a control group against which to measure efficacy of therapies. He writes:

"The final proof of the value of any therapy can only lie in its ability to improve the condition of, or cure, individuals who otherwise would continue to suffer psychiatric symptoms or would recover only after much longer periods of hospitalization and care. While most previous research seems to indicate that the shock therapies *do* alleviate symptoms and shorten hospitalization time, still the aforementioned difficulties of comparing data obtained at different times on different samples and with varying amounts of incidental therapy make it imperative that a control group be studied *in conjunction with* treatment evaluation."

If Ulett's admonition was heeded, a large percentage of the "scientific" papers now published in the psychiatric journals would be returned to the authors with the request that they do comparison studies on their wondrous new "treatments" before presenting them to a palpitating audience as panaceas. An astounding amount of faith healing and self-hypnosis passes today for scientific, controlled experimentation among some of the more prominent psychiatric cults.

A number of careful evaluative studies are needed to test the claims being made for many new therapies. For example, the last few years have seen the emergence of a whole school devoted to the propagation of carbon-dioxide therapy. The carbon-dioxide treatment consists of inducing anesthesia in the patient by administering a combination of oxygen and carbon dioxide over a five-to-eight minute period. The resultant drop in oxygen in the brain induces increased cerebral activity following a short period of unconsciousness.

Dr. L. J. Meduna, the distinguished father of metrazol shock, has moved away from his early love of metrazol to a passionate advocacy of carbon dioxide, which he has administered more than twenty thousand times, with as many as one hundred and fifty treatments to a patient. However, in his book on carbon-dioxide therapy, Meduna gives the reader little outside of his own personal experience with the treatment.

At the 1950 Milbank Conference, Dr. Heinz Lehmann of McGill University gave a brief paper on the use of nitrous oxide, which produces effects similar to those of carbon dioxide. In discussing the difficulties of scientific evaluation of a treatment, Dr. Lehmann voiced the almost universal complaint of his scientific colleagues who are continually pounced upon by the apostles of one school or another.

"When we give a physical treatment, the rabid psychodynamicist might call it a sadistic assault, and when we try to interpret what this treatment means to the patient, the organicist might accuse us of philosophic speculation," Dr. Lehmann moaned. "And the 'constitutionalist' will not even look at our results because we cannot furnish him with the pedigree of the patient. Yet no matter what they say, I think we are all practicing more or less integrated psychiatry and, therefore, I am going to present the treatment for what it is: one of the treatments in psychiatry."

Evaluations at the State Hospital Level

With a patient population in excess of half a million, the state mental hospital system offers an almost ideal proving ground for setting up comparative studies on the efficacy of various treatments. However, until the advent of the new drugs, very little advantage was taken of the research opportunities presented by the availability of such a large mass of patients in a relatively closed system.

At the Stockton State Hospital in California, a pioneer study has been completed on the value of "total push" therapy. Total push is an all-out effort using all known available treatments and a large number of skilled therapists, to surround the patient with the optimistic conditions conducive to recovery.

In the Stockton experiment, four hundred male patients were selected from the chronically ill groups. They were then split up into groups of two hundred each, matched as closely as possible as to age, length of hospitalization, education, etc. Patients in the control group received the same "treatment" as the rest of the patients in the hospital. Those in the experimental group were placed in two special cottages, with a much larger staff assigned to them. Group therapy sessions were held, a lot of medical attention was given for minor physical ailments, extra attention was given to the preparation and serving of food, and so on.

The results achieved so far document the thesis that intensified treatment with additional personnel pays off, both from the humanitarian and economic points of view. The number of patients in the intensive treatment group able to leave the hospital was almost three times that in the control group, and the same ratio held for patients able to leave the hospital on convalescent leaves. However, many more experiments of the Stockton type are needed to determine the specific methods by which such results are achieved.

There have been similar attempts to compare state hospital discharge rates over a period of years. The most ambitious and challenging is one reported on at the 1955 convention of the American Psychiatric Association by a team from Warren State Hospital in Pennsylvania. The study covered discharge and readmission rates to Warren State of all schizophrenics for a forty-year period, from 1913 through 1952. In presenting the paper, Dr. Robert H. Israel, Warren State superintendent, unburdened himself of some powerful criticisms of both the quantitative and qualitative shortcomings of current evaluation studies.

" . . . Over-all statistics on discharges from mental hospitals are quite misleading because they report only on discharge rates in relationship to residual resident populations in the hospitals," Dr. Israel noted. "There have been a number of studies in which first admissions of schizophrenics are followed up to the point of hospital discharge or for varying periods after discharge, such periods ranging from one to twelve years. However, the number of cases in each series of follow-up reports is usually small. . . . Confusion also arises from the varying criteria which are used in defining 'improvement' or 'recovery.' . . . Over-all improvement rates, without regard to similarity of follow-up periods, range from 23 per cent to 53 per cent, with the majority of reports of improvement clustering around 40 per cent. There are, to the best of our knowledge, no studies at all which have followed massive numbers of first admissions to one hospital over such a long period of time that one could derive an historical picture of any changes which might have taken place in the prognosis for schizophrenic new admissions nowadays, compared with the patients of ten, twenty or thirty years ago."

The Warren State study avoided many of the previous pitfalls. It followed each individual admission to the point of discharge, and it standardized the term "discharge" to mean physical movement alive out of the hospital.

The study turned up some surprising data. Over the entire forty-year period covered in the survey, the discharge rate for schizophrenia had never been below 54 per cent. In the third decade, it rose to about 61 per cent, and in the 1943–52 period, hit a high of 72 per cent. These figures led the authors to some optimistic conclusions, tempered by their honest admission that the Warren State experience would not hold for many state hospitals with less active treatment and activity programs.

"The authors feel that this study, along with others completed and in process at the Warren State Hospital, demonstrates that the old pessimism about schizophrenia was quite unjustified, at least in cases of this illness coming to this hospital. From these studies it appears that three out of four schizophrenics currently coming to the hospital can be discharged and that only three out of ten of the discharged patients will require permanent readmission. These studies also seem to contradict the oft-expressed views that shock and other modern therapies have not really effected any change in prognosis for the schizophrenic patients. The figures demonstrate quite clearly a sharply improved outlook. There is no longer any reason for the family physician or the psychiatrist to talk in gloomy terms with the family of the schizophrenic patient. There is every reason to believe that new therapies and improvement of presently available therapies will brighten the already encouraging picture even more in the future."

Topeka State Hospital, which Dr. Karl Menninger and his colleagues converted from a snake pit to a hospital in the seven-year span from 1948 to 1955, recently released some interesting figures on discharge percentages. In 1948, for every three patients admitted, only one left the hospital cured or improved. In 1953, for every two who entered, one was discharged and one sent home on convalescent leave. The number of patients at Topeka State has dropped from eighteen hundred to fourteen hundred, a remarkable decrease when viewed against the yearly rise of patients in the majority of our state mental hospitals.

Increasing efforts are being made to compare present hospital populations with those in previous decades. Under the aegis of the National Institute of Mental Health, seven states—Arkansas, California, Louisiana, Michigan, Nebraska, Ohio, and Virginia—agreed to follow all patients admitted for the first time in 1948 for a full twelve-month period to determine at the end of that time how many had been discharged or released on trial visit in each disease category. These figures were then compared with some remarkably complete data on patients admitted to New York State hospitals in 1914.

The comparisons indicate very significant changes in the mental hospital population in a generation. While not as striking as the Warren State figures, the data indicate a considerable increase in the number of schizophrenics either discharged or on trial leave—56 per cent in 1948 as against 33 per cent in 1914. In the involutional psychotic group, the proportion of patients discharged doubled, from 35 per cent in 1914 to 70 per cent in 1948. On the other hand, patients with senile dementia increased significantly, from 27 per cent in 1914 to 42 per cent in 1948.

However, comparisons such as the above are quite crude. It is somewhat arbitrary to compare one state's discharge picture in 1948 with that of another state in 1914; the variables are almost endless. However, discussion of this pioneer study is useful, if for no other reason than to indicate the need for scores of additional, much more precise studies of significant changes in mental hospital populations.

Follow-Up of Patients

What happens to a mental patient after he is discharged and returned to the community? Did the treatment do him any good? Is he really strong enough to go back into the same family and job situation and now conquer the stresses which smashed him just a year or two back? Has he relapsed and returned to the same hospital, or to another?

You can ask scores of questions of this kind, but you will get few answers. The lack of adequate data on the whereabouts and welfare of discharged mental patients is a national disgrace.

In 1949, I talked to the chief psychiatric social worker at the Topeka State Hospital. In the previous year, Dr. Karl Menninger had taken over the staffing problems of a state hospital which had no trained social workers. Now there were eight. The patients valued them above all other therapists. Why?

"I guess it's because we have almost resurrected some patients from the limbo of lost identity," the chief social worker explained to me. "When we came to this hospital, there weren't even adequate records on many of the patients. We had to find out who they were. We became amateur detectives, hunting their long lost brothers, sisters, wives, children. We had to find out where they had lived before, what jobs they had had—really who they had been before they came here. We found a number who weren't really mentally ill, and we were able to discharge them to families which had been out of contact with them for as long as twenty years. Many of the patients who had left on trial leave were lost to us. Where were they? What were they doing? We had to introduce a new concept into the hospital—that of establishing the full and important identity of each patient and then making sure we would never lose it again, even after the patient was discharged."

Over the past six years, the medical and social service departments at Topeka State have done a remarkable job in ferreting out elderly people who are not really psychotic. By visiting relatives and by helping to find suitable nursing homes, staff workers have discharged more than three hundred nonpsychotic elderly people.

At the 1953 Mental Hospital Institute of the American Psychiatric Association, Dr. William L. Jacquith, Superintendent of the Mississippi State Hospital, reported that he had surveyed 180 state hospitals and found only a handful conducting any kind of research on what happens to their patients after they are fully discharged. Pointing out that state hospitals discharge approximately two hundred thousand patients a year, Dr. Jacquith said:

"I am of the opinion that one of the greatest sources of research lies in the forgotten files of our mental hospitals. There are certainly millions of our citizens who have been discharged from mental hospitals, yet our profession has done little to study their cases and the 'why' of their well-being. . . . Here we may find the answers to many of our unsolved problems in the practice of psychiatry, and in finding these answers offer new hope to the mentally ill."

Along the same lines, the Director of the National Institute of Mental Health had this to say in October, 1953, to the House Interstate and Foreign Commerce Committee:

"Of patients who have been discharged, how many relapse and how soon? How are relapse rates related to diagnosis, sex, age on admission, length of hospitalization, therapy? Furthermore, we should like to know what social and environmental factors encountered by discharged patients are related to relapse or successful readjustment. Follow-up studies of patients discharged from tuberculosis sanatoria have proven very profitable in our understanding of that disease. There is no reason to suppose that such studies would be less valuable in the study of mental illness. Accurate follow-up data on discharged mental patients can serve as the basis for 'discharge prediction' techniques, weighting significant factors in the patient's life history. . . . Furthermore, better understanding of relapse factors would greatly aid the development of rehabilitation programs for patients, while they are still in the hospital and later when they have returned to the community."

A Significant Follow-Up Study

The oldest private hospital for the mentally ill in the country, the Pennsylvania Hospital, has recently published some very important data covering one period, 1925–34, preceding the use of shock treatments, and the period 1940–46 when shock treatments became standard procedure at the hospital. The study has followed both groups of patients for five years after discharge in an effort to evaluate the effectiveness of shock treatments.

In the schizophrenia study, 393 patients admitted during the period 1925–34 are compared with 440 patients admitted in the 1940–46 period when insulin and electric shock series were frequently used. On the surface, the results are encouraging. Twenty-two per cent of the 1940–46 group maintained recoveries, as against 9 per cent in the 1925–34 group. Also, the rate of improvement was significantly higher in the 1940–46 group. However, Dr. Earl Bond and his colleagues at the Pennsylvania Hospital did some digging into the records of patients who were listed as recovered up to the fifth year, but then showed relapses. Dr. Bond summarized these findings in a report in the June, 1954, issue of *The American Journal of Psychiatry*:

"The shock treatments seem to be a push in the upward direction in schizophrenia: there are more recoveries sustained to the fifth year, more slightly improved, fewer unimproved, many more recovered and relapsed in the five years, and more recovered in the group that could not be followed. Relapsed cases, both in and later than the fifth year period, raise the question as to whether shock treatments are enough. . . . More patients recover and stay well under shock therapies but also more recover and relapse."

In the manic-depressive psychoses, the recovery rate in the 1940–46 group is not much higher than in the 1925–34 group—66 per cent after five years as against 64½ per cent. Electric shock did shorten the attacks, so that among the recovered cases the average hospital stay was only a little more than two months as against four and a half months in the earlier 1925–34 group. However, the earlier group sustained recoveries better than the shock group. Of 227 manic-depressives who were discharged as recovered after a series of electric shock treatments, 65 broke down in the first year, 66 from the second to fourth years, and 9 in the fifth year. Only 87 maintained the recovery for five years.

In the involutionary psychoses, shock proved the most effective. It reduced the average stay from twelve months to two months, and it produced twice the number of recoveries in the later group over the earlier group, both initially and five years after admission.

The Pennsylvania Hospital studies offer several significant findings. They document the effectiveness of shock treatments in shortening hospital stays and in giving patients additional years in society. However, they also point up the failure of these shock treatments to put a really solid foundation under many so-called "recoveries." They highlight the need for more basic knowledge of the workings of the human metabolism, so that rational rather than empirical treatments may be given some day.

As noted in previous chapters, the same basic evaluation needs hold for the newer drugs. Although most investigators agree that the drugs produce a more durable, basic improvement than shock therapy, much more evidence is needed to substantiate these claims. In recognition of this need, the National Mental Health Committee devoted its major efforts in 1955 to presenting the case for a nation-wide evaluation of both the therapeutic and the metabolic action of all new drugs being used in clinical practice.

Leaders in American psychiatry are becoming increasingly convinced of the urgent need for more precise evaluation techniques. Within a week's time in October, 1954, two of the top authorities on psychiatric therapy, speaking at widely distant points of the compass, sounded the call to arms.

Addressing the Sixth Mental Hospital Institute of the American Psychiatric Association in Minneapolis, Dr. Lauren H. Smith, distinguished Philadelphia psychiatrist and vice-chairman of the American Medical Association Council on Mental Health, warned that psychiatric research was seriously endangered by this indifference to scientific evaluation.

"At the present time there are only about a dozen good statistical evaluations in the whole psychiatric literature that are carefully made both with respect to immediate results and follow-up studies which also include comparison of the effect of hospitalization alone or different forms of psychotherapy," Dr. Smith told Institute members. "Yet these statistics provide little orientation for future investigations on somatic treatments. This lack of orientation, or frame of reference, constitutes perhaps the greatest block for scientific progress in psychiatric research. The need of a solid foundation that rests on scientific criteria is well recognized and can be alleviated only by research projects adhering strictly to present concepts in psychiatry and correlating them with basic sciences. There is too much speculation and a tendency to play on hunches without an appreciation of psychophysiological principles."

A few days later, at a symposium on directions of current progress in psychiatry held in Washington, D.C., Dr. Paul Hoch, Chairman of the Committee on Therapy of the American Psychiatric Association, pleaded for a better methodology in evaluating treatment.

"We . . . lack a comprehensive methodology of evaluating improvement in a patient," Dr. Hoch told his colleagues. "Criteria of improvement are judged by different psychiatrists in different ways, because there is no agreement as to criteria. For example, one psychiatrist judges a patient's improvement on social adjustment, another on sexual adjustment, and a third on insight. Some use descriptive manifestations, others special psychodynamic formulations which vary with the different psychodynamic schools. . . .

"The lack of evaluation of therapy is especially conspicuous in the realm of psychotherapies. The efficacy of many of these therapies rests on belief, not on scientific factual evidence. There have been very few systematic attempts to evaluate claims concerning psychotherapy. In fact, there is virtually no precedent for studying effects of psychotherapy in any form of mental disturbance by a control design. The opinion is often expressed that no form of psychotherapy can ever be evaluated by a control design because of the irreducible differences between patients and therapists, the multifactorial and intangible nature of the therapeutic process, etc. Just because of these doubts, experiments in evaluation of psychotherapy are urgently needed. . . . What kind of patient needs what kind of psychotherapy, which one will benefit most from a certain form of psychotherapy are unsolved issues. Conclusions about short psychotherapy versus prolonged psychotherapy, symptomatic psychotherapy versus reconstructive psychotherapy are based on subjective clinical impressions, not on scientific evaluations."

Rehabilitation of the Mentally Ill

Through the superb leadership of Dr. Howard A. Rusk, rehabilitation of the physically handicapped is at last becoming an important segment of medicine. Rehabilitation of the mentally ill has lagged far behind, with old prejudices and fears playing a large part in slowing its advance. In the past few years, however, there has been an increasing development of family care and foster home programs which help the mentally ill individual back into community life.

Both the Federal government's Office of Vocational Rehabilitation and the National Institute of Mental Health are pioneering new programs in rehabilitation of the emotionally handicapped. The latter is aiding in the financing of several projects of great interest. One, being conducted at a state hospital, is designed to measure the effectiveness, cost, and savings resulting from a carefully planned rehabilitation program. Another, under the sponsorship of a school of public health, is designed to measure both those community influences which tend to support and to continue the rehabilitation of discharged mental hospital patients and those which tend to crush even the most promising recovery. Many more studies along these lines are needed. It is folly to spend thousands of dollars on the treatment of a patient, only to see that patient's struggle toward recovery smashed by unknowing people and excessive environmental stresses.

There are a few shafts of light pushing through the current darkness. Down in New Orleans, Dr. Ian Stevenson of the Louisiana State University Medical School did some work in 1953 on a group of supposedly hopeless unemployables crippled by severe emotional handicaps. After short periods of psychiatric treatment at New Orleans' Charity Hospital, a number of them were taken off the relief rolls and placed in gainful occupations. These people are now paying taxes instead of costing the State of Louisiana thousands of dollars each year.

However, much more needs to be done. At the 1955 convention of the American Psychiatric Association, Past President Dr. Kenneth Appel publicly spanked his colleagues for their indifference to rehabilitation.

"In 1943, the Barden-Lafollette amendment to the Federal Rehabilitation Law was passed," Dr. Appel pointed out. "By this law every psychiatrically disabled patient is entitled to federal help in job finding, vocational guidance and training, books, tuition, transportation and maintenance. Very few psychiatrists have apparently ever even heard of these facilities. In 1948, only five states offered such services to more than one hundred cases of mental illness. . . . Rennie demonstrated that only 23 per cent of potentially employable discharges from Brooklyn State Hospital asked for rehabilitation services. At Norwich State Hospital, a review of charts revealed that in 62 per cent of patients on convalescent status no reference was made to future employability. These statistics suggest that rehabilitation is often not considered in the therapeutic program."

Turning to the brighter side of the picture, Dr. Appel cited the tremendous effectiveness of rehabilitation techniques in the few instances where they had been applied to the psychiatrically disabled.

" . . . There are many pleasing statistics which demonstrate the value of rehabilitation," Dr. Appel informed his colleagues. "For example, in the Traverse City State Hospital in Michigan as many as seventy patients a day worked out in 1945. In Iowa, of forty-six patients placed out in family care, only ten returned and, in 20 months, $27,000 was saved by the state and earned by the patients. At the Roanoke Veterans Hospital, where an active rehabilitation program is in use, only nine out of sixty-eight patients who left the hospital in the last three years have returned. . . . In New York State, recovery of family care patients averaged 30 per cent higher than in institutions. It should be emphasized that, generally speaking, these were chronic long continued hospital cases who would not have left the hospital had it not been for the program. . . . In Boston's Southard Clinic in 1951, 175 potential new hospital admissions were maintained in the community and seventy-three former patients were prevented from relapsing. It was estimated that this operation saved the state an ultimate $683,000."

At hearings last year before the Senate Subcommittee on Health, E. B. Whitten, Executive Director of the National Rehabilitation Association, documented a disheartening story of resistances to rehabilitation of the psychiatrically disabled.

"I think there are twelve or fifteen states that have one or more counselors working in the mental hospitals," Whitten told the Senators. "In practically all instances, those arrangements have been made at the initiative of the rehabilitation people and not at the initiative of the people who operate the mental hospitals. And I regret to have to say that, because I think the initiative really should have come from the other direction. . . .

"Now to show you the extent to which this has gone, in 1954 3,790 mentally handicapped people were rehabilitated by the state agencies—rehabilitation agencies. That number constitutes 7 per cent of the total number rehabilitated during the year, although I am sure everybody would agree that the potentiality for caseload there is many times higher than that proportion would indicate."

Among the many reasons mentioned by Whitten for this shamefully low percentage of rehabilitation of the psychiatrically disabled, here are just a few cited in his official testimony:

"Some problems have been revealed in this experimental work in rehabilitation. For one thing, it has been awfully difficult for rehabilitation agencies to find the people to do this job. In the first place, it is difficult for them to get consultative services from psychiatrists and from psychiatric social workers who might be expected to lead in the training of the remainder of the rehabilitation staff in order to handle these cases more efficiently.

"Now another problem that has been run upon is this, that even where you go to a mental institution and you make arrangements to provide the institution with this counseling service aimed at job placement, and you place your counselor there, you find after a year or two of frustration that the concept of rehabilitation is not really accepted by the people in the hospital. They have given academic acceptance to it by allowing a counselor to come there, but the concept has never trickled down, at all, from the person who gave permission to place a counselor there, to the members of the medical staff and other staff, so the counselor finds himself in a straitjacket wondering for a long time why he can't get anything done, and finally it dawns on him that they don't really understand what he is trying to do."

PSYCHIATRIC RESEARCH: THE FUTURE

22. SOME
RESEARCH
TASKS AHEAD

It is enormously difficult to try to climb up on the mountain top to survey the big tasks ahead in psychiatric research. One of England's most distinguished psychiatrists recently summed up the size of the challenge in these words:

"As scientists, we must be prepared to wait perhaps another hundred years or more before even starting to learn how the human brain really works. I would not change my present line of work because we are only at the very beginning of its possibilities rather than near the end of an already over-explored and dogma-ridden field."

In practically every field of knowledge necessary to an understanding of the whys and wherefores of human behavior—from the involved workings of the endocrine system to the mechanisms involved in the transmission of nervous impulses—we are only at the very threshold, the very beginning of the accumulation of the tremendous body of data needed to round out a clear picture of the organic functionings underlying normal or abnormal behavior. We are as the Pilgrims who landed on the Rock; there is still a whole continent to be explored, and thousands upon thousands of man-hours of detailed chopping-away ahead of us.

Over the past few years, I have attempted to keep up with research on the organic aspects of mental illness. Most of it is buried in the technical magazines: *The American Journal of Psychiatry;*

The Archives of Psychiatry and Neurology; The Journal of Nerv-
ous and Mental Disease; The Journal of Clinical Investigation; The
American Journal of Physiology; The Proceedings of the Associa-
tion for Research in Nervous and Mental Disease, and many, many
more. Occasionally a blessed book comes along that attempts a
description of the new plants being raised in the psychiatric vine-
yard. Books such as R. G. Hoskins' *The Biology of Schizophre-*
nia; Hans Selye's *Stress;* Robert G. Heath's *Studies in Schizophre-*
nia, and a few others of like nature give the layman a view—somewhat restricted and involved, to be sure—of the new lines of experimentation.

Here we face one of the biggest problems in convincing the
American people and their legislative representatives of the desira-
bility of supporting greatly enlarged research on the biologic aspects of mental illness. Most of the physiologists, chemists, neuro-
pathologists, anatomists, *et al.,* who are doing a great deal of the
painstaking exploration of the vast continent of the mind are poor
communicators. True, it is a very difficult job to explain to a person
who has only a limited knowledge of the physiology of the body
what you are attempting to do in studying cerebral blood circulation
or in investigating the output of the adrenal glands under stress.

However, that it can be done is readily seen when one thinks of
the job general medicine has done in this country in educating the
public to an understanding of both the nature of many disease processes and the need for further research. For example, both in pamphlets and in several superb films, the American Cancer Society has
spelled out the story of cellular growth and its aberrations in remarkably clear fashion. When the Cancer Society testifies each year
before House and Senate Appropriations committees in support of
additional research funds for the National Cancer Institute, the
congressmen are not inundated with a flood of indigestible concepts. Dr. Cornelius P. Rhoads, Scientific Director of the Sloan-
Kettering Institute, uses films, slides, and a number of graphic devices of his own creation to spell out the basic problems in cell
growth. Dr. Sidney Farber of Boston's Children's Hospital makes
the devastating course of leukemia a dramatic and not easily forgotten thing. And that job of education has paid off beautifully.
In the floor debates in both House and Senate on the cancer appropriations, you hear very few passages that give off the ethereal

aura of the "ghost" factory. The congressmen have learned to toss around "metastasis" and "carcinoma" with the greatest of ease, and no professional translators are employed during the debate.

In the field of psychiatric research, Dr. Heath of Tulane is one of the few who has succeeded in giving the Congress the "feel" of basic physiologic investigation. Through the use of films, he was able to convey to a House Appropriations subcommittee a real understanding of his complex neurological experiments in stimulating deep areas of the brain. The education "took," too; the following year, when a different set of witnesses appeared, they were peppered with a number of intelligent questions on Heath's work.

Heath is successful in this regard because he has given a great deal of thought to the problem of communicating his complex ideas. For a demonstration of this most difficult of arts, I commend to one and all the opening chapter of *Studies in Schizophrenia,* a masterful presentation of a series of quite advanced physiological concepts.

Because the biological boys have this communication difficulty, they feel they are not getting a sufficient share of what little psychiatric research money there is, both governmental and private. One of them complained about it this way recently:

"Look at the bulk of the research grants which are made by the National Institute of Mental Health. They go to support endless studies in psychotherapy, or elaborate epidemiological surveys as to who in the community has what mental illness, what economic class he comes from, and whether or not he ever used a yo-yo when he was a child. They get taxpayers' moneys for these surveys, and yet they can't even define the metabolic characteristics of the disease they are looking for. They get these grants because the psychotherapists and epidemiologists are skilled verbalists who have been busy all their lives communicating their lack of information in very persuasive fashion. We in the organic fields don't have these skills and, besides, we don't have proportionate representation on the study sections which make the grants."

If the above indictment is valid, and there are many who would dispute it violently, the onus really falls on the plaintiffs. In the competition for research moneys, they must learn the techniques required to get their ideas across to the public.

That they have ideas—hundreds of exciting ones with great promise in the treatment of mental illness—is all too apparent to anyone who digs into the technical literature. To describe these ideas in detail would require a book in itself. In the following pages, an attempt will be made to highlight some of the more challenging ones. This summary owes much to a remarkable symposium, "The Biology of Mental Health and Disease," conducted by the Milbank Memorial Fund in 1950. At that symposium, more than one hundred scientists working mostly in organic aspects of mental illness spent four days trying to chart the present status of knowledge in the various fields and to project future lines for fruitful inquiry. The general impression gained from the more than six hundred pages of recorded proceedings is of a small band of dedicated men with much to explore and so little in the way of personnel and financial support with which to do the job.

The Chemical Constitution of the Brain

Lipids (organic substances which are insoluble in water and have a greasy feel) are the main components of brain tissue. Chemists have been working on lipids for the past century and a half, but only recently have tools been developed to study them minutely.

Brain proteins are also important brain constituents, and most, if not all, brain proteins are linked with lipids in the form of lipoproteins. As to what we know about these proteins, here is what Dr. J. Folch-Pi, Director of Scientific Research, McLean Hospital, Waverley, Massachusetts, has to say:

"In the case of brain proteins the span of our knowledge was comprehensively reviewed in the book, *Chemistry of the Brain* by Dr. I. H. Page in 1937. One-half page was devoted to the subject out of a total of 430 pages."

Pointing out how little we know of the vitally important development of brain tissue from its inception as a neural tube to its fulfillment in the adult brain, Dr. Folch-Pi continues:

"This is a fascinating subject of study and such work as has already been done promises to be a rich and rewarding field of research for biochemists. Most of our present knowledge has unfortunately been gathered by methods that have become obsolete. . . ."

New methods are being developed for the isolation of these various minute brain components. A technique has been devised for the preparation of pure brain lipids, and several new lipids and lipoproteins have been discovered.

Knowledge of the kind Folch-Pi and his colleagues are seeking is absolutely essential to an understanding of the basic workings of the brain, yet their work is little known and suffers from a severe shortage of technicians.

Cerebral Circulation and Metabolism

Basic to an understanding of the brain is the study of its blood flow and its oxygen consumption. Many of the modern drug treatments for mental illnesses achieve an appreciable part of their effect through disruption of the existing oxygen flow through the brain. However, these effects are achieved empirically, without any real understanding of just what occurs.

Studies of schizophrenic patients subjected to insulin shock therapy have shown that while the cerebral blood flow stays comparatively constant throughout the whole procedure, the oxygen consumption of the brain shows profound changes.

Recently, a few studies of great importance have been conducted upon patients suffering from senile dementia. These studies have shown, first of all, a somewhat higher blood pressure in the senile psychotics because there is definite hardening of the arteries. Further, cerebral blood flow in the seniles is considerably below normal and is connected with the narrowing of blood vessels in the aging brain. The oxygen consumption of seniles is also much below par. From these studies, Dr. Seymour Kety, the distinguished physiologist who is Scientific Director of both the National Institutes of Mental Health and Neurological Diseases and Blindness, concludes:

"It is suggested that this reduction in oxygen consumption is on the basis of a reduction in blood flow and that the oxygen consumption change is responsible for, or in some way associated with, the mental changes in this disease."

An increasing number of scientists are in agreement with Dr. Kety that improvement of blood flow and oxygen consumption in aged patients would release untold numbers from our mental hospitals. It certainly holds more promise than rug-weaving and television.

Kety has observed no significant differences between the schizophrenic brain and the normal brain with respect to blood flow and oxygen consumption, but he is strongly persuaded, based upon several pioneer studies, of a definite correlation between the oxygen consumption of the brain and the mental functioning of an individual.

The effect of a deficiency of oxygen (anoxia) upon the nervous system and the brain is being studied by several basic science teams. These studies have shown that oxygen deficiency induces marked structural alterations in the brain, with consequent impairment of behavior.

Dr. William F. Windle and his team at the University of Pennsylvania have been working on the problem of severe oxygen deficiency during the birth of many infants.

"Not only do many infants die each year at birth because of asphyxiation, but many others are deeply asphyxiated and heavily narcotized at birth, and yet survive," Dr. Windle writes. "From clinical observations it would seem that some of the latter suffer permanent damage to the central nervous system as the result of asphyxia. . . . One may raise the question, do infants suffering asphyxia at birth, but escaping symptoms of permanent brain damage, reach maturity with neural mechanisms fully equal to those of individuals born normally?"

In describing the results of a large number of experiments in which severe lack of oxygen was produced in guinea pigs, Dr. Windle, now Chief, Laboratory of Neuroanatomical Sciences, National Institute of Neurological Diseases and Blindness, continues:

"We are prone to blame inferior human mentalities on poor environment and especially on defects of the germ plasm. It is probable that asphyxiation at birth is partly responsible in man as it was in our guinea pigs."

Dr. Ross A. McFarland of the Harvard School of Public Health has done a number of experiments, including some at fantastically high altitudes in the Andes Mountains in Chile, on chemical changes in the brain resulting from varying degrees of oxygen deficiency. He sums up his findings in this way:

"The approach is a biologic one, demonstrating that sensory and mental deterioration and even loss of insight may result from altered metabolism in the nervous tissue. This concept is in sharp contrast to the view that repression or regression influenced by emotional mechanisms form the basis of certain mental diseases."

Dr. Alvin L. Barach of Columbia University and Dr. Harold E.

Himwich of the Galesburg State Research Hospital in Illinois have further observed in several experiments that normal persons kept in artificially high oxygen concentrations for as long as sixty days do not suffer any impairments, but persons with cerebral arteriosclerosis become "irrational, paranoid, depressed or grandiose." They are unable to explain the mechanisms underlying these impairments.

The Nervous System and Its Electrical Activity

From microscopic examination of the neuron, the nerve cell which is the structural unit of the nervous system, to large investigations and electrical stimulations of precisely mapped zones of the brain, a beginning has been made for several decades of work ahead in relating the physical activity of the complex human nervous system to its end result—human behavior, whether normal or abnormal.

The most dramatic development in increased understanding of the workings of the nervous system has been the remarkable growth of the science of electrophysiology, the recording of changes in the electrical output of nerve cells. As Dr. Mary A. Brazier of Massachusetts General Hospital puts it:

"The growth and development of electrophysiology has worked a profound change in neurophysiology in the last twenty-five years. I do not mean only the experimental advance, but the change in concepts of the nervous system. In brief, it is a change from the concept of a passive, static nervous system to an active dynamic one.... No longer do we think of the nervous system as having to respond only when it is stimulated."

This dynamic concept of the nervous system as a vast electrical network, superbly co-ordinated and integrated in the healthy but punctuated with "shorts" in the abnormal, is at the very foundation of the revolutionary work of Heath and of others in the field of electrical stimulation.

The challenge is to relate this electrical activity of the brain to specific behavior. If this is done, then one can apply the very electrical forces which nerve cells exhibit to improve their functioning and possibly normalize certain abnormal behavior patterns. As Dr. George H. Bishop of the Washington University School of Medicine states it:

"Every chemical process in a nerve cell is presumably represented by an electrical charge, and every electrical phenomenon presumably correlates with mental function. However precisely measured, at present these potentials are in a sense nonspecific; an electrical change does not tell what chemical change produced it, nor what mental phenomenon results from it. But we recognize that all electrical changes in tissues are electrochemical, and no physiologist would hesitate to presume a fairly inclusive correlation between the pattern of electrical activity in groups of neurons and the mental behavior that accompanies it. Between the oxidative metabolism of nerve cells and the mental behavior of the nervous system, the electrical record of activity is the natural bridge, the common medium, in which both of these can be evaluated. How shall we use this intermediary?"

However, in order to achieve this desired correlation between the electrical output of the nervous system and human behavior, there must be much more detailed knowledge of the various zones of the brain and their functions. We are many years away from a functional Rand-McNally of the human brain.

Dr. John C. Lilly, formerly of the University of Pennsylvania Medical School and now with the National Institute of Mental Health, has actually worked up a combination electrode array and camera device to record minute waves of electrical activity occurring in various parts of the brain. This device can portray the activity of only twenty-five small zones of the brain, but Lilly is years ahead of this in his thinking:

"This work hints that if we can work with many zones at once, we can begin to understand the brain mechanisms more thoroughly. Some of the implications of future work with several thousands or millions of zones at once or their equivalent can be imagined as follows: Given the necessary technical advances, it may be possible to by-pass the usual inputs and outputs through the body to and from the central nervous system. At that time with, say, a million subelectrodes or their equivalent, it may be possible for the first time to see and record enough of the electrical action of the brain concurrently with bodily behavior to begin to offer evidence useful in psychiatric research. Pushing this fantasy a little further than is cautious, we may imagine the day when one brain can electrically 'look' into parts or the whole of another brain directly without interposing the confusion inherent in communication by speech and hearing."

Tissue Study and Mental Illness

Tissue is an aggregation of similarly specialized cells united in the performance of a particular function. Over the past half-century, there have been numerous studies of the minute structure and function of these vital tissues, with particular relation to brain tissue and schizophrenia. Investigators at the beginning of the century were in more or less general agreement that the brain tissue of schizophrenics, examined in autopsies, showed no pathologic abnormalities. However, the invention of more refined chemical techniques and the use of living tissue in examination have led an increasing number of investigators to believe abnormal tissue-functioning is present in the schizophrenic brain and nervous system.

Dr. N. W. Winkelman of the Graduate School of Medicine of the University of Pennsylvania, who has devoted thirty years to the problem, sums up the more recent view in these words:

"The most common feature of the schizophrenic brain is not only a general decrease in the number of nerve cells in the cortex [outer layer] of the anterior [front] half of the brain but also numerous areas are found in which the ganglion [nerve] cells have either completely disappeared or the nerve cells are in the process of disintegration. . . . Different types of cell disease have been noted in schizophrenia. We have encountered a variety of cell changes; the most constant has been the so-called chronic cell disease, including cell shrinkage and ghost cells and at times loss of polarity."

On the basis of these studies, Winkelman concludes:

"It is universally agreed that there is a definite predisposition to the development of schizophrenia. It usually attacks those who are biologically vulnerable, known clinically as a 'schizoid personality.' . . . An increasing array of evidence in many related fields is accumulating to bolster the contention that schizophrenia should be included among the 'organic' psychoses."

Many able scientists would disagree with the above statement, but none would dispute the need for further exploratory work to test this and other findings on the role of nerve-tissue functioning in mental illness.

Endocrines, Personality, and Behavior

Since the turn of the century, there has been a fast-accumulating posse of investigators trying to track down the activities of the endocrines, those glands which secrete into the blood and the lymphatic vessels substances which are of vital importance to the maintenance of the human metabolism. Summing up progress to this point, Dr. Robert A. Cleghorn of McGill University writes:

"With the development of the experimental approach, more has been accomplished in the last fifty years than in the preceding five thousand. It has been possible to reproduce both deficit and excess hormonal states and to unravel, to some extent, the complexities of the interdependence of the endocrines and their various effects on form and function."

In recent years, the administration of hormonal agents has not only proved therapeutically beneficial—for example, ACTH and cortisone in arthritis—but has been observed to result in marked behavioral changes, such as pronounced euphoria and even mood changes reaching the stage of mania.

Many scientists believe that endocrine disturbances are implicated in many major mental illnesses. R. G. Hoskins, in his *Biology of Schizophrenia*, makes out a strong case for thyroid deficiency in schizophrenics. Dr. James J. Smith has argued strongly for adrenal insufficiency in the causation of alcoholism, and he has published several papers on the effective treatment of alcoholics with ACTH, the hormone which causes the release of cortisone. In psychotic depressions, a number of investigators have reported success with testosterone, the male hormone.

Probably the most exciting work in glandular abnormalities as they relate to mental illness has been going on since 1941 at the Worcester Foundation for Experimental Biology and at the Worcester State Hospital. The core of the studies at Worcester has been the finding that the adrenal glands of schizophrenics do not secrete normally under situations involving stress. These secretions have been measured in an elaborate series of urinary and blood tests.

Dr. Hudson Hoagland, Executive Director of the Worcester Foundation, states the group findings in this way:

"Schizophrenic patients as a group have failed to meet the daily stresses of living and have developed bizarre forms of behavior necessitating hospitalization. We were interested to find that these patients, in general, displayed abnormal and inadequate adrenal stress responses as compared to controls [normal people]."

In additional tests of his hypothesis, Hoagland and his co-workers have conducted experiments in which ACTH has been injected into both schizophrenics and normals. In the schizophrenics, the adrenal glands are unable to respond adequately to injections of ACTH.

Hoagland and his group realize that a tremendous amount of additional work needs to be done in the field of the adrenals, and they make no unwarranted therapeutic claims.

"We do not think that the adrenal abnormality is 'the cause' of schizophrenia, but that it may be one of several factors involved is possible, especially in view of our finding that the better a patient's adrenal responsivity, the better is his prognosis with electroshock therapy," Hoagland writes. " . . . We have used ACTH and cortisone therapeutically but without beneficial results. Cortisone is only one of fifteen adrenal steroids produced by the beef adrenal in response to ACTH. We believe it desirable to learn more specifically what the patients' adrenals produce in comparison to normal persons' before doing much more along therapeutic lines."

Enzymes and Mental Disease

Enzymes are organic compounds which govern the metabolic events that yield and utilize energy in all living cells. While it is generally agreed that their significance is as great, or greater than, any other chemical constituents of protoplasm, there has been a painful shortage of studies relating enzyme activity to mental illness.

Some leads show great promise. In the mental illness known as pellagra psychosis, which results from a deficiency of niacin, it is believed that the aberrational behavior is partially due to interference with normal enzyme activity. Enzymatic changes in brain tissue have been related to other psychoses, particularly those caused by organic damage to the brain. Recently, a pioneer study has reported abnormalities in the distribution of carbonic anhydrase, a very important enzyme, in the brains of schizophrenics.

With the advent of psychosurgery, it has become possible for physiologists, through biopsies, to obtain living tissue for the intensive study of enzyme activities. For example, at McLean Hospital in

Waverley, Massachusetts, Dr. Alfred Pope and his associates are using newly discovered microanalytic techniques for the minute examination of key enzymes. Of this work, Dr. Pope writes:

" . . . It seems probable that the study of cerebral enzymes can be one pertinent way of attacking the manifold problems related to the physical substratum of behavior, and that the use of quantitative histochemical [tissue-fluid measuring] technics not only has special advantages for such study but also may be counted on to furnish considerable insight into the finer chemical anatomy of the nervous system."

And Dr. Winifred M. Ashby, who has done the pioneer work on carbonic anhydrase, outlines the big problem ahead in these words:

"We are only at the threshold of the studies necessary for an understanding of the part that brain enzymes must play in mental disease. Practically all is in the future."

Heredity and Mental Disease

Probably no more significant psychiatric research has been done in the past several decades than that of Dr. Franz Kallman of the New York Psychiatric Institute on heredity as a factor in mental illness, with particular reference to schizophrenia, manic-depressive psychosis, and involutional melancholia.

In an elaborate series of studies of twins over a long period of years, Kallman has demonstrated dramatically the much higher incidence of mental illness among the blood relatives of persons already afflicted with one of the major psychoses. Furthermore, he has pushed his studies back to the fetal egg. Twins born of the same egg (identical twins) parallel each other in the onset of mental illness in families with a high incidence of the disease, whereas twins born of separate eggs show significant differences in the development of mental illnesses.

Kallman observes that his statistical investigations of the incidence of mental illness shows a remarkably consistent pattern of distribution in widely different population samples, irrespective of income levels, size of families, environmental stresses, etc. Putting a gentle damper on the psychodynamic boys, who go overboard in attributing mental illness to purely external stresses, he writes:

"The list of frustrations, known to produce no severe psychosis in some people, is practically unlimited and extends to physical hardships such as starvation, complete exhaustion, and prolonged malignant disease, to extreme emotional stress and to a great number of behavioral inadequacies of the parents. . . . From a genetic standpoint there is reason to believe, therefore, that some persons, namely the carriers of a specific type of predisposition or potential vulnerability, have the biologic capacity for reacting to precipitating environmental stimuli with either a schizophrenic or another type of psychosis, while this capacity is not possessed by a number of ordinary people."

The Kallman studies, patiently executed and beautifully carried out, have lent great weight to the organic school, which believes that psychotic mental illness is fundamentally a failure of the human metabolism to handle stress successfully. Its leaders agree with Kallman that the inheritance of a certain kind of metabolism is of crucial importance in the individual's ability to withstand the trials of life.

Commenting on the significance of Dr. Kallman's studies, Dr. Sheldon Clark Reed, Director of the renowned Dight Institute of Human Genetics at the University of Minnesota, writes:

"It is a source of amazement both to us and to the head social worker at the State Institution that so many of the patients turn out to have a common affected ancestor. The various branches of the large families of the rural Middle West are quite often unaware of their rather close blood relationship. . . . In the genetic counseling which we do for individuals and the county and state welfare agencies, we need such follow-up data on the expectations for schizophrenia and manic-depressive psychosis. We need it very badly and soon!"

And Dr. Jan A. Böök of the University of Lund, whose samplings in Swedish communities bear out Kallman's findings, comments:

"It is obvious that the genetic approach to the problems of schizophrenia and manic-depressive psychosis is not so pessimistic, deterministic or sterile as many psychiatrists are still inclined to believe . . . The genetic theory explains that only some individuals develop these psychoses and why they do. The psychodynamic approach has not been able to give a satisfactory answer to this question. Many observational facts contradict theories based on sociologic or psychic contamination, and there is much evidence in support of a theory of fundamental biological differences."

Summary

The foregoing is obviously a very truncated discussion of just a few areas in which psychiatric research might fruitfully pursue hundreds upon hundreds of leads in the next several decades. It is obvious to anyone who has even a superficial familiarity with biological studies of mental illness that it is one of the most neglected areas in the total medical research picture. It is inadequately staffed, poorly financed, and shunted off into the corner. There are only a few places in the country, such as the Worcester Foundation for Experimental Biology, where intensive interdisciplinary basic research can be pursued on a widespread scale. There is need for a hundred more Worcesters right now—solidly financed research institutes pulling physiologists, anatomists, neurologists, chemists, geneticists, and psychiatrists into a total-push attack upon the many unsolved mysteries of human metabolism.

In addition, there has been little effort to climb up onto the mountain top and plot out the big stretches of land to be surveyed and developed. Commenting on this, the report of the twenty-seventh annual conference of the Milbank Memorial Fund states:

"To the bystander some implications of this situation for research on the biological aspects of mental health and disease are plain. The data that have accumulated are, for the most part, unassembled and unorganized. There is little or no opportunity to cross professional lines, to meet together and trade experience. Hence, there is too little chance to broaden or sharpen individual research projects through inclusion of technics and viewpoints from allied specialties."

23. WHERE DO WE GO FROM HERE?

WHERE do we go from here? In strengthening public support of psychiatric research and training, what weaknesses must be overcome and what assets beefed up?

In undertaking such an analysis, the year 1955 serves as an ideal proving ground. It was one of considerable ferment in the mental health field. A number of singular victories were won, but the cruel absence of a strong nation-wide citizens' movement cost us dearly on a number of important fronts.

At the crucial Congressional level, we split a three-game series—we won one, lost one, and the third was called when the lights went out.

We took a pretty bad licking on appropriations for the National Institute of Mental Health. We proposed a Citizens' Budget of approximately $30,000,000, of which $8,000,000 was for construction of psychiatric research laboratories. The Eisenhower Administration proposed a little more than $17,000,000, with no moneys allocated to research construction.

We lost the ball game on the House side because we couldn't get into the ball park. Although we had appeared for a number of years before the House Appropriations Subcommittee having jurisdiction over moneys for the Institute, no citizen witnesses were heard in 1955. The House committee voted out the Eisenhower budget, plus an additional sum of $250,000 for research on mental deficiency obtained through the brilliant efforts of Congressman Fogarty.

The Senate Appropriations Subcommittee, under the brilliant leadership of Alabama's Lister Hill, did everything in its power to repair the damage. After hearing the evidence presented by our witnesses, it voted close to $22,000,000 for the Institute, the exact amount of our request except for research construction, which was handled in a separate bill. The Senate ratified this figure but, when the bill went to conference, the entire increase was wiped out. So we lost a million and a half for drug research, a million and a half to expand the training of desperately needed psychiatric personnel, and a million to provide more preventive clinics in all parts of the country.

We did a little better on research construction. The Senate Subcommittee on Health, also headed by Senator Hill, held three days of hearings on a bill providing $90,000,000 in matching grants over a three-year period for the construction of laboratory facilities in the fields of mental illness, cancer, heart disease, neurology, and arthritis.

Our witnesses—Dr. Robert P. Knight of the Austen Riggs Foundation, Dr. Gardner Murphy of the Menninger Foundation, and Dr. Robert T. Morse of the American Psychiatric Association—did a beautiful job. Dr. Murphy, attacking the present "horse-and-buggy provision for research" in scathing terms, moved the Senators deeply with these closing words:

"Research is often associated in people's minds with the problem of psychosis or insanity. But I would like, in concluding, to remind you that it is not only insanity but apathy, failure of nerve, demoralization, irresponsibility, alcoholism, drug addiction, gnawing fears, doubts, anxieties, self hate, and hate of one's fellows that often surrounds and leads into the problem of insanity and in the long run becomes ever more important. Insanity is, in a certain sense, the region of total eclipse around which the partial eclipse of human nature through mental anguish appears. If we believe in a vigorous mental health program, what can be more important than basic investigation into the roots both of psychosis and of the violence, irresponsibility, and apathy which threaten so many of our citizens?"

The research construction bill swept unanimously through the

Senate in July, but our real trouble came on the House side. Both the American Psychiatric Association and the National Mental Health Committee put heavy pressure on House members, but it wasn't enough to get the bill out of the House Interstate Commerce Committee.

Our failure on this bill pointed up again several damaging weaknesses in the national mental health movement. The National Association for Mental Health, the senior citizens' organization in the field, followed its usual dynamic policy of doing absolutely nothing. Afraid that some congressman might bite them—an unwarranted fear, since congressmen prefer good, vigorous beef—the leaders of the NAMH sat knitting and tatting in their custodial hayloft at 1790 Broadway in New York City while a few of us burned up down in Washington. The American Medical Association, powerful and prestigious in membership, finances, and Washington lobbyists, emitted a few negative burps and went about the business of trying to repeal the twentieth century by legislative rider.

Our one clear-cut victory came in the passage of the Mental Health Study Act of 1955, appropriating $1,250,000 in Federal assistance over a three-year period for a nongovernmental "nationwide analysis and reevaluation of the human and economic problems of mental illness."

The real steam which generated the nation-wide survey concept originated with Dr. Kenneth Appel. From May, 1953, to May, 1954, during his tenure as President of the American Psychiatric Association, Dr. Appel constantly pounded home the need for an entirely fresh look at our whole approach to the mentally ill. He wanted the decks swept clean, in the same manner in which the famous Flexner report of 1910 on the nation's medical schools had revolutionized medical education in this country, putting an end to scores of fly-by-night diploma mills and tying the modern training of physicians into the universities. Dr. Appel insisted that the broom-sweeping should be done by a nongovernmental commission, with private foundations supplying the major financing. He wanted this commission truly representative of all professional organizations in the field.

The idea really took hold in October, 1954, during an American Psychiatric Association-sponsored conference on research to which a number of private foundation representatives had been invited.

Pulling no punches, Dr. Appel attacked present programs for the care and treatment of the mentally ill as hopelessly outmoded and ludicrously out of tune with the industrial might and know-how of America. When Dr. Appel had finished, Dr. Leo Bartemeier, Chairman of the Council on Mental Health of the American Medical Association and a Past President of the American Psychiatric Association, got to his feet and echoed Dr. Appel's denunciation of conditions in our public mental hospitals. The Foundation people were deeply impressed, and the Field Foundation authorized an immediate grant of $10,000 to aid in the formation of a Joint Commission. The following January, the APA and the AMA invited seventeen allied professional organizations to a meeting to chart the first steps in the massive undertaking.

Independently of all this, several Senators were preparing legislation for national surveys. Senator William Purtell of Connecticut introduced, in the early days of the Eighty-fourth Congress, a bill providing for a Presidential Commission on Mental Health. Senator Hill, Chairman of the powerful Labor and Public Welfare Committee, preferred the nongovernmental approach. He called the American Psychiatric Association and the National Mental Health Committee in for a number of conferences, and together we drafted Senate Joint Resolution 46. We then did a little personal visiting, and we recruited thirty-one Senatorial sponsors for the Resolution.

The House Interstate Commerce Committee held hearings early in March, and Dr. Blain and I testified the first morning. There was an amusing touch the next day when the American Medical Association representatives testified. During 1953 and 1954, this same Committee, then under the chairmanship of Republican Charles A. Wolverton, had held extensive hearings on the whole national health picture. The brilliant Wolverton and his colleagues had constantly rapped AMA leaders for their negative testimony, demanding that they come up with a positive program which would endorse something more than "temporary" motherhood. As the AMA representatives testified in 1955 for the mental health survey bill, careful to qualify their cautious endorsements with liberal sprinklings of "temporary" and "limited," a number of the Committee members had a difficult time concealing their amusement. A ranking member of the Committee summed up Congressional feeling about the AMA testimony when he remarked to me, at the close of the hearing: "Never have so many negative words been used to endorse so few positive ideas."

The bill swept through the House in April, and then moved over to the Senate side where it encountered easy sailing. Senator Hill tacked the $250,000 for the first year of the study onto a supplemental appropriations bill for the Department of Health, Education and Welfare, and it rolled through the Congress.

Since the enactment of the legislation, things have moved at a rapid pace. The Joint Commission on Mental Illness and Health was formally incorporated late in the summer of 1955. It now comprises more than twenty powerful lay and professional national organizations. At the first formal meeting of the full Commission in Washington, D.C., on October 8, Dr. Appel was elected President and a sweeping series of objectives for the three-year study were adopted.

If it follows the high aspirations of Dr. Appel, Dr. Blain, and the other progressive leaders of the American Psychiatric Association, the Joint Commission can produce a document which will have a profound impact in burying for all time some of our obsolete concepts and practices in treating mental illness. However, it must constantly be on guard against those elements in American medicine which support the survey because it gives them another excuse for inaction during the period consumed by the study.

The actions of the American Medical Association will, in the final analysis, pretty much determine the success or failure of this ambitious survey.

After decades of looking the other way, the AMA has recently discovered that mental illness is the biggest health problem in the country. In 1952, it set up a Committee on Mental Health, and in 1954 it signified it really meant business when it elevated the Committee to Council status with a full-time executive director and a generous budget.

Its current President, Dr. Elmer Hess of Erie, Pennsylvania, means business. In his inaugural address at the 1955 AMA convention, Dr. Hess had more pertinent, courageous things to say about mental illness than all of his distinguished predecessors.

"One of the greatest medical problems in the United States today is that of mental and emotional illness," Dr. Hess told thousands of doctors at the Atlantic City meeting. "Leading psychiatrists believe that at least 50 per cent of all patients who come to physicians' offices have a mental or emotional disturbance along with their physical disability. And because at least half of our patients seem to fall in this category, I think that mental health becomes automatically a concern of all practicing physicians, not just of the psychiatrists. Currently about ten million Americans are suffering from mental and emotional disturbances and more than half of the nation's hospital beds are occupied by these patients. If any medical situation ever deserved the attention of every physician, this is it.

"In my book, the nation's physicians should be the leaders in any campaign to overcome the ravages of mental illness. Great numbers of mental patients could be returned to useful, productive lives if they receive the proper medical as well as psychiatric treatment. Instead, today we have a system of understaffed, overcrowded institutions in which the mentally ill have little hope for cure—they are virtually tossed on a human junk pile."

Mighty strong words! A decade ago, when we newspaper reporters used just such terms to describe conditions in the mental hospitals, our most severe critics were state medical society leaders who charged us with everything from "meddling" to "inducing unwarranted fears in the families of the mentally ill."

Dr. Hess did not content himself with indulging in a few generalities. In the body of his address, he proposed a number of specific ways in which the nation's physicians could transform themselves from Rip Van Winkles into powerful therapeutic agents for the mentally ill. Since the severe shortage of psychiatrists will be with us for another decade or two, his suggestions are of the utmost importance.

"There are a number of specific ways in which our members can help to put this program across," Dr. Hess informed his colleagues. "Physicians should take an increasingly active part in the development of more psychiatric units in general hospitals. Standards for such units are now published by the American Psychiatric Association.

"Another important step which we can take, and one which I have recommended previously, is that physicians give one day a week to work in state or county hospitals near their homes. They need our help desperately, and we should offer it. In some states arrangements have already been made for these hospitals to retain young physicians on a part-time basis as attending staff physicians. I believe this procedure should be encouraged, because it would be one good way to arouse the interest of general physicians in this type of work.

"I think that the interest of general physicians in mental health work can also be stimulated through development of residency training programs for nonpsychiatric residents in state mental hospitals. At least two states, Illinois and Massachusetts, have already developed programs of this nature. Others should be encouraged to follow suit.

"A suggestion has been made to me that state and county medical societies be encouraged to establish psychiatric consultation services for their general physician members. These services would be provided by the psychiatrists who are members of the societies. Consultation services of this nature now exist in Boston, New York, and San Francisco. I think this suggestion is worthy of serious consideration."

An excellent program, which I respectfully commend to the AMA's own Council on Mental Health. Although boasting a glittering array of psychiatric talent, the Council acts like so many characters in search of a script. Dr. Hess has prescribed for them a very fine one, and it is hoped they will busy themselves with its immediate production. The same holds for the forty state medical association committees on mental health, which Dr. Hess referred to very proudly in his address. Up to the present time, many of these committees continue to follow the conditioned reflexes of negativism. In his own state of Pennsylvania, Dr. Hess would be interested to learn that the state mental health committee has dragged a ponderous foot on an excellent bill to strengthen the state's central mental health authority. In Pennsylvania, as in many other states, the mental health committees are influenced too much by the reactionary medical lobbyists who "represent" medicine in the various legislative cloakrooms. The new broom must sweep some of this away before Dr. Hess's program can become a reality.

The American Psychiatric Association presents a picture almost the reverse of the American Medical Association's. Its programs and policies are clear-cut and progressive, and it has assumed broad public responsibilities which are a constant drain upon its limited manpower and finances. However, it wasn't until 1948 that it accumulated enough money to set up a central office with a full-time medical director.

Under the whirlwind leadership of Dr. Daniel Blain, the APA has been engaged in a constant effort to lift the standards of psychiatric care in this country. The Association is not content with publishing medical standards for the better treatment of mental patients. Its Central Inspection Board, despite chronic financial malnutrition, has inspected more than 120 state mental hospitals, and its painstaking reports have had an enormous influence upon both state aspirations and appropriations.

Dr. Blain's particular baby is the comprehensive state mental health survey. Since the pioneer one in Louisiana, valuable state blueprints have been completed in Indiana, Arkansas, and Kentucky. Currently surveys are under way in the pivotal states of Ohio and Pennsylvania.

A few fainthearts in the APA have constantly carped at this survey activity, arguing that the organization is too small to take on such big public responsibilities. They have also nervously warned about the dangers of politics, since these surveys are made for state governors. Blain has replied impatiently that if it is not the business of the national professional psychiatric organization to fight for better care for mental patients, then whose business is it?

The APA Governing Council has also shaken off a lot of barnacles these past few years. It now devotes considerable time to consideration of national and state legislation, and it has taken an increasingly forthright stand on both appropriations and proposed laws. Along these lines, the National Mental Health Committee is deeply in the debt of scores of prominent psychiatrists who, over the past seven years, have journeyed to Washington at their own expense to appear before Congressional committees.

Psychiatrists are found increasingly in legislative conferences and in Governors' offices. Dr. Blain bounces from state to state, appearing before legislative committees and advising state administrators on programs and policy. Dr. Will Menninger addressed joint sessions of the Ohio and Pennsylvania legislatures during the past year. In a number of states, psychiatrists play key roles on mental health advisory councils formed to blueprint new legislation for Governors and legislatures.

In evaluating the assets of the public mental health movement, top place must go to the governors of the forty-eight states and their operating mechanism, the superbly staffed Council of State Governments.

At the 1955 National Governors' Conference in Chicago, the state chief executives again proved they were far out in front of the professionals in tackling the root causes underlying our shabby care of the mentally ill. With Governor Williams of Michigan presiding at a special panel on mental illness, the Governors waived all polite preliminaries and opened up on the doctor shortage as the key factor in inadequate staffing of state mental hospitals. Governor George Craig of Indiana, who in the past three years has had his fill of professional obfuscation on the doctor shortage, compared the current competitive bidding contests between states for scarce psychiatrists to university raids upon rival football talent. Governor George Leader of Pennsylvania echoed his sentiments, pointing out that if it didn't stop the states would have to adopt "a reciprocal trade agreement for highly trained psychiatrists and staff workers."

State Government, the official publication of the Council of State Governments, printed the following summary of the highly charged discussion in its September issue:

"Attention first centered on what, it was generally agreed, was the most crucial present problem—obtaining and holding the trained professional personnel needed in the mental health field, including psychiatrists. With this, necessarily, was linked the training and educating of personnel.

"A number of Governors specifically decried current 'raiding' from state to state in order to obtain psychiatrists. As one of them summarized, the states must now compete with private medicine, with the federal government and with each other for trained mental health personnel. Governors underlined the necessity of increasing the total supply by drawing more young people into the profession and by giving them the training required.

"There was no disposition to minimize the difficulties to be overcome in this matter. One of the Governors, pointing to a present woeful inadequacy in the number of psychiatrists, nurses and other professionals, said the solution required, first, training of adequate numbers in the medical schools and, secondly, the willingness of many more doctors to choose service in mental hospitals over private practice. We do not have enough physicians, generally, in our smaller communities, he added; and the shortage of psychiatrists is still greater. In similar vein, another participant suggested a study that would evaluate how many trained mental health personnel are needed and that we look at the medical schools to see how big a gap exists between the number required and those prepared."

The Governors are very determined on this issue. On the concluding day of the conference, they unanimously passed a resolution directing the Chairman of the Governors' Conference "to appoint a committee to work with representatives of the American Medical Association and the American Psychiatric Association to seek means of increasing the number of doctors and other technical personnel available for state institution services."

Governor Williams was appointed chairman of the committee, and the other members include Craig, Harriman of New York, Knight of California, Hall of Kansas, Griffin of Georgia, Smylie of Idaho, Roberts of Rhode Island, and Foss of South Dakota. It is a powerful group, including in its membership governors who have tangled publicly on a number of occasions with leaders of organized medicine on the subject of the doctor shortage. Establishment of the committee is stern warning to the American Medical Association that the nation's governors are through listening to long-winded discourses about a plentiful supply of doctors. They want action, and there will be some hot words around the conference tables in the months to come.

At the state legislative level, tremendous increases in appropriations for psychiatric research and training continued to be the big story in the closing months of 1955. As one indication of the booming trend, an official memorandum drafted by the Council of State Governments for the 1955 Governors' Conference noted that "funds being set aside by the states for training in 1955 may be as much as five or six times the amount of any preceding year."

In a number of states, sweeping organizational reforms were instituted to emphasize the cardinal importance of research and training.

For example, in Ohio a new Bureau of Psychiatric Research and Training was created, headed by a psychiatrist with the rank of Assistant Commissioner. In addition, three psychiatric training institutes were established, in Cleveland, Cincinnati, and Columbus.

The three receiving hospitals in these cities will be converted to base units of the new institutes. These institutes will become associated training faculties on the order of the Massachusetts plan. They will be tied in closely with the medical schools in the three cities, and they will affiliate with surrounding private and public psychiatric facilities.

The Ohio legislature appropriated a whopping $10,000,000 for the first two years of the new training plan, making it the most ambitious ever launched by an individual state. Under the new program, Ohio will raise the number of psychiatrists in training in the three major cities by 340 per cent! Over and above this, the legislature provided sizable additional sums to increase the number of staff psychiatrists by 137 per cent, nurses by 140 per cent, and social workers and psychologists by 50 per cent.

The much smaller state of Florida is now engaged in an equally ambitious research and training undertaking. In addition to providing millions of dollars for two new state mental hospitals and a number of preventive clinics, the 1955 legislature passed major legislation creating a Council on Mental Health composed of six professionals and five members from the general public. This Council is given the job of planning and administering all research and training moneys in the state, with particular emphasis upon the granting of sizable training stipends for the production of additional psychiatrists, psychologists, social workers, and nurses.

The Florida Council plan is a direct outgrowth of the Florida research and training committee created to carry out a state survey as part of the Southern Regional Mental Health Program. I think it fair to state that Florida has effected more basic reforms in its mental health program than any other state in the country. The contrast between the medieval barbarism which I reported in 1949 and the magnificent ferment of 1955 is a striking tribute to the enlightened actions of an aroused citizenry.

Equally gratifying are recent developments in New York State. The appointment of Dr. Paul Hoch as State Mental Hygiene Commissioner in July dramatized, more than any other single action, the new importance of psychiatric research. Dr. Hoch is one of the nation's most gifted research workers, and the National Mental Health Committee is very proud to have had a part in working for his appointment.

Dr. Hoch has lost little time swinging into action. On September 14, he announced a series of projects designed to treat the mentally ill before they slide down the hill into chronicity. He is not only expanding intensive treatment facilities for new arrivals at a number of state hospitals, but is using after-care clinics and day-care hospitals to treat mental illness in the community. To obtain the additional psychiatric personnel needed for this ambitious treatment program, he is tapping the large private psychiatric manpower pool in the state, buying up scarce psychiatric time on a part-time basis.

Dr. Hoch is also pioneering in an attack upon arteriosclerosis and the senile psychoses, which together account for a staggering 40 per cent of New York State's first admissions to mental hospitals. He has set up special treatment teams to work on the rehabilitation of these oldsters, and is pushing expanded research upon the physiological phenomena underlying hardening of the arteries of the brain.

In striking a balance sheet of strengths and weaknesses in the mental health movement, we come last, and least, to the National Association for Mental Health.

Citizen action in the field of mental health has a proud early tradition to live up to. One magnificent citizen, Dorothea Lynde Dix, was responsible for the establishment or expansion of more than thirty mental hospitals in the United States and abroad during the middle decades of the nineteenth century. However, in the later years of her life, Miss Dix saw many of "her" institutions sink to the level of snake pits because of medical Toryism and public apathy. As Albert Deutsch has noted, it was beyond the capacity of any individual at that time to create a national citizens' organization to enforce better care for the mentally ill.

In the first decade of the twentieth century, Clifford Beers, a former mental patient, wrote *A Mind That Found Itself*. In the book, Beers outlined his plans for the creation of a strong national citizens' organization to work for better care and treatment of the mentally ill. On February 19, 1909, the National Committee for Mental Hygiene was born at a meeting in New York City.

Serving as its secretary for three decades, Beers proved an indispensable spark plug. Under him and under two excellent medical directors—Dr. Thomas W. Salmon, who served from 1915 to

1922, and Dr. Frankwood E. Williams, who succeeded Dr. Salmon and served until 1932—the old NCMH sponsored numerous state and local surveys of mental hospital conditions, played a vital role in the birth of the new profession of psychiatric social work, pioneered in fostering public understanding of the need for psychiatric classification and treatment of prisoners, and made its greatest contribution in leading the fight for more preventive services, particularly child guidance clinics.

Beers died in 1943, and the history of the citizens' mental health movement since then has been a pretty sorry one. World War II brought an enormously heightened interest in psychiatry, and in state after state major reform movements blazed into action. All across the land citizens were begging for technical help in building state mental health societies, but the reply of the National Committee was a feeble and inept one.

In Oklahoma, in 1945 and 1946, we built a strong citizens' movement by many a trial and many more errors. Most of these mistakes could have been avoided if we had had any kind of help from the national movement. After more than a year of pleading and ranting, we finally got one field worker for a couple of weeks. He gave us a considerable lift, but he was handicapped severely because the national organization treated him as though he were the carrier of an infectious disease. He and one co-worker were not even paid by the National Committee. Mrs. Albert D. Lasker, then Secretary of the NCMH, provided the funds because she saw the desperate need to channel this bursting citizen energy into permanent state and local mental health associations.

However, her fellow officers showed little enthusiasm for the field work project, and it collapsed after only two years of limited activity. At the 1948 annual convention of the Committee, I protested bitterly against the folding of the project to key staff members. I pointed out rather angrily that Clifford Beers, who had founded the pioneer state society in Connecticut in 1908, had stressed as one of the cardinal duties of a national organization maximum help in the creation and development of new state societies. I reminded them that for the past three years we in the field had been emphasizing the need for a set of manuals on state organization, programming, fund-raising, etc. I expressed my fear that this great citizen movement of the forties would prove just an-

other disheartening graph line in the boom-and-bust cycle of mental
health reform unless we got about the urgent business of setting up
some permanent guide lines and bench marks.

All to no avail. They retreated to the position the Committee had
taken in a one-sentence letter to me early in 1946. Bursting with
enthusiasm at that time, I had written the Committee a long letter
outlining the exciting developments in Oklahoma. I informed the
staff that a newly born, lusty infant recently christened The Oklahoma Committee for Mental Hygiene desired to affiliate with the
National Committee. Furthermore, we regarded this affiliation as
so vital to the future well-being of our precious baby that we were
willing to send $1,000 of our hard-earned campaign money to pay
for the privilege. Some weeks later, I received the following warm
expression of fellowship from the national offices in New York
City:

> The National Committee for Mental Hygiene has no mecha-
> nism for the affiliation of state mental health societies.

We survived this comradely note of cheer, but the National Committee began to slide deeper into the pit, controlled by a Board of
Trustees concerned mostly with its own self-perpetuation. The
large, weary staff continued to send out negative, dreary missives.

Preceding my tour of the Florida mental hospitals in 1949, the
newly formed Southeastern Florida Mental Health Society notified
the National Committee of my impending visit. A reply came from
the head of a section of the Committee supposedly devoted to encouraging state organization, informing the eager Floridians that
my contemplated safari was "premature." Premature? I was several decades late! And if I was premature, how premature then
was Dorothea Lynde Dix?

Sensing that the inactivity of the National Committee was creating a series of vacuums which had to be filled if we were to go
forward, a group of conscientious objectors who had done magnificent work in state mental hospitals formed the National Mental
Health Foundation in the immediate postwar years. Abandoning
the ostrichlike tactics of the National Committee, they published a
series of harrowing eyewitness reports on conditions in state mental
institutions.

The American Psychiatric Association also moved in to fill the breach. At its 1946 annual convention, it adopted a courageous report by its Committee on Psychiatric Standards and Policies urging the entire Association membership, "including state mental hospital superintendents, to call forcefully to the attention of the public and their legislators all of the shortcomings and deficiencies in state hospitals, and to demand the assistance and backing necessary to maintain mental hospitals in fact as well as in name." In furtherance of these and other aims, leaders of the APA formed the American Psychiatric Foundation to raise funds for the inspection of mental hospitals and the promotion of research.

In 1950, the three organizations amalgamated into the present National Association for Mental Health. However, the dreary bureaucrats of the old National Committee for Mental Hygiene continued to hold the balance of power. The young firebrands of the National Mental Health Foundation, many of whom had taken staff positions with the new organization, soon found themselves gasping for air amid the encircling smog of the hayloft at 1790 Broadway. Most of them left for greener and more lively pastures.

Paradoxically, the amalgamated organization is more conservative and much more timid than the old National Committee for Mental Hygiene. Although the old committee lacked the foresight and imagination to build a strong national citizens' movement, it did play a key role in the Congressional testimony which led to passage of the National Mental Health Act of 1946. Major credit for this move must go to Dr. George S. Stevenson, then medical director of the committee.

The key provision of the 1946 act led to the creation of the National Institute of Mental Health, the strong psychiatric arm of the Federal government. Furthermore, the National Committee came down to Washington in 1947, 1948, and 1949 to testify effectively in behalf of increased funds for the fledgling Institute. All of us in the mental health field are deeply grateful to Dr. Stevenson and his colleagues for their farsighted efforts in this important area of the public psychiatric movement.

However, this promising activity was abruptly terminated by the board of the amalgamated association in 1950. The drastic surgical move was spearheaded by several Philadelphians who went into a deep state of shock when they learned that the organization was engaged in presenting the citizens' case for more Federal money for the mentally ill. These enlightened Philadelphians, who equated the "radical" activities of the Federal government with those of Beelzebub himself, had contributed a sizable amount of money to the organization, so their wishes naturally prevailed. Although a number of key board members resigned in bitter protest against this benighted castration of the citizens' movement, the 1950 decision has remained in force for the past six years.

It is really most difficult to portray the negativism of the "new" National Association for Mental Health. The name implies that it takes a stand for mental health. As to mental illness, it has never taken a clear-cut position one way or the other. Like Calvin Coolidge's minister, who was against sin, I believe the NAMH is against both sin and mental illness, but I have little evidence to go on.

At the important Federal level, the Association has constantly refused to face up to its responsibilities. It seems terrified that the Congress will bite it. The annual battle for increased appropriations for the National Institute for Mental Health is a fierce one, and even a small effort by the NAMH over the past few years would have undoubtedly resulted in an expansion of desperately needed funds for research, training, and clinical work.

Its leaders hold to the view that visible efforts for increased federal moneys might be construed as "lobbying." Well, what's wrong with some good, well-placed lobbying? More than a century ago, Dorothea Lynde Dix spent six years lobbying the Federal Congress for a land-grant program to aid mental patients whom she described as "wards of the nation." Sixty years later, Clifford Beers described one of the major purposes of the newly formed National Committee for Mental Hygiene in these words: "To enlist the aid of the Federal Government so far as may seem desirable."

Fortunately, the National Mental Health Association's point of view is not shared by its sister health organizations. The American Cancer Society, the American Heart Association, the National Committee for Research in Neurological Disorders, the United Cerebral Palsy Associations, the Arthritis and Rheumatism Foundation—they all send top medical scientists and lay leaders to Washington each year to testify both for increased appropriations and new legislation. They don't stop with formal testimony, either. In the past seven years, I have seen some of America's most noted medical researchers pursuing panting Congressmen through the intricate catacombs of the Capitol.

At the state level, it's the same sad story. Although most of the state mental health associations are now affiliated with the National Association, they get little NAMH support at the legislative level. I have pounded scores of state legislative corridors these past few years, and I have yet to bump into a representative of the NAMH. The major traffic hazard on these jaunts is Dr. Dan Blain of the American Psychiatric Association, who holds the track record for whizzing down Capitol corridors.

Many of these state societies are a refreshing contrast to the NAMH. They have clear-cut eight- and ten-point programs, and they know how to work a state capitol from stem to stern. If the national leaders really want to learn how to convert citizen heat into legislative light, they might start by visiting Ohio, Pennsylvania, and Florida. In each of these states, state and local mental health societies have blueprinted dynamic new programs and then stormed the state capitols to get them enacted.

It is shameful that these state and local societies are not tightly welded into a national movement with a unified, forward-looking program. Sam Whitman, who has done a magnificent job over a decade as Executive Director of the Cleveland Mental Hygiene Association, put it beautifully in a recent conversation. "We are isolated pockets of influence," he told me. "When are we going to tie the spur tracks together and run the big railroad right?"

In the past two years, the state societies have begun to bare their teeth at the annual wakes of the National Association. They threatened to withdraw in 1954 unless the then NAMH President Richard Weil gave up a reorganization plan which would have placed the selection of the Board of Trustees in the hands of a few members of a powerful inner clique. Weil backed down, and the state societies got considerably increased representation on the national Board.

During the past year, the entire leadership of the National Association has changed hands. The new President, F. Barry Ryan, Jr., and the new Executive Director, experienced and competent Richard P. Swigart, seem to understand that the ultimate fate of the national organization is completely dependent upon the degree to which it draws upon the strength and experience of the affiliated state societies. The state societies not only have practically a monopoly on legislative and program know-how, but they raise most of the funds which support their ailing national parent. If Ryan and Swigart can convince the Board of Trustees, still weighted down with too many guardians of the past, that it is absolutely vital to inaugurate democratic working relationships with the state societies, they will have performed a feat which none of their numerous predecessors was able to bring off.

There are some auspicious signs of revived activity. For example, the new leadership has reversed the old policy of refusing "tainted" moneys from outside sources. It recently accepted a grant of $50,000 from the Smith, Kline and French drug company to be used in setting up new field services around the country. Although some of us had hoped the National Association would use a good share of its own money on a continuing basis for this important work, we are delighted that even a pilot project is under way.

However, the time of decision is near at hand. In my recent travels around the country, I sensed a growing restiveness among state and local mental health people. Unless the national organization pulls itself up by the boot straps and moves strongly into the public arena in the next year or two, it will sink out of sight.

For a decade now, many of us in the mental health field have spent many a long evening discussing the possibility of a new national mental health organization. We have gotten to the edge of the water on several occasions, but we have always been dissuaded by those who have asked "more time" for the present organization to assert itself. Next year will be better, they argue, but next year never is. When we bring this home, they serve up their trump card: How would it look to have two national organizations competing for public support?

I cannot understand this line of reasoning. Isn't our fundamental concern the welfare of the millions of mentally ill in this country? How long must they wait, when every waiting day is a sickly, dragging one? What do we say to the families of the mentally sick—that we refuse to do what we know to be right because we are afraid of the mincing displeasure of a few bureaucrats and a few professionals? Isn't it our main job to create a powerful citizens' mental health movement, existing organization or no? When we battled at the state level for a new day for the mentally ill, we tore down many a time-honored citadel and chopped off scores of bureaucratic heads. And many a state mental health society was born out of the needs of the time, replacing older societies which were fiddling with pamphlets while the citizenry burned with indignation. If the present national organization is unable to do the job for which it was created, then in all honesty it should dissolve itself. If it refuses to do so, then those of us who want action have an inescapable duty to create a new democratic vehicle through which the good citizens of this great land can give expression to their deep and burning interest in this problem.

All arguments pale in the light of a major necessity—we must create a powerful national voice for those who are unable to speak for themselves. We have temporized long enough, and we have forgiveness enough to ask of our brothers who are tormented in mind. And if we falter anywhere along the way, we have only to look to the life of little, frail Miss Dix for guidance, she who during her forty-five-year battle for the mentally ill bowed to no one, not even the President of the United States.

ACKNOWLEDGMENTS

THE author and The World Publishing Company herewith thank the following individuals and institutions for material quoted in *Every Other Bed*. If any errors have accidentally occurred they will be corrected in subsequent editions, provided notification is sent to the publisher.

INTRODUCTION. Honorable Harry Shapiro and the Philadelphia *Inquirer:* editorial of Feb. 17, 1955.

CHAPTER 1. Dr. Kenneth Appel, the American Psychiatric Association, and Robert L. Robinson: speech before the Fifth Mental Hospital Institute of APA, 1953.

CHAPTER 2. Dr. Lawrence Kubie and *Science:* "Research in Psychiatry Is Starving to Death," Vol. 116, Sept. 5, 1952. The Washington *Post:* "House Restores Slashes, Votes Agriculture a Billion," April 15, 1954.

CHAPTER 3. Dr. Mesrop A. Tarumianz: speech before the Delaware Com. on Research and Training, May 18, 1954. Drs. John Whitehorn, Gregory Zilboorg, and the *American Journal of Psychiatry:* "Present Trends in American Psychiatric Research," Vol. 13:303-12, 1933. Dr. Kenneth Appel: address before the APA, May, 1954. Dr. Karl Menninger and the *Bulletin of the Menninger Clinic:* "The Contribution of Psychoanalysis to American Psychiatry," May, 1954. Dr. Alan Gregg and the *Amer. Jour. of Psychiatry:* "A Critique of Psychiatry," Vol. 101, No. 3. Paul Huston and the GAP: Report No. 25 "Collaborative Research in Psychopathology," Jan., 1954. Dr. Lawrence Kubie and the *American Scientist:* "Some Unsolved Problems of the Scientific Career," Jan., 1954.

CHAPTER 4. Dr. William Menninger and the *Menninger Quarterly:* "Industrial Mental Health," Fall, 1954.

CHAPTER 6. Dr. Jules H. Masserman and the *Bulletin of the Menninger Clinic:* "Psychotherapy—A Review and an Integration," July, 1954. Drs. L. J. Meduna, Nolan D. C. Lewis, and the *Journal of Nervous and Mental Disease:* Dr. Meduna's "The Place of Biological Psychiatry in the Evolution of Human Thought," Jan., 1955. Dr. William B. Terhune and the *American Journal of Psychiatry:* "Physiological Psychiatry," Vol. 106, No. 4, Oct., 1949. The *Atlantic Monthly:* "A Psychiatrist's Choice," July, 1954. Albert Q. Maisel and the *Ladies' Home Journal:* "Is Mental Disease Mental?" July, 1953. Dr. Hans Selye and the *Practitioner:* "The Adaptation Syndrome in Clinical Medicine," Jan., 1954. Dr. Karl Menninger and the *Bulletin of the Menninger Clinic:* "Regulatory Devices of the Ego Under Major Stress," May, 1954.

CHAPTER 7. Dr. Robert W. Wilkins, his associates, Ciba Pharmaceutical Products, Inc., and *Proceedings, New England Cardiovascular Society:* "Preliminary

Observations on Rauwolfia Serpentina in Hypertensive Patients," from "The Rauwolfia Story," 1952. Dr. Raymond Harris and *Annals,* The New York Academy of Sciences: "Clinical Use of Reserpine (Serpasil) in Geriatrics," Vol. 59:95, 1954. Dr. Nathan S. Kline and *Annals,* N. Y. Acad. of Sci.: "Use of *Rauwolfia Serpentina* Benth in Neuropsychiatric Conditions," Vol. 59:107, 1954. Drs. David B. Williams, Robert H. Noce, Walter Rapaport, and the *Journal of the American Medical Association:* "Reserpine (Serpasil) in the Management of the Mentally Ill and Mentally Retarded," Vol. 156, No. 9, and "Reserpine (Serpasil) in the Management of the Mentally Ill," Vol. 158, No. 1. Dr. Anthony Sainz and *Annals,* N. Y. Acad. of Sci.: "The Use of Reserpine in Ambulatory and Hospitalized Geriatric Patients," Vol. 61:72. Dr. Dean C. Tasher and *Annals,* N. Y. Acad. of Sci.: "The Use of Reserpine in Shock-Reversible Patients and Shock-Resistant Patients," Vol. 61:108. Dr. Leo E. Hollister and *Annals,* N. Y. Acad. of Sci.: "Treatment of Chronic Schizophrenic Reactions with Reserpine," Vol. 61:92. Dr. William L. Kirkpatrick and *Annals,* N. Y. Acad. of Sci.: "Clinical Evaluation of Reserpine in a State Hospital," Vol. 61:123. Dr. Jay L. Hoffman and *Annals,* N. Y. Acad. of Sci.: "Clinical and Psychological Observations on Psychiatric Patients Treated with Reserpine," Vol. 61:144. Dr. Sydney Kinnear Smith and *Annals,* N. Y. Acad. of Sci.: "The Use of Reserpine in Private Psychiatric Practice," Vol. 61:206.

CHAPTER 8. Drs. J. Sigwald, D. Bouttier, the French *Annals of Medicine,* and H. Lawley: "R. P. 4560 in Current Neuropsychiatric Practice." Dr. Heinz E. Lehmann and the AMA *Archives of Neurology and Psychiatry:* "Chlorpromazine," Vol. 71, No. 2, Feb., 1954. Dr. N. W. Winkelman, Jr. and the *Jour. of the AMA:* "Chlorpromazine in the Treatment of Neuropsychiatric Disorders," Vol. 155:18. Dr. Joseph F. Fazekas, his associates, and *Medical Annals of the District of Columbia:* "The Use of Chlorpromazine in the Treatment of Acute Alcoholism," May, 1954. Dr. Vernon Kinross-Wright and *Postgraduate Medicine:* "Chlorpromazine—A Major Advance in Psychiatric Treatment," Vol. 16:297. Dr. Douglas Goldman: "Treatment of Psychotic States with Chlorpromazine," before convention of APA, 1955. Dr. Herman C. B. Denber, his associates, and the *Amer. Jour. of Psychiatry:* "Chlorpromazine in the Treatment of Mental Illness: A Study of 750 Patients," June, 1955. Drs. Nathan S. Kline, George T. Nicolaou, and the *Psychiatric Research Reports* of the APA: "Reserpine in the Treatment of Disturbed Adolescents," Vol. 1:122. Dr. Herbert Freed: "Treatment of Hyperkinetic Emotionally Disturbed Children with Prolonged Administration of Chlorpromazine," before convention of APA, 1955. Dr. Frank Ayd, Jr.: "Thorazine and Serpasil Treatment of Private Neuropsychiatric Patients," before convention of APA, 1955. Dr. Thomas P. Rees and Smith, Kline and French Laboratories: Videclinic before convention of APA, 1955.

CHAPTER 9. Earl Ubell and the New York *Herald Tribune:* "New Era: Drugs for Mental Disease?" May 15, 1955. Dr. Howard Fabing and the *Amer. Jour. of Psychiatry:* "Clinical Studies on Meratran, A New Anti-Depressant Drug," Vol. 111, No. 11. Dr. Julius Pomeranze and the *Journal of Gerontology:* "A New Anti-Depressant in Geriatrics," Vol. 9:486, Oct., 1954. Dr. H. E. Himwich, The Wm. S. Merrell Co.: "The Use of Frenquel in the Treatment of Disturbed Patients with Psychoses of Long Duration," before convention of APA, 1955.

CHAPTER 10. Dr. Winfred Overholser and the *Jour. of the AMA:* editorial, March 5, 1955.

CHAPTER 11. Dr. William Menninger and the Cleveland *Plain Dealer:* "Menninger's Tip to Ohio: 'Buy Brains,'" Feb. 17, 1955. Dr. Daniel Blain, Robert

L. Robinson, and the *Amer. Jour. of Psychiatry:* "A New Emphasis in Mental Health Planning," March, 1954.

CHAPTER 14. Drs. Robert P. Knight, Eugene B. Brody, and the International Universities Press, Inc.: Dr. Knight's statement in the Preface, Dr. Frederick C. Redlich's "The Concept of Schizophrenia and Its Implication for Therapy," and Dr. Brody's "The Treatment of Schizophrenia: A Review," from *Psychotherapy with Schizophrenics,* edited by Brody and Redlich. Dr. D. M. Palmer and the *Amer. Jour. of Psychiatry:* "Insulin Shock Therapy, A Statistical Survey of 393 Cases," Vol. 106:918, 1950. Dr. Melvin L. Kohn and the National Institute of Mental Health: "Social Isolation and Schizophrenia." Dr. Harry Solomon: report on LSD by the Boston Psychopathic Hospital before convention of APA, 1954. Dr. Robert G. Heath, his associates, Drs. Herbert S. Gaskill, George C. Ham, the Commonwealth Fund, and Harvard University Press: Dr. Heath's statement on pp. 28, 33, Dr. Gaskill's statement on p. 501, and Dr. Ham's statement on p. 505 from *Studies in Schizophrenia,* by the Tulane Department of Psychiatry and Neurology, published for the Commonwealth Fund by Harvard University Press, 1954.

CHAPTER 15. Dr. Sol Levy and the *Journal of the AMA:* "Pharmacological Treatment of Aged Patients in a State Mental Hospital," Dec. 5, 1953. Dr. Gunther E. Wolff and *Mental Hospitals:* "Use of Electroshock on Seniles," Sept., 1954. Drs. Lothar B. Kalinowsky, Paul Hoch, and Grune & Stratton, Inc.: *Shock Treatments and Other Somatic Procedures in Psychiatry,* by Hoch and Kalinowsky, 2nd Ed., 1952. Dr. Walter Bruetsch and Paul B. Hoeber, Inc.: pp. 316-17 of *The Biology of Mental Health and Disease,* 1952. Dr. Edward J. Stieglitz, The Wm. S. Merrell Co., *Geriatrics:* "Constructive Medicine in Aging," April, 1955. Dr. Lloyd James Thompson, The Wm. S. Merrell Co., *Geriatrics:* "Stresses in Middle Life from the Psychiatrist's Viewpoint," April, 1955.

CHAPTER 16. Drs. Clemens E. Benda and Malcolm J. Farrell: material from a discussion before convention of APA, 1953. Dr. Theodore H. Ingalls and Paul B. Hoeber, Inc.: p. 394 of *The Biology of Mental Health and Disease,* 1952. The *Jour. of the AMA:* "Amino Acid Metabolism and Mental Deficiency," May 14, 1955.

CHAPTER 17. Drs. Daniel J. Feldman, Howard D. Zucker, and the *Jour. of the AMA:* "Present-Day Medical Management of Alcoholism," Nov. 7, 1953. Raymond G. McCarthy, Sidney Spector, and *State Government:* Mr. McCarthy's "State Action on Alcoholism," Dec., 1954. Dr. Eugene F. Carey and *Annals,* N. Y. Acad. of Sci.: "A New Approach to the Emergency Treatment of Sickness Caused by Narcotic Withdrawal," Vol. 61:222.

CHAPTER 18. Dr. Ian Stevenson and *Harper's Magazine:* "Psychosomatic Medicine," Part I, July, 1954. Dr. Franz Alexander and The Ronald Press Company: *Studies in Psychosomatic Medicine,* by Alexander and French, 1948. Dr. Roy R. Grinker and Blakiston Div., McGraw-Hill Book Company, Inc.: *Psychosomatic Case Book,* by Grinker and Robbins, 1954. Dr. Franz Alexander and the Columbia University Press: New York Academy of Medicine: *Modern Attitudes in Psychiatry* (March of Medicine, 1945), 1946.

CHAPTER 19. Dr. Franz Alexander and The Ronald Press Company: *Psychoanalytic Therapy,* by Alexander and French, 1946. Dr. Rudolf Dreikurs, Raymond Corsini, and the *Amer. Jour. of Psychiatry:* "Twenty Years of Group Psychotherapy," Feb., 1954. Dr. Hilde Bruch: speech before the International Institute for Child Psychiatry, 1954. Dr. Paul Lemkau: speech before the Fifth International Congress on Mental Health, 1954.

CHAPTER 20. Dr. Paul Lemkau and the *Amer. Jour. of Psychiatry:* "The Epidemiological Study of Mental Illnesses and Mental Health," May, 1955. Dr. Robert P. Knight: *The Epidemiology of Mental Disorder,* and remarks on pp. 112-13, Milbank Memorial Fund, 1950. Drs. Ivan Belknap and E. Gartly Jaco: *Interrelations Between the Social Environment and Psychiatric Disorders,* Milbank Mem. Fund, 1953, and the paper "The Epidemiology of Mental Disorders in a Political-Type City, 1946-52." Dr. Thomas Francis, Jr. and The Milbank Mem. Fund: *The Epidemiology of Mental Disorder,* and remarks in "Evaluation of This Material," Milbank Mem. Fund, 1950. Dr. John Clausen: "Social Isolation and Schizophrenia," before annual meeting of the American Sociological Society, 1954. Dr. Thomas A. C. Rennie: *Interrelations Between the Social Environment and Psychiatric Disorders,* Milbank Mem. Fund, 1953.

CHAPTER 21. Dr. Harold E. Himwich and Paul B. Hoeber, Inc.: p. 548 in *The Biology of Mental Health and Disease,* 1952. Dr. Lothar B. Kalinowsky and Paul B. Hoeber, Inc.: p. 563 in *The Biology of Mental Health and Disease,* 1952. Dr. George A. Ulett, his associates, and the *Bulletin of the Menninger Clinic:* "The Use of Matched Groups in the Evaluation of Convulsive and Subconvulsive Photoshock," Vol. 18, No. 4. Dr. Heinz E. Lehmann and Paul B. Hoeber, Inc.: p. 578 in *The Biology of Mental Health and Disease,* 1952. Dr. Robert H. Israel: "Discharge and Readmission Rates Among 4254 Consecutive First Admissions of Schizophrenia to Warren State Hospital," before convention of APA, 1955. Dr. William Jacquith: "Follow-Up of Mental Patients," before the Fifth Mental Hospital Institute of the APA, 1953. Dr. Earl D. Bond and the *Amer. Jour. of Psychiatry:* "Results of Treatment in Psychoses—With a Control Series," June, 1954. Dr. Lauren H. Smith: "Critique of Somatic Therapies," before the Sixth Mental Hospital Institute of the APA, 1954. Dr. Paul H. Hoch and the *Amer. Jour. of Psychiatry:* "Progress in Psychiatric Therapies," Oct., 1955. Dr. Kenneth Appel: "Rehabilitation in Psychiatry," before convention of APA, 1955.

CHAPTER 22. Drs. J. Folch-Pi, William F. Windle, Ross A. McFarland, George H. Bishop, John C. Lilly, Robert A. Cleghorn, Hudson Hoagland, Alfred Pope, Winifred M. Ashby, Franz J. Kallmann, Sheldon Clark Reed, Jan A. Böök, and Paul B. Hoeber, Inc.: p. 12, p. 331, p. 335, p. 160, pp. 207, 209, p. 265, pp. 437, 446-47, p. 466, p. 467, p. 284-85, p. 299, and p. 301, from *The Biology of Mental Health and Disease,* 1952.

CHAPTER 23. Dr. Elmer Hess and the *Jour. of the AMA:* June 25, 1955.

INDEX

ABOUT THE AUTHOR

MIKE GORMAN was born in New York City on December 7, 1913. He received his B.A. at New York University, where he also did graduate work. After four years of service in the Army, in 1945 he joined the Oklahoma City *Daily Oklahoman,* where he started his work on mental health. In five years on the paper he wrote more than 400 stories, 60 editorials, a book, and several pamphlets. His book, *Oklahoma Attacks Its Snake Pits,* was a book condensation in the *Reader's Digest* in 1948, the same year in which he became the first newspaperman in the country to receive the Lasker Award of the National Committee for Mental Hygiene, for his distinguished writing in the field of medicine, and particularly for psychiatric writing. The following year he was selected one of the nation's ten outstanding young men by the United States Chamber of Commerce, for his crusading efforts in the field of mental health. From 1949 to 1951 he lectured and wrote on mental health problems. He became the chief writer and director of public hearings for the President's Commission on Health Needs of the Nation in 1952, and in 1953 he accepted the post of Executive Director of the National Mental Health Committee.